MICROBIAL POPULATION OF OCEANS AND SEAS

A. E. Kriss, I. E. Mishustina,

N. Mitskevich and E. V. Zemtsova.

Translated by K. Syers, M.A.

Edited by Professor Gordon E. Fogg, F.R.S.,

Professor of Botany, Westfield College, University of London.

EDWARD ARNOLD (PUBLISHERS) LTD. LONDON

First English translation 1967
Translated and prepared for press by Scripta Technica Ltd.
from the Russian title
Mikrobnoye naseleniye mirovogo okeana
published in Moscow by Nauka, 1964

Printed in Great Britain by
Fletcher and Son Ltd., Norwich

CONTENTS

III Geography of marine microorganisms

IV Conclusion

Editor's preface

Bacteria, yeasts and other microorganisms are presumably as important in the oceans as they are in terrestrial habitats but information about their occurrence and activities, which is essential for full understanding of the chemical and biological processes taking place in the marine environment, is as yet meagre. In this state of our knowledge the extensive microbiological surveys of the oceans carried out by Professor Kriss and his colleagues are a particularly interesting contribution for they provide for the first time a synoptic picture of the distribution of marine microorganisms. Professor Kriss's work having recently come under criticism it is particularly valuable to have this full account available in English, for it will undoubtedly provide the starting point for much future investigation.

In editing this translation I have added a few footnotes giving my personal comment on certain controversial points and drawing the attention of the reader to publications which have appeared too recently for mention in the original text.

G. E. FOGG

I

INTRODUCTION

Introduction

We know very little about the species of microorganisms inhabiting the depths of the high seas. Investigators have not been greatly concerned with determining the species composition of the marine microflora, but have concentrated rather on the search for physiological groups of microbes taking part in the circulation of biologically important elements.

A brief review of published data in microbial species of marine provenance was compiled by ZoBell and Upham (1944). The great majority of these had been found in coastal waters, usually in the surface layers. The authors also describe sixty species occurring in Pacific Ocean water and mud within 600 miles of shore. The authors do not indicate the depth at which any particular species was found.

Since 1954 workers from the Department of Marine Microbiology of the USSR Academy of Sciences Institute of Microbiology have been taking part in a series of expeditionary studies of vast areas of the world's seas and oceans. In the central Arctic the drifting station 'North Pole 3' was engaged in microbiological work at latitude 88° in July 1954 and again in September of that year, when the ice-floe took it almost to the Pole (Kriss, 1955). During the 1955 high latitude expedition microbiological studies were carried out at two drifting stations- 'North Pole 3' (86°N) and 'North Pole 5' (83°N) and in 1956 at 'North Pole 4' (87°N) and 'North Pole 5' (86°N) (Kriss, 1955a, 1957).

Again in 1956, the expeditionary ship *Ob* worked three latitudinal sections in the Greenland Sea (78°, 79° and 80°N) with 34 microbiological stations, four of them in the Arctic, near the north-eastern tip of Greenland (Mishustina, Mitskevich, 1963).

Extensive research on the distribution of heterotrophs in the Indian Ocean was carried out during the *Ob's* 1956–7 oceanographical voyage, when microbiological observations were made at a series of 58 stations in the sector between Africa and Antarctica, Antarctica and Asia and along the Antarctic coast (Kriss et al., 1958; Lebedeva, 1959). In 1957–8 microbiological work in the central parts of the Pacific was done by the *Vityaz'* in two parallel sections along the meridians 174°W and 172°E between latitudes 37°N and 41°S, at 63 stations (Kriss et al., 1958). In 1958 the *Sevastopol'* worked at 51 stations in the Norwegian Sea. In 1959, during the Atlantic voyage of the *Mikayl Lomonossov*, the opportunity was taken to collect microbiological material showing the range of heterotrophs at 41 stations in a section along the 30th meridian from 66°N to the Tropic of Capricorn (Kriss, Mitskevich et al., 1960). The co-ordinates of the microbiological stations in the various seas and oceans are shown in Table 1.

The following areas have thus been covered for microbiological research purposes: the subtropical, tropical, and equatorial parts of the Central Pacific; the equatorial, tropical, subtropical, sub-Antarctic and Antarctic areas of the Indian Ocean; the equatorial, tropical, subtropical and sub-Arctic areas of the Atlantic; and the high-latitude sea areas up to the North Pole (Fig. 1).

The material collected gives us a picture not only of the quantitative distribution of heterotrophic microorganisms in different parts of the water column and in different parts of the ocean, but also of the species composition of the heterotrophic microbial population and its biochemical activity.

At this point we must consider whether modern microbiology has at its disposal methods of quantitatively evaluating the various processes affected by microorganisms under natural conditions, in this case in seas and oceans.

Omelyanskiy, as long ago as 1924, referred to microorganisms as sensitive chemical reagents. It is certainly possible to tell the relative concentration of substances used by microorganisms as body-building materials or sources of energy by knowing the concentration of multiplying members of particular physiological groups of these organisms. It is profoundly erroneous to maintain, as do some investigators (Kuznetsov, 1961, and others) that in estimating the activity of processes caused by any given physiological group of microorganisms in a body of water one must discount large numbers of the microorganisms comprising that group. These authors are in fact assuming, that the high concentration of the microorganisms is due not to multiplication, resulting from abundance of accessible food, but to accumulation of microbial cells surviving in the latent state. This is to ignore the elementary fact that the spores of microorganisms are as subject to death as their vegetative cells and remain viable for only comparatively short periods of time if conditions are against them.* (See note on p.3.)

The surface layer of the Black Sea bottom contains saprophytic bacteria, capable of breaking down organic sulphur-containing material and forming hydrogen sulphide (Kriss, Rukina, 1949a), which are no less numerous and active and form no less hydrogen sulphide than the sulphate-reducing microorganisms. Yet this does not mean that the hydrogen sulphide in the Black Sea is the product of putrefactive processes, a view wrongly ascribed to the present authors by Kuznetsov (1961, 1962); the inference is rather that the two processes of hydrogen sulphide formation, reduction of sulphates and breakdown of organic sulphur compounds are actively occurring in the Black Sea bottom and that for the moment we lack data on which to base any serious judgement as to which is the more important.†

The occurrence of large numbers of highly active microorganisms in a natural substrate is evidence of intensive multiplication and always indicates that the substrate contains a sufficient quantity of food for these organisms. In connection with the above-mentioned example of saprophytic bacteria, it is interesting that chemists have corroborated the results of microbiological research in finding that the bottom sediments of the Black Sea contain relatively large amounts of organic sulphur compounds (Ostroumov, 1953).

Chemical methods, however, do not always reveal substances which, the moment they are formed by a certain species of microorganisms in a natural substrate, are immediately used as food by other species living in that substrate. This was what led us (Kriss, Rukina, 1949b) to start looking for nitrifiers in the Black Sea mud, after it had been found to contain a considerable concentration of microorganisms actively reducing nitrates and nitrites. The search was successful and the high concentration of active denitrifiers in the Black Sea bottom was explained by the comparatively large number of nitrifying bacteria, not by hypothetical nitrification (as Kuznetsov, who usually gives the results of our investigations wrongly, states, 1961, 1962). Since the population and activity of the nitrifying bacteria were very high, we are justified in thinking that the nitrites and nitrates formed by nitrifiers in the Black Sea mud will be used by denitrifying microorganisms in *statu nascendi* and, consequently, cannot be determined by chemical methods.

* (Editor's footnote). It is probably generally true that cells which have ceased active metabolism do not survive under natural conditions but it seems premature to imply that this is invariably so. Bacterial spores certainly do remain viable for an appreciable time under circumstances in which the vegetative cells are killed and the curious organic oozes found in Pilkington Bay, Lake Victoria, and other places provide an apparently clear exception to Professor Kriss' generalization. These oozes have the remarkable property of not decaying in a warm, wet oxidizing environment and yet appear to contain an enormous bacterial flora which is viable but dormant as though held static by nutrient limitation or by an antibiotic (unpublished results of V. Collins, Freshwater Biological Association, Ambleside, England; see also B. S. Newell, 1958, *Microbiology of lake deposits*. East African Fisheries Research Organization, Annual Report. 1956–7, pp. 27–28).

† (Editor's footnote). F. A. Richards (in *Chemical Oceanography*, 1, edited by J. P. Riley and G. Skirrow, Academic Press, London and New York, 1965, pp. 642–3) points out that the data from the Black Sea show a relationship between the concentrations of sulphate and those of hydrogen sulphide and supports the conclusion that the hydrogen sulphide in these waters is derived largely from the reduction of sulphates.

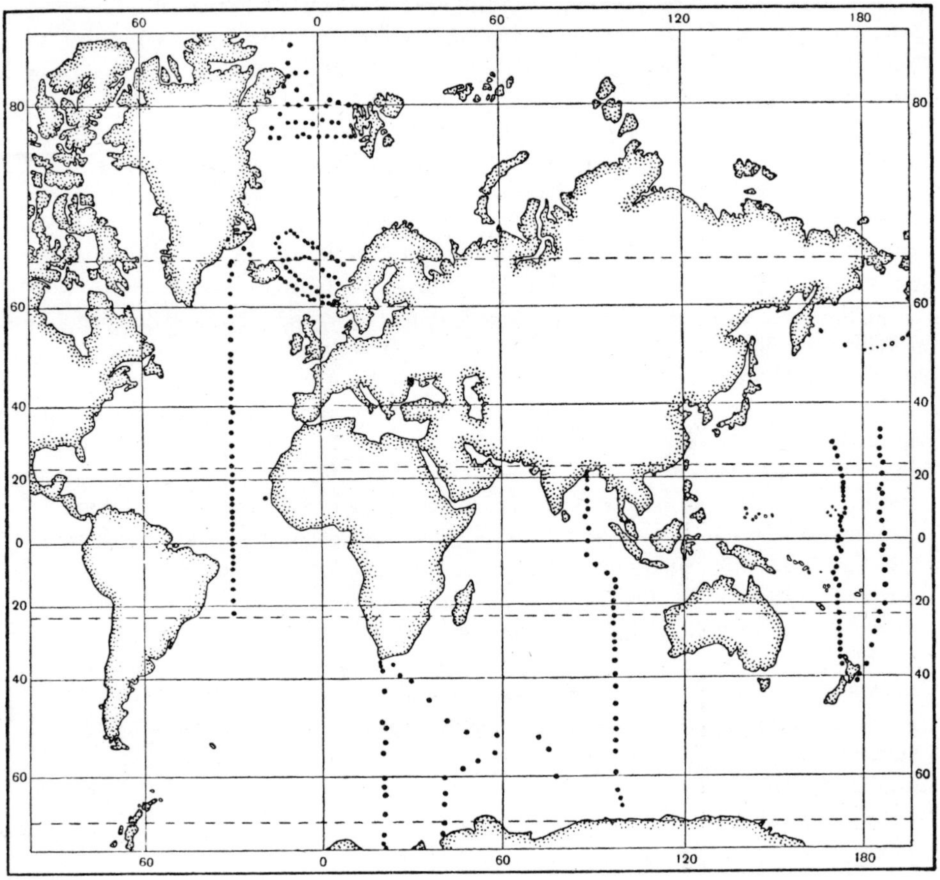

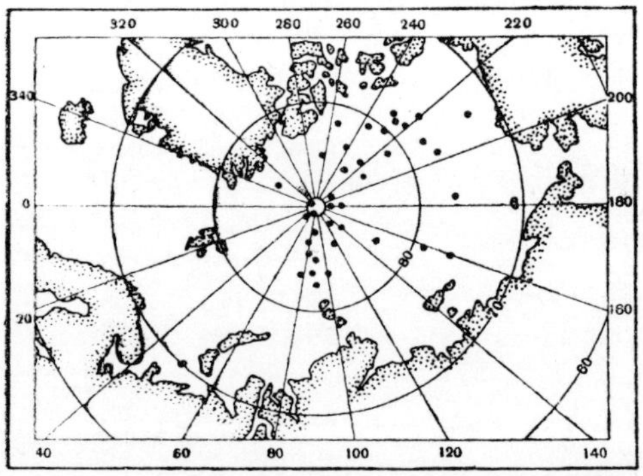

Fig. 1 Maps of microbiological stations in the world's seas and oceans

Leaving aside, for the moment, the question of oxygen sources for chemosynthetic processes or energy for other manifestations of microbic autotrophy in the sulphur-containing depths of the Black Sea, we must emphasize that it was precisely the quantitative determinations of physiological groups of microorganisms in the water layers and at the bottom of the sea that enabled us to estimate the intensity of the diverse biochemical reactions produced by microorganisms in that body of water (Kriss, 1959). Sorokin too (1962) refers to the large number of nitrifiers and sulphur bacteria in the deep bottom deposits (1600, 1700 m) of the hydrogen sulphide zone of the Black Sea, where the peak concentrations of that compound have been determined and free oxygen is lacking.

It is, indeed, obvious that the microbiological conversion of biogenic matter occurs at considerably greater intensity in the deep-water mud of the Black Sea than in the deeper-lying bottom deposits of the Sea of Okhotsk, or in the north-west Pacific or in the North Pole area, since the members of physiological groups of microorganisms contributing to carbon, nitrogen and sulphur exchange in the Black Sea is greater by two, three or more orders of magnitude than in the other waters mentioned, where similar investigations have been performed.

It is equally obvious that the importance of microorganisms in the biological productivity of the Black Sea can scarcely be overestimated, for the biomass of microorganisms (the biomass itself, not its production – another of Kuznetsov's errors (1962), per m^2 in the deep part of the Black Sea is almost double the total biomass of zooplankton and phytoplankton (Kriss, Lebedeva, 1953). The method of determining the microbial biomass – counting the number of microorganisms on a membrane ultrafilter and measuring their volume – in no way differed from the method used by Kuznetsov (1951, 1952) in his research on the microorganic biomass in natural bodies of water.

We can thus get a clear idea of the intensity of the microbiological processes at work in a given part of a body of water at the moment a sample is taken, from the quantity of microorganisms in the water and at the bottom and from their activity, particularly in first inoculations on selective media. Unfortunately however, although such data are of great value in comparative studies where large differences are involved, they do not enable us to estimate, in absolute terms, the activity of the microbiological processes at work in converting and forming organic matter in a body of water; for culture methods produce underestimates of the true quantity of bacteria belonging to any particular physiological group in the material under study.

In particular, we have as yet no method which could enable us to make a quantitative assessment of the primary production of a body of water due to chemosynthesizing bacteria will the same degree of approximation to natural conditions as do the bottle methods used in studying the photosynthesizing activity of phytoplankton.

By way of example we may take the attempts of Kuznetsov (1955) and

Sorokin (1955, 1957) at quantitative determination of chemosynthetic processes in bodies of water by the radiocarbon method suggested by Steeman-Nielsen (1952) for measuring photosynthesis in natural waters. These authors put carbonate containing C^{14} into sample bottles of water or mud and, after one or more days, determined the quantity of carbon assimilated by bacterial cells; from this value they calculated the bacterial biomass which, in their opinion, had been produced by chemosynthesis.

Kuznetsov and Sorokin claim that by placing bottles containing water or mud samples in a refrigerator or thermostat (depending on the temperature in the natural body of water), or even in a natural body of water, they had thereby 'set up experiments with isolated water samples under conditions approximating as nearly as possible to natural' (Kuznetsov et al., 1962, p. 34). We might have passed over this unfounded claim in silence, but for certain important circumstances which invalidate their use of the radiocarbon method to determine bacterial assimilation of carbon dioxide in the water or at the bottom of a natural body of water.

As we know, conditions are created in isolated samples of water or mud irrespective of the temperature at which they are kept, favouring the multiplication of one, two or, more rarely, three species of heterotrophic bacteria. Within a short time the number of heterotrophs in the sample bottles will be greater by three or four orders of magnitude than in the natural body of water and the species composition of the microbial coenosis will be drastically altered. The Kuznetsov-Sorokin method consequently not only obscures the essence of the process of carbon dioxide assimilation by bacteria in the sample bottles (instead of chemosynthesis, this method gives us a quantitative statement of heterotrophic carbon dioxide assimilation by the heterotrophs breeding in the bottle), but also greatly exaggerates the actual intensity of the processes of bacterial carbon dioxide assimilation in a natural body of water.

Unfortunately, Sorokin still does not realize the unsuitability of the radiocarbon method for estimating the rate of bacterial carbon dioxide fixation processes in natural waters. Moreover, he refers to 'its great advantages over the quantitative count method' and arrives at such conclusions as that the bacterial population in a body of water 'often reaches its peak when the substrate has already been exhausted and the vital activity of the bacteria is depressed' (Sorokin, 1962c, p. 685).

According to Sorokin, the radiocarbon method 'permits' even determination of physiological groups of microorganisms, without the usual procedure of seeding in selective media. Using this method in the Black Sea, he considered the introduction of thiosulphate into the sample bottles as sufficient grounds for attributing the quantity of $C^{14}O_2$ assimilated in the bottles to the activity of sulphur bacteria (Sorokin, 1962c). It is curious, also that the radiocarbon method 'permitted' him even to trace separately the vertical distribution of sulphur-producing aerobes and anaerobes.

Equally frivolous is Sorokin's conclusion (1962c) that there are almost no viable bacteria at depths greater than 500 m in the Black Sea, merely because he did not succeed in detecting fixation of tagged carbon dioxide in his bottles. If the radiocarbon method were really so universally applicable it would open untold possibilities in microbiology!

The use of isotopes can undoubtedly offer new possibilities of studying the physiology of microorganisms under natural conditions and consequently provide new approaches for evaluating the intensity of microbiological metabolic processes in natural waters; but more work on these methods is still needed. Attempts at simplified solutions are not merely unhelpful; on the contrary, compared with existing methods of determining the quantity of microorganisms in a body of water and their activity in the relevant media, such attempts take us further away from the possibility of building up a picture of the extent of biochemical activity on the part of various microbial species in their hydrospheric habitats.*

The present monograph describes the species of deep-dwelling microorganisms occurring in the great ocean areas and the global distribution pattern of the marine microbial population.

Part I contains previously published data on microbial species of marine origin and deals with certain problems in the taxonomy of marine microorganisms. Then follows an account of sampling techniques and preliminary treatment of water and mud samples and of the investigation procedure for species determination of the strains isolated. There are separate sections on the salt tolerance of marine microorganisms, their survival capacity in the process of prolonged culture in the laboratory and the distribution of organic matter in the oceanic water column. Much space is devoted to describing species and variants of non-sporulating and sporulating bacteria, coccal forms, mycobacteria, Proactinomycetes, Actinomycetes and yeast organisms represented in our collection of heterotrophic microorganism cultures from the high seas. This part contains data on antagonism among marine organisms and on the lysogenetic properties or marine heterotrophs.

In Part II we deal with problems of the geography of marine microorganisms. Geogrophical patterns in the density distribution of the heterotrophic microbial population in the seas and oceans are shown; heterotrophic microorganisms in various geographical zones of the world's seas and oceans are compared in respect to their biochemical activity; the range of species which have extensive areas is described; the possibility of using microorganisms as deep-current indicators is demonstrated.

* (Editor's footnote). Interpretation of the results obtained by the radiocarbon technique is indeed a difficult matter and calls for a much greater understanding of the inter-relations of metabolic processes than we at present possess (see E. Steemann Nielsen, 1960, *Physiol. Plant.*, **13**, pp. 348–57; G. E. Fogg, 1963, *Brit. Phys. Bull.*, 2, pp. 195–205). For Sorokin's recent views see I. I. Sorokin in *Symposium on Primary Productivity in Aquatic Environments, Mem. Ist. Ital. Idrobial.*, 1965, 18 suppl., pp. 187–205.

Table 1. Co-ordinates and depths of marine microbiological stations

Central Arctic

Station number	Latitude N	Longitude	Depth, m
	1954		
'North Pole 3'(July)	88°04'3"	151°16' W	3450
'North Pole 3'(Sept.)	89°29'5"	65°43' W	4116
	1955		
'North Pole 3'	85°53'	27°30' W	3440
'North Pole 5'	82°55'	151°32' E	2712
	1956		
'North Pole 4'	87°28'3"	177°12'4" W	3950
'North Pole 5'	86°26'	79°19' E	3544

Greenland Sea, 1956

Station number	Latitude N	Longitude E	Depth, m
1	78°04'	09°48'	214
2	78°03'	08°50'	1144
3	78°04'	05°54'	2158
4	78°06'	02°35'	3039
		Longitude W	
5	78°02'	00°04'	3021
6	78°04'	03°20'	2870
7	78°08'	04°53'	1447
8	78°03'	06°45'	348
11	78°00'	13°36'	136
12	78°00'	15°47'	501
14	78°38'	15°48'	56
17	79°25'	13°06'	212
20	81°00'	11°41'	77
22	81°59'	09°58'	2581
23	82°52'	09°04'	3306
24	81°36'	07°44'	1304
26	81°29'	09°30'	257
27	80°02'	10°04'	131
29	78°56'	09°56'	244
30	78°56'	07°26'	244
32	79°58'	06°53'	298
34	80°46'	06°57'	1049
36	81°35'	04°13'	3500
38	80°13'	03°56'	2117
42	78°54'	03°53'	2147
43	78°55'	01°26'	2656
45	79°47'	01°31'	2754
		Longitude E	
46	79°58'	02°44'	2690

Table 1 (continued)

Station number	Latitude N	Longitude E	Depth, m
48	79°06′	01°44′	2520
49	80°08′	03°48′	1485
50	80°03′	06°54′	659
51	79°57′	09°53′	476
54	78°56′	06°34′	1280
55	78°59′	04°53′	1907

Indian Ocean, 1956-7

Station number	Latitude S	Longitude E	Depth, m
212	56°00′2″	56°54′1″	>4000
213	57°23′6″	51°16′0″	5320
214	58°36′6″	46°19′2″	5365
215	60°04′1″	40°17′2″	5300
217	62°38′7″	40°19′6″	5054
219	64°24′2″	40°02′8″	4810
221	66°34′3″	40°06′0″	4540
222	68°00′8″	39°41′0″	2150
235	69°46′3″	20°19′6″	2960
236	69°21′2″	19°42′3″	3396
238	68°08′3″	19°59′5″	4080
240	65°30′2″	20°07′4″	4924
242	62°46′1″	20°19′0″	5190
243	61°33′8″	20°00′5″	5226
246	60°07′0″	19°58′3″	5360
248	55°58′5″	20°00′0″	4720
249	53°58′9″	20°10′8″	3750
251	50°58′0″	20°28′0″	4150
252	50°03′2″	19°57′1″	4780
256	42°54′0″	20°06′7″	4980
259	37°49′2″	19°45′6″	4580
260	36°18′9″	19°36′9″	1820
261	35°52′8″	19°41′7″	204
265	36°20′5″	23°14′2″	2240
266	38°70′2″	25°35′4″	2700
267	40°37′8″	29°13′5″	4400
269	45°03′4″	35°02′6″	2700
271	49°49′3″	41°21′3″	4250
272	52°11′3″	47°40′3″	4300
274	52°32′3″	57°43′9″	4720
276	53°07′5″	71°48′9″	1570
278	55°29′5″	74°49′8″	3010
280	60°08′5″	77°28′3″	2270
281	62°27′3″	97°35′5″	3962
282	64°03′5″	98°33′5″	430
283	63°32′4″	98°18′3″	1632

Table 1 (continued)

Station number	Latitude S	Longitude E	Depth, m
285	59°29′0″	97°06′7″	4540
287	55°54′8″	96°58′2″	4500
288	53°50′0″	96°54′2″	3970
289	51°36′1″	97°02′9″	3670
291	49°35′0″	97°06′0″	3520
293	46°31′2″	97°04′0″	3050
295	42°29′1″	97°05′5″	3350
297	39°23′0″	97°01′3″	3900
299	36°05′5″	97°02′6″	4510
301	32°28′6″	97°02′7″	4290
302	30°36′2″	97°03′0″	3130
303	29°13′0″	97°01′1″	3804
305	25°22′6″	96°53′8″	5360
306	23°40′7″	97°01′4″	5820
307	21°31′3″	96°48′9″	5380
308	19°09′7″	96°56′9″	5590
309	16°48′5″	96°54′8″	5820
310	14°40′2″	97°02′7″	4720
311	12°49′3″	96°58′4″	4590
312	10°48′2″	94°50′8″	5230
314	7°48′3″	90°38′8″	5250
316	4°45′3″	88°12′7″	5020
318	00°01′8″	88°21′8″	4495
	Latitude N		
320	03°55′0″	88°40′7″	4140
322	07°57′7″	88°02′6″	3680
323	10°07′8″	88°08′0″	—
324	12°21′0″	88°09′2″	3200
326	16°41′0″	88°27′1″	2634
327	18°41′3″	88°10′6″	2240
328	19°58′4″	88°09′0″	972
329	20°55′2″	88°01′5″	39

Pacific Ocean, 1957-8

Station number	Latitude N	Longitude E	Depth, m
3777	32°48′3″	185°58′0″	5520
3778	31°13′3″	185°52′0″	5540
3780	27°37′0″	185°45′0″	5316
3781	25°50′3″	185°50′2″	2794
3782	24°03′2″	186°29′0″	4923
3784	20°21′5″	186°24′2″	5238
3786	16°51′0″	186°19′7″	5337
3787	15°49′0″	186°14′3″	5250
3788	14°04′5″	186°27′5″	5802

Table 1 (continued)

Station number	Latitude N	Longitude E	Depth, m
3791	11°02′8″	186°15′0″	5530
3793	8°33′6″	185°52′6″	5948
3795	5°58′0″	186°27′7″	5765
3797	1°57′8″	187°06′2″	5370
	Latitude S		
3801	2°25′0″	186°33′0″	5230
3802	3°19′6″	186°46′8″	5350
3805	6°47′8″	187°02′2″	5570
3808	10°06′6″	187°23′0″	3875
3812	14°49′0″	187°04′0″	6860
3814	17°50′0″	183°19′5″	
3818	20°08′6″	186°52′8″	8560
3823	23°26′5″	185°20′6″	10000
3825	25°39′0″	184°35′4″	5770
3827	28°24′5″	183°55′1″	9280
3831	32°09′0″	182°42′5″	9500
3834	37°00′1″	181°03′8″	
3837	40°12′4″	177°48′7″	1960
3838	41°18′2″	177°40′3″	3000
3839	36°53′0″	172°31′5″	1758
3840	35°16′8″	172°12′0″	1244
3842	33°16′0″	171°59′4″	2080
3843	31°46′9″	171°54′2″	2060
3844	29°51′7″	172°00′5″	2520
3845	27°39′8″	171°55′7″	3868
3846	25°41′0″	171°50′3″	3170
3847	23°21′2″	171°55′0″	4814
3850	20°01′1″	171°02′0″	3240
3851	18°12′5″	171°00′2″	2992
3853	14°31′0″	171°20′0″	3059
3854	12°36′1″	170°27′2″	3500
3855	10°30′0″	170°15′3″	5180
3856	8°27′7″	170°39′0″	5250
3857	6°32′0″	171°05′7″	4832
3859	3°22′5″	172°01′8″	4122
3860	2°40′2″	171°57′1″	3643
3861	0°44′3″	171°55′2″	4343
3862	0°04′3″	171°53′2″	4672
	Latitude N		
3863	0°55′4″	171°50′5″	4403
3864	2°56′0″	172°42′8″	2900
3865	4°05′0″	172°08′0″	4415
3866	5°04′8″	172°16′2″	4381
3867	6°28′0″	172°49′3″	4776
3868	7°59′0″	173°11′8″	5020
3869	9°23′0″	173°35′7″	5251
3871	12°23′5″	173°19′8″	5570
3872	13°29′5″	173°13′7″	5738

Table 1 (continued)

Station number	Latitude N	Longitude E	Depth, m
3873	14°20′3″	173°16′0″	5550
3874	16°08′0″	173°10′3″	5480
3875	18°02′4″	173°09′1″	3220
3876	19°57′3″	172°37′1″	5070
3877	21°59′0″	172°20′0″	5540
3879	25°56′9″	171°14′1″	5960
3880	27°59′5″	170°32′0″	5855
3881	29°55′0″	169°55′0″	5600

Norwegian Sea, 1958

Station number	Latitude N	Longitude E	Depth, m
1699	66°02′0″	07°52′6″	370
1701	66°23′8″	06°01′1″	680
1703	66°54′7″	04°02′4″	1345
1705	67°19′9″	02°07′0″	1385
		Longitude W	
1708	68°00′9″	00°46′3″	3680
1709	68°13′1″	01°40′5″	2845
1710	68°26′0″	02°41′2″	3785
1711	68°39′5″	03°38′3″	3680
1712	68°53′5″	04°33′9″	3705
1715	69°32′2″	07°20′9″	2510
1716	69°44′1″	08°15′2″	945
1717	69°55′6″	09°10′4″	1840
1719	69°53′0″	10°51′1″	1950
1721	69°15′7″	13°52′0″	1670
1723	68°34′8″	14°04′8″	1280
1724	68°10′1″	13°28′0″	1685
1725	67°32′1″	13°15′0″	1730
1727	66°32′5″	12°01′6″	1250
1729	66°35′7″	10°04′4″	1480
1732	66°41′2″	07°07′2″	1740
1733	66°43′0″	06°08′5″	2360
1734	66°44′7″	05°10′0″	3300
1736	66°48′2″	03°12′2″	2760
1738	66°09′9″	01°25′7″	3540
		Longitude E	
1740	65°15′2″	01°07′3″	3020
1742	64°36′0″	02°50′8″	2510
1744	64°04′0″	04°33′6″	1360
1746	63°35′9″	05°48′5″	240
1752	61°31′0″	03°02′0″	390
1754	61°33′9″	01°07′5″	176
		Longitude W	
1756	62°11′5″	00°26′8″	695

Table 1 (continued)

Station number	Latitude N	Longitude W	Depth, m
1758	62°44′4″	02°41′9″	890
1760	63°21′4″	04°35′1″	2500
1762	63°57′5″	06°27′5″	2870
1764	64°28′5″	08°09′9″	1915
1766	65°13′3″	10°00′0″	750
1767	65°30′0″	11°00′0″	855
1770	67°18′0″	23°33′0″	511
1773	68°05′0″	25°12′5″	1090
1778	63°55′1″	12°44′5″	585
1781	63°31′6″	11°22′7″	330
1786	62°58′8″	08°59′4″	465
1789	62°38′2″	07°36′2″	220
1795	61°42′4″	04°50′8″	320
1797	61°27′8″	03°42′2″	1190
1798	61°14′7″	02°59′5″	1280
1800	61°00′8″	01°54′2″	380
		Longitude E	
1806	60°35′5″	01°34′1″	135
1808	60°35′9″	03°09′7″	180
1809	60°36′0″	03°53′5″	303
1810	60°40′6″	04°30′8″	340

Atlantic Ocean, 1959

Station number	Latitude N	Longitude W	Depth, m
345	64°50′	29°08′	980
346	66°22′	29°47′	340
347	66°00′	30°00′	375
348	64°00′	30°00′	2280
349	62°00′	30°00′	2160
350	60°00′	30°00′	1170
351	58°30′	30°00′	2250
352	56°30′	30°00′	2853
353	54°30′	30°00′	3120
354	51°30′	30°00′	1880
355	50°00′	30°00′	3280
356	48°00′	30°00′	3400
357	46°00′	30°00′	3327
358	44°00′	30°00′	2820
359	42°00′	30°00′	2540
360	40°00′	30°00′	1450
361	38°59′	29°52′	720
362	36°10′	30°00′	3050
363	33°30′	30°00′	2350
364	30°00′	30°00′	4400

Table 1 (continued)

Station number	Latitude N	Longitude W	Depth, m
365	27°00′	30°00′	5600
366	24°00′	30°00′	5600
367	21°24′4″	30°00′	4870
368	19°00′	30°00′	4650
369	16°30′	30°00′	5080
370	14°00′	30°00′	5420
371	12°30′	30°00′	5686
372	10°30′	30°00′	5430
373	08°30′	30°00′	4500
374	06°30′	30°00′	3760
375	04°30′	30°00′	3430
376	01°40′	30°00′	3240
377	00°05′	30°00′	3370
	Latitude S		
378	02°00′	30°00′	4870
379	04°00′	30°00′	4840
380	06°00′	30°00′	5300
381	08°00′	30°00′	5200
383	11°40′	30°00′	5220
385	14°40′	30°00′	4900
387	18°00′	30°00′	4760
389	22°00′	30°00′	4960
	Latitude N		
393	14°00′	18°34′	3220

1

Species of microorganisms found in the sea (published data)

The following attempt at systematizing our information on microbial species isolated from sea water and mud and from marine animals and plants is based largely on the seventh edition of Bergey's Manual (1957), which as a rule indicates habitat and place of occurrence. Important sources for species not listed there were works by ZoBell and Upham (1944) and Brisou (1955), which, along with certain other publications, contain both previously published and original data. Lastly, the list has been completed from that given in the 1963 monograph by Kriss.

The list in Table 2, though based on Bergey, includes also species mentioned as occurring in the sea by ZoBell and Upham (1944), Brisou (1955), Issachenko (1914) and others, though not by Bergey (1957) himself.

The classification follows the system adopted in the seventh edition of Bergey's *Manual*.

As can be seen from Table 2, the microorganisms which have been isolated from a marine habitat belong to the class Schizomycetes von Naegeli, the orders Pseudomonadales Orla-Jensen, Eubacteriales Buchanan, Actinomycetales Buchanan, Beggiatoales Buchanan, Myxobacterales Jahn, Spirochaetales Buchanan, and the families Thiorhodaceae Molisch, Athiorhodaceae Molisch, Chlorobacteriaceae Lauterborn, Methanomonadaceae Breed, Thiobacteriaceae Janke, Pseudomonadaceae Winslow et al., Spirillaceae Migula, Azotobacteraceae Bergey et al., Rhizobiaceae Conn, Achromobacteraceae Breed, Enterobacteriaceae Rahn, Bacteroidaceae Breed et al., Micrococcaceae Pribram, Brevibacteriaceae Breed, Lactobacillaceae Winslow et al., Propionibacteriaceae Delwiche, Bacillaceae Fischer, Mycobacteriaceae Chester, Actinomycetaceae Buchanan, Streptomycetaceae Waksman et Henrici, Beggiatoaceae Migula, Vitreoscillaceae Pringsheim, Leucotrichaceae Buchanan, Achromatiaceae Massart, Cytophagaceae Stanier, Spirochaetaceae Swellengrebel and Treponemataceae Robinson. They belong to the following genera: *Thiosarcina* Winogradsky, *Thiopedia* Winogradsky, *Thiocapsa* Winogradsky, *Thiodictyon* Winogradsky, *Thiothece* Winogradsky, *Thiocystis* Winogradsky, *Lamprocystis* Schröter, *Amoebo-*

Table 2. Species of microorganisms of marine origin described in Bergey's *Manual* (1957)

CLASS Schizomycetes von Naegeli, 1857
Order Pseudomonadales Orla-Jensen

Family Thiorhodaceae Molisch
Thiosarcina rosea (Schröter, 1886) Winogradsky, 1888
Thiopedia rosea Winogradsky, 1888
Thiocapsa roseopersicina Winogradsky, 1888
Thiodictyon elegans Winogradsky, 1888
Thiothece gelatinosa Winogradsky, 1888
Thiocystis rufa Winogradsky, 1888
Thiocystis violacea Winogradsky, 1888
Lamprocystis roseopersicina (Kützing, 1849) Schröter, 1886
Amoebobacter granula Winogradsky, 1888
Amoebobacter roseus Winogradsky, 1888
Thiopolycoccus ruber Winogradsky, 1888
Thiospirillum jenense (Ehrenberg, 1838) Winogradsky, 1888
Thiospirillum rosenbergii (Warming, 1875) Winogradsky, 1888
Thiospirillum violaceum (Warming, 1876) Winogradsky, 1888
Rhabdomonas gracilis (Warming, 1876) Bergey et al., 1923 (*Rhodocapsa suspensa* Molisch)
Rhabdomonas rosea Cohn, 1875
Rhodothece pendens Molisch, 1907
Chromatium gobii Issachenko, 1914
Chromatium minus Winogradsky, 1888
Chromatium minutissimum Winogradsky, 1888
Chromatium okenii (Ehrenberg, 1838) Perty, 1852
Chromatium vinosum (Ehrenberg, 1838) Winogradsky, 1888
Chromatium warmingii (Cohn, 1875) Migula, 1900
Chromatium weissei Perty, 1852

Family Athiorhodaceae Molisch, 1907
Rhodopseudomonas capsulata (Molisch, 1907) van Niel, 1944
Rhodopseudomonas palustris (Molisch, 1907) van Niel, 1944 (*Rhodobacterium capsulatum* Molisch)

Family Chlorobacteriaceae Lauterborn
Chlorobium limicola Nadson, 1912
Chlorobium thiosulfatophilum Larsen, 1952

Family Methanomonadaceae Breed
Methanomonas methanica (Söhngen, 1906) Orla-Jensen, 1909

Family Thiobacteriaceae Janke
Thiobacterium bovista (Molisch, 1912) Janke, 1924
Thiovulum majus Hinze, 1913 (*Thiovulum mulleri* Lauterborn)
Thiospira bipunctata (Molisch, 1912) Vislouch, 1914
Thiobacillus denitrificans Beijerinck, 1904
Thiobacillus neapolitanus Parker
Thiobacillus thioparus Beijerinck, 1904

Family Pseudomonadaceae Winslow et al.
Pseudomonas calciprecipitans Molisch, 1925
Pseudomonas calcis (Drew, 1912) Kellerman et Smith, 1914
Pseudomonas fluorescens liquefaciens Migula, 1895
Pseudomonas gelatica (Gran, 1902) Bergey et al., 1930
Pseudomonas halestorga Elazari-Volcani, 1940
Pseudomonas ichthyodermis (Wells et ZoBell, 1934) ZoBell et Upham, 1944
Pseudomonas iridescens Stanier, 1941
Pseudomonas marinoglutinosa (ZoBell et Allen, 1935) ZoBell, 1943
Pseudomonas membranoformis (ZoBell et Allen, 1935) ZoBell, 1943
Pseudomonas phosphorescens Fisheri, 1887
Pseudomonas stutzeri (Lehmann et Neumann, 1896) Kluyver, 1942
Photobacterium fischeri Beijerinck, 1889
Photobacterium harveyi (Johnson et Shunk, 1936) Breed et Lessel, 1954
Photobacterium phosphoreum (Cohn, 1878) Ford, 1927
Photobacterium pierantonii (Zirpolo, 1918) Krasil'nikov, 1949
Alginomonas alginica (Waksman, Carey et Allen, 1934) Kåss et al., 1945
Alginomonas alginovora (Waksman, Carey et Allen, 1934) Kåss et al., 1945
Alginomonas fucicola (Waksman, Carey et Allen, 1934) Kåss et al., 1945
Alginomonas terrestralginica (Waksman et al., 1934) Kåss et al., 1945
Mycoplana bullata Gray et Thornton, 1928
Mycoplana dimorpha Gray et Thornton, 1928

Table 2 (continued)

Halobacterium cutirubrum (Lochhead, 1934) Elazari-Volcani, 1940
Halobacterium halobium (Petter, 1931) Elazari-Volcani, 1940 (*Bacillus halobius ruber*, Klebahn, 1919)
Halobacterium marismortui Elazari-Volcani, 1940
Halobacterium salinarium (Harrison et Kennedy, 1922) Elazari-Volcani, 1940 (*Pseudomonas salinaria* Harrison et Kennedy, 1922)
Halobacterium trapanicum (Petter, 1931) Elazari-Volcani, 1940

Family Spirillaceae Migula
Vibrio adaptatus ZoBell et Upham, 1944
Vibrio agarliquefaciens (Grey et Chalmers, 1924) Bergey et al., 1934
Vibrio beijerinckii Stanier, 1941
Vibrio fuscus Stanier, 1941
Vibrio granii (Lundestad, 1928) Stanier, 1941
Vibrio hyphalus ZoBell et Upham, 1944
Vibrio indicus (Beijerinck, 1889) Lehmann et Neumann, 1896
Vibrio luminosus Beijerinck, 1888
Vibrio marinopraesens ZoBell et Upham, 1944
Vibrio phytoplanktis ZoBell et Upham, 1944
Vibrio pierantonii (Zirpolo, 1918) Meissner, 1926
Desulfovibrio aestuarii (van Delden, 1904) ZoBell, 1948 (*Bacterium hydrosulfureum ponticum*, Zelinskyi, 1893)
Desulfovibrio desulfuricans (Beijerinck, 1895) Kluyver et van Niel, 1936
Desulfovibrio rubentschikii (Baars, 1930) ZoBell, 1948
Spirillum serpens (Müller, 1786) Winter, 1884
Spirillum virginianum Dimitroff, 1926
Spirillum volutans Ehrenberg, 1832 (*Spirillum colossus*)

Order Eubacteriales Buchanan

Family Azotobacteraceae Bergey, Breed et Murray
Azotobacter agilis Beijerinck, 1901
Azotobacter chroococcum Beijerinck, 1901

Family Rhizobiaceae Conn
Agrobacterium stellulatum Stapp et Knösel, 1954

Chromobacterium marismortui Elazari-Volcani, 1940

Family Achromobacteraceae Breed
Achromobacter aquamarinus ZoBell et Upham, 1944
Achromobacter fisheri Johnson et Shunk, 1936
Achromobacter stenohalis ZoBell et Upham, 1944
Achromobacter superficialis (Jordan, 1890) Bergey et al., 1923
Achromobacter thalassius ZoBell et Upham, 1944
Flavobacterium balustinum Harrison, 1929
Flavobacterium diffusum (Frankland et Frankland, 1889) Bergey et al., 1923
Flavobacterium dormitator (Wright, 1895) Bergey et al., 1923
Flavobacterium fucatum Harrison, 1929
Flavobacterium halmephilum Elazari-Volcani, 1940
Flavobacterium halohydrium ZoBell et Upham, 1944
Flavobacterium lutescens (Migula, 1900) Bergey et al., 1923
Flavobacterium marinotypicum ZoBell et Upham, 1944
Flavobacterium marinum Harrison, 1929
Flavobacterium marinovirosum ZoBell et Upham, 1944
Flavobacterium neptunium ZoBell et Upham, 1944
Flavobacterium okeanokoites ZoBell et Upham, 1944
Flavobacterium piscicida Bein, 1954
Flavobacterium solare (Lehmann et Neumann, 1896) Bergey et al., 1923
Agarbacterium amocontactum (ZoBell et Allen, 1935) Breed
Agarbacterium aurantiacum Angst, 1929
Agarbacterium boreale (Lundestad, 1928) Breed
Agarbacterium bufo Angst, 1929
Agarbacterium ceramicola (Lundestad, 1928) Breed
Agarbacterium delesseriae (Lundestad, 1928) Breed
Agarbacterium mesentericum Angst, 1929
Agarbacterium polysiphoniae (Lundestad, 1928) Breed
Agarbacterium reducans Angst, 1929

Table 2 (continued)

Agarbacterium rhodomelae (Lundestad, 1928) Breed
Agarbacterium uliginosum (ZoBell et Upham, 1944) Breed
Beneckea chitinovora (Benecke, 1905) Campbell
Beneckea hyperoptica (Campbell et Williams, 1951) Campbell
Beneckea indolthetica (Campbell et Williams, 1951) Campbell
Beneckea labra (Campbell et Williams, 1951) Campbell
Beneckea lipophaga (Campbell et Williams, 1951) Campbell
Beneckea ureasophora (Campbell et Williams, 1951) Campbell

Family Enterobacteriaceae Rahn
Serratia kiliensis (Lehmann et Neumann, 1896) Bergey et al., 1923
Proteus vulgaris Hauser, 1885

Family Bacteroidaceae Breed, Murray et Smith
Bacteroides fragilis (Veillon et Zuber, 1898) Castellani et Chalmers, 1919
Bacteroides halosmophilus Baumgartner, 1937
Bacteroides serpens (Veillon et Zuber, 1898) Hauduroy et al., 1937

Family Micrococcaceae Pribram
Micrococcus agilis Ali-Cohen, 1889
Micrococcus colpogenes Campbell et Williams, 1951
Micrococcus morrhuae Klebahn, 1919
Micrococcus varians Migula, 1900
Sarcina litoralis Poulsen, 1879
Sarcina ureae (Beijerinck, 1901) Löhnis, 1911
Methanococcus vannielii *Stadtman* et Barker, 1951
Peptococcus glycinophilus (Cardon et Barker, 1946) Douglas

Family Brevibacteriaceae Breed
Brevibacterium immotum (ZoBell et Upham, 1944) Breed, 1953
Brevibacterium marinopiscosum (ZoBell et Upham, 1944) Breed, 1953
Brevibacterium maris (Harrison, 1929) Breed, 1953
Brevibacterium sociovivum (ZoBell et Upham 1944) Breed, 1953
Brevibacterium stationis (ZoBell et Upham, 1944) Breed, 1953

Family Lactobacillaceae Winslow et al.
Peptostreptococcus putridus (Schottmüller, 1910, amend. Prévot, 1933) Smith
Eubacterium niosii (Hauduroy et al., 1937) Prévot, 1938
Ramibacterium ramosum (Veillon et Zuber, 1898) Prévot, 1938

Family Propionibacteriaceae Delwiche
Zymobacterium oroticum Waksman et Barker, 1954

Family Bacillaceae Fischer
Clostridium caproicum Prévot, 1938
Clostridium kluyveri Barker et Taha, 1942
Clostridium lacunarum Prévot, 1948
Clostridium limosum Prévot, 1948
Clostridium pasteurianum Winogradsky, 1895
Clostridium propionicum Cardon et Barker, 1946
Clostridium setiense (Prévot et Raynaud, 1944) McClung et McCoy
Methanobacterium omelianskii Barker, 1936

Order Actinomycetales Buchanan

Family Mycobacteriaceae Chester
Mycobacterium marinum Aronson, 1926

Family Actinomycetaceae Buchanan
Nocardia atlantica (Humm et Shepard, 1946) Waksman
Nocardia marina (Krasil'nikov, 1949) Waksman

Family Streptomycetaceae Waksman et Henrici
Streptomyces marinus (Humm et Shepard, 1946) Waksman

Order Beggiatoales Buchanan

Family Beggiatoaceae Migula
Beggiatoa alba (Vaucher, 1803) Trevisan, 1845
Beggiatoa arachnoidea (Agardh, 1827) Rabenhorst, 1865
Beggiatoa gigantea Klas, 1937
Beggiatoa leptomitiformis Trevisan, 1842
Beggiatoa minima Winogradsky, 1888
Beggiatoa mirabilis Cohn, 1865
Thioploca ingrica Wislouch, 1912
Thioploca minima Koppe, 1923
Thioploca schmidlei Wislouch, 1914

Table 2 (continued)

Thiothrix anulata Molisch, 1912
Thiothrix longiarticulata Klas, 1936
Thiothrix marina Molisch, 1912
Thiothrix voukii Klas, 1936

Family Vitreoscillaceae Pringsheim
Microscilla marina Pringsheim, 1951

Family Leucotrichaceae Buchanan
Leucothrix mucor Oersted, 1884 (*Chlamydothrix longissima* Molisch, 1912)

Family Achromatiaceae Massart
Achromatium oxaliferum Schewiakoff, 1893 (*Achromatium gigas* Nadson)
Achromatium volutans (Hinze, 1903) van Niel, 1948 (*Thiophysa volutans* Hinze)

Order Myxobacterales Jahn

Family Cytophagaceae Stanier
Cytophaga diffluens Stanier, 1940
Cytophaga krzemieniewskae Stanier, 1940
Cytophaga sensitiva Humm, 1946

Order Spirochaetales Buchanan

Family Spirochaetaceae Swellengrebel
Spirochaeta lurystrepta Zuelzer, 1912
Spirochaeta marina Zuelzer, 1912
Spirochaeta plicatilis Ehrenberg, 1838
Saprospira grandis Gross, 1911
Saprospira lepta Dimitroff, 1926
Saprospira punctum Dimitroff, 1926
Cristispira anodontae (Keysselitz, 1906) Gross, 1912
Cristispira balbianii (Certes, 1882) Gross, 1912
Cristispira pinnae (Gonder, 1908) Zuelzer, 1912

Family Treponemataceae Robinson
Leptospira biflexa (Wolbach et Binger, 1914) Noguchi, 1918

bacter Winogradsky, *Thiopolycoccus* Winogradsky, *Thiospirillum* Winogradsky, *Rhabdomonas* Cohn, *Rhodothece* Molisch, *Chromatium* Perty, *Rhodopseudomonas* Kluyver et van Niel, *Chlorobium* Nadson, *Methanomonas* Orla-Jensen, *Thiobacterium* Janke, *Thiovulum* Hinze, *Thiospira* Vislouch, *Thiobacillus* Beijerinck, *Pseudomonas* Migula, *Photobacterium* Beijerinck, *Alginomonas* Thjøtta et Kåss, *Mycoplana* Gray et Thornton, *Halobacterium* Elazari-Volcani, *Vibrio* Müller, *Desulfovibrio* Kluyver et van Niel, *Spirillum* Ehrenberg, *Azotobacter* Beijerinck, *Agrobacterium* Conn, *Chromobacterium* Bergonzini, *Achromobacter* Bergey et al.,* *Flavobacterium* Bergey et al., *Agarbacterium* Angst, *Beneckea* Campbell, *Serratia* Bizio, *Proteus* Hauser, *Bacteroides* Castellani et Chalmers, *Micrococcus* Cohn, *Sarcina* Goodsir, *Methanococcus* Kluyver et van Niel, *Peptococcus* Kluyver et van Niel, *Brevibacterium* Breed, *Peptostreptococcus* Kluyver et van Niel, *Eubacterium* Prévot, *Ramibacterium* Prévot, *Zymobacterium* Waksman et Barker, *Clostridium* Prazmowski, *Mycobacterium* Lehmann et Neumann, *Nocardia* Trevisan, *Streptomyces* Waksman et Henrici, *Beggiatoa* Trevisan, *Thioploca* Lauterborn, *Thiothrix* Winogradsky, *Microscilla* Pringsheim, *Leucothrix* Oersted,

* (Editor's footnote). Species of *Achromobacter* and *Flavobacterium* have been placed in Grey and Thornton's genus *Mycoplana* by Wood (see E. Ferguson Wood, 1965, *Marine Microbial Ecology*, London, p.35). These organisms are stated to be highly pleomorphic when first isolated but to stabilize on prolonged culture to forms ascribable to *Achromobacter* and *Flavobacterium.* Wood points out that the characterization of marine bacteria by cultural features rather than by the morphological attributes which they show in their natural habitats may sometimes be misleading.

Achromatium Schewiakoff, *Cytophaga* Winogradsky, *Spirochaeta* Ehrenberg, *Saprospira* Gross, *Cristispira* Gross and *Leptospira* Noguchi.

Table 3 lists microorganisms species found in the sea and mentioned or described in detail by ZoBell and Upham (1944) but not listed in the seventh edition of Bergey's key (1957). Some of them had appeared in earlier editions but, as the authors of the key state, those which had not been sufficiently fully described or which did not fit into accepted classification were omitted from the seventh edition.

For convenience of comparison the order in which the species are listed in Table 3 follows the generic sequence in Bergey's key. As can be seen by comparing Tables 2 and 3, species which do not appear in the seventh edition of Bergey's key belong, for the most part, to the genera listed in Table 2. The exceptions are *Gallionella, Diplococcus, Actinomyces, Cladothrix, Sarcinastrum, Bacterium* and *Torula,* of which the last three do not appear in Bergey (1957).

Brisou (1955) suggested a different classification of marine microorganisms from that adopted in the 1957 edition of Bergey's key. The Brisou classification has been used for Table 4, which lists species described by that author but not appearing in Bergey's key. According to Brisou (1955) these species belong to the following genera: *Micrococcus, Pseudomonas, Phytobacterium, Aplanobacter, Achromobacter, Acinetobacter, Flavobacterium, Protaminobacter, Vibrio, Spirillum, Bacteridium, Infabilis, Clostridium, Sporovibrio, Spherocillus, Treponema,* of the families Micrococcaceae, Pseudomonadaceae, Vibrionaceae Prévot, Spirillaceae, Bacillaceae, Clostridiaceae, Sporovibrionaceae, Spherophoraceae, which are distributed among the orders Micrococcales, Bacteriales, Spirillales Prévot, Bacillales, Clostridiales, Sporovibrionales Prévot, Actinobacteriales, Spirochaetales Buchanan.

The following species do not appear in the works by Bergey (1957), ZoBell and Upham (1944) or Brisou (1955): *Spirillum Egunovi* Issach., 1914, *Bact. chordale* Issach., 1914, *Bact. lactis aerogenes, Bacillus probatus, B. undulatus, Pectinobacter amylophylum,* (all discovered by Issachenko, 1914, 1937, in Arctic seas); the luminescent bacteria *Bact. ponticum, Bact. meotidum, Bact. Issachenkoi* and *Bact. Knipowitchii* (described by Yegorova, 1929, from the Black Sea); the lipolytic bacilli *B. Andrussovi* and *B. lipolyticus* (discovered by Ginzburg-Karagicheva, Pryanishnikova and Rodionova (1934) in deep-sea mud from the Black Sea); *Bact. rubidium (Eisenberg)* Chester from Pacific mud (Mefedova, 1955); *Micrococcus aeroroseus, M. aurantioluteus, M. inactivus, M. leukos, Sarcina ocros, Pseudomonas adhaerens,* var. A, *Ps. adriatica, Ps. indolgena, Ps. variabilis, Ps. variabilis* var. A, *Ps. variabilis* var. B, *B. uniflagellaris* (all isolated by Vlajnić, 1955, from Adriatic water), *Azotobacter nigricans* Kras., 1949, *Az. vinelandii* Lipmann, 1904, *Az. smyrnii* Lipmann, 1915 and *Az. insigne* (from Pshenin's (1959) collection of nitrogen-fixers from the Black Sea; Pshenin, 1959).

Table 3. Species of marine microorganisms mentioned or described in detail by ZoBell and Upham (1944) but not appearing in the seventh edition of Bergey's *Manual* (1957)

Thiobacterium beijerincki Issachenko et Salimowskaja
Thiobacterium nathansoni Issachenko et Salimowskaja
Thiobacillus thiogenes (Molisch) Ellis (1932)
Pseudomonas aestumarina ZoBell et Upham (1944)
Pseudomonas azotogena ZoBell et Upham (1944)
Pseudomonas coenobios ZoBell et Upham (1944)
Pseudomonas enalia ZoBell et Upham (1944)
Pseudomonas felthami ZoBell et Upham (1944)
Pseudomonas hypothermis ZoBell et Upham (1944)
Pseudomonas indigofera Elazari-Volcani (1940)
Pseudomonas marinopersica ZoBell et Upham (1944)
Pseudomonas membranula ZoBell et Upham (1944)
Pseudomonas neritica ZoBell et Upham (1944)
Pseudomonas obscura ZoBell et Upham (1944)
Pseudomonas oceanica ZoBell et Upham (1944)
Pseudomonas perfectomarinus ZoBell et Upham (1944)
Pseudomonas periphyta ZoBell et Upham (1944)
Pseudomonas pierantonii Bergey et al. (1939)
Pseudomonas pleomorpha ZoBell et Upham (1944)
Pseudomonas sessilis ZoBell et Upham (1944)
Pseudomonas stereotropis ZoBell et Upham (1944)
Pseudomonas vadosa ZoBell et Upham (1944)
Pseudomonas xanthochrus ZoBell et Upham (1944)
Photobacterium annulare Fischer (1885-1886)
Photobacterium caraibicum Fischer (1885-1886)
Photobacterium coronatum Fischer (1885-1886)
Photobacterium degenerans Fischer (1885-1886)
Photobacterium delgadense Fischer (1885-1886)
Photobacterium glutinosum Fischer (1885-1886)
Photobacterium hirsutum Fischer (1885-1886)
Photobacterium papillare Fischer (1885-1886)
Photobacterium tuberosum Fischer (1885-1886)
Halibacterium aurantiacum Fischer (1894)
Halibacterium liquefaciens Fischer (1894)
Halibacterium pellucidum Fischer (1894)
Halibacterium polymorphum Fischer (1894)
Halibacterium purpureum Fischer (1894)
Halibacterium roseum Fischer (1894)
Halibacterium rubrofuscum Fischer (1894)
Gallionella reticulosa Butkewitch (1928)
Gallionella tortuosa Butkewitch (1928)
Vibrio algosus ZoBell et Upham (1944)
Vibrio balticus Lehmann et Neumann (1931)
Vibrio haloplanktis ZoBell et Upham (1944)
Vibrio hydrosulfureus Zelinsky (1893)
Vibrio marinagilis ZoBell et Upham (1944)
Vibrio marinoflavus ZoBell et Upham (1944)
Vibrio marinofulvus ZoBell et Upham (1944)
Vibrio marinovulgaris ZoBell et Upham (1944)
Vibrio ponticus ZoBell et Upham (1944)
Vibrio splendidus Lehmann et Neumann (1931)
Microspira murmanensis Issachenko (1914)
Spirillum levocolelaenum (Koch) Issachenko (1912)
Spirillum marinum Russel (1891)
Spirillum ostreae Noguchi - Dimitroff (1926)
Spirillum rectiphyseteris Beauregard (1897)
Achromobacter galophilum Bergey (1939)
Achromobacter halophilum Bergey (1939)
Achromobacter luminosum Katz (1891)
Achromobacter pellucidum Harrison (1929)
Achromobacter pikowskyi Bergey (1939)
Achromobacter phosphoreum Katz (1891)
Achromobacter phosphoricum Katz (1891)
Flavobacterium droebachense Lundestad (1928)
Flavobacterium turcosum Zimmerman et Bergey (1939)
Flavobacterium halophilum Bergey (1939)
Agarbacterium cyanoides Angst (1929)
Agarbacterium viscosum Angst (1929)
Serratia marinorubra ZoBell et Upham (1944)

Table 3 (continued)

Serratia sp. *a* Gibbons (1937)
Serratia sp. *b* Gibbons (1937)
Micrococcus albus translucens Hanzawa et Takeda (1931)
Micrococcus aquivivus ZoBell et Upham (1944)
Micrococcus boreus Issachenko (1914)
Micrococcus cartharinensis Issachenko (1914)
Micrococcus centropunctatus Issachenko (1914)
Micrococcus euryhalis ZoBell et Upham (1944)
Micrococcus gelatinosus Issachenko (1914)
Micrococcus halophilus Bergey (1939)
Micrococcus infimus ZoBell et Upham (1944)
Micrococcus lentulentus Hanzawa et Takeda (1931)
Micrococcus litoralis Kellerman (1915)
Micrococcus marinus Issachenko (1914)
Micrococcus maripuniceus ZoBell et Upham (1944)
Micrococcus minutissimus Issachenko (1914)
Micrococcus pikowskyi Bergey (1939)
Micrococcus sedentarius ZoBell et Upham (1944)
Micrococcus sedimenteus ZoBell et Upham (1944)
Micrococcus selenicus Brenner (1916)
Sarcina morrhuae Klebahn Elazari-Volcani (1940)
Sarcina pelagia ZoBell et Upham (1944)
Sarcina sp. (Lochhead) Gibbons (1937)
Diplococcus gadidarum Beckwith (1911)
Bacillus abysseus ZoBell et Upham (1944)
Bacillus argenteo-phosphorescens Katz (1891)
Bacillus borborokoites ZoBell et Upham (1944)
Bacillus cirroflagellosus ZoBell et Upham (1944)
Bacillus cyaneo-phosphorescens Katz (1891)
Bacillus epiphytus ZoBell et Upham (1944)
Bacillus filicolonicus ZoBell et Upham (1944)
Bacillus granulosis Russel (1891)
Bacillus halophilus Russel (1891)
Bacillus imomarinus ZoBell et Upham (1944)
Bacillus indigoferus (Voges) Bergey (1939)
Bacillus kildini Issachenko (1914)
Bacillus limicola Russel (1893)
Bacillus limosus Russel (1891)
Bacillus litoralis Russel (1891)
Bacillus litorosus Russel (1893)
Bacillus maritimus Russel (1893)
Bacillus pelagicus Russel (1893)
Bacillus sporonema Schaudinn (1903)
Bacillus submarinus ZoBell et Upham (1944)
Bacillus thalassokoites ZoBell et Upham (1944)
Bacillus thalassophilus Russel (1891)
Actinomyces albus Gasperini Issachenko (1914)
Actinomyces halotrichis ZoBell et Upham (1944)
Actinomyces marinolimosus ZoBell et Upham (1944)
Beggiatoa marina Molisch et Bergey (1939)
Achromatium mulleri (Warming) Bergey et al. (1939)
Spirochaeta halophilica Browne (1922)
Spirochaeta icterogenes Zuelzer (1928)
Cristospira interrogationis (Gross) Bergey (1939)
Cristospira mina Dimitroff (1926)
Cristospira modiolae (Schellack) Dimitroff (1926)
Cristospira spiculifera (Schellack)Dimitroff (1926)
Cristospira tenua Dimitroff (1926)
Cladothrix intricata Russel (1891)
Bacterium actinopelte Baur (1902)
Bacterium amforeti Issachenko (1914)
Bacterium arcticum Issachenko (1914)
Bacterium balticum Feitel (1903)
Bacterium balbianii Billet (1888)
Bacterium barentsianum Issachenko (1914)
Bacterium bauri Parlandt (1911)
Bacterium beijerincki Issachenko (1914)
Bacterium brandti Issachenko et Rostowzew (1910)
Bacterium breitfussi Issachenko (1914)
Bacterium costatum Lloyd (1931)
Bacterium chitinochroma Hock (1941)
Bacterium chitinophilum Hock (1941)
Bacterium fausseki Issachenko (1914)
Bacterium feiteli Parlandt (1911)
Bacterium flavum Issachenko (1914)

Table 3 (continued)

Bacterium granii Parlandt (1911)	*Bacterium russelli* Issachenko et Rostowzew (1910)
Bacterium halophilicum Browne (1922)	*Bacterium septentrionale* Issachenko (1914)
Bacterium helgolanicum Nadson (1903)	*Bacterium spirilloides* (Zuelzer) ZoBell et Upham (1944)
Bacterium henseni Gran (1901)	*Bacterium smaragdinophosphorescens* Katz (1891)
Bacterium knipowitchi Issachenko (1914)	*Bacterium spirale* Issachenko (1914)
Bacterium laminariae Billet (1888)	*Bacterium siccum* Issachenko (1914)
Bacterium lonkoi Issachenko (1914)	*Bacterium triviale* Gran (1901)
Bacterium lobatum Baur (1902)	*Sarcinastrum urosporae* Lagerheim (1900)
Bacterium marinum Issachenko (1914)	*Torula wehmeri* Hanzawa et Takeda (1931)
Bacterium ornatum Feitel (1903)	
Bacterium pappillare Issachenko (1914)	
Bacterium repens Gran (1901)	

Bergey's 1957 key contains 183 species of marine origin, or about 12% of the total number of species (about 1550) belonging to the class Shizomycetes. Many of these species have been found not only in the sea and its inhabitants, but also in soil and other habitats; the number which can be regarded as peculiarly marine species is small.

Of the 188 genera belonging to the class Schizomycetes, listed by Bergey (1957), there are 59 which include both marine- and land-living species. There are only three genera of which all the species were isolated either from the sea water or from marine animals: *Photobacterium* Beijerinck, *Zymobacterium* Waksman et Barker and *Saprospira* Gross.

If we make the bold assumption that all the species listed above and in Tables 3 and 4 but not appearing in the seventh edition of Bergey's *Manual* (1957) are new, the percentage of species occurring in a marine milieu will be almost doubled and will account for roughly a quarter of all listed species of microorganisms. It must be remembered, however, that most of the species listed in the text above or in Tables 2, 3 and 4 were taken from closely inshore parts of the sea. These lists, accordingly, give some idea of the whole range of microbial population in the shelf part of the sea and of the continental slope at shallow depths; only a very few of the several hundred species listed are mentioned in the literature as having been found in open, deep-water parts of the sea and ocean.

More detailed information on deep-sea microflora was obtained by the 1946, 1948 and 1949 expeditions to central areas of the Black Sea, well away from the coasts (Kriss, Rukina, Biryuzova, 1950; Kriss, Markianovich, Rukina, 1954; Markianovich, 1954). Taking the standard hydrographic levels, these expeditions investigated the whole water column, from surface to bottom, as well as the surface layers of mud brought up from maximum depths. The resultant collection of 700 microorganism cultures gives a fairly comprehensive picture of the microflora inhabiting the oxygen and hydrogen sulphide zones of the Black Sea.

Species affiliation was determined in accordance with the criteria of Krasil'nikov's *Key* (1949). This key differs from Bergey's in that the

Table 4. Microorganism species of marine origin described by Brisou (1955) but not listed in Bergey's *Manual* (1957)

EUBACTERIA

Order Micrococcales

Family Micrococcaceae

Micrococcus halophilus Bergey et coll., 1927
Micrococcus petrolei Renault, 1897
Micrococcus pikowskyi Bergey et coll., 1930

Order Bacteriales

Family Pseudomonadaceae

Pseudomonas cyanoides (Angst) Brisou, 1954
Pseudomonas dispersum (Humm) Brisou, 1954
Pseudomonas elongata Humm, 1946
Pseudomonas floridana Humm, 1946
Pseudomonas proteus (Humm) Brisou, 1954
Pseudomonas viscosum (Angst) Brisou, 1954
Phytobacterium atlantica (Humm) Brisou, 1954
Phytobacterium beaufortensis (Humm) Brisou, 1954
Phytobacterium cryosthasia (Campbell et Williams) Brisou, 1955
Phytobacterium roseola (Humm) Brisou, 1954
Phytobacterium subrubra (Campbell et Williams) Brisou, 1955
Aplanobacter corallina (Humm) Brisou, 1954
Aplanobacter droebachense (Lundestad) Brisou, 1954
Aplanobacter inertia (Humm) Brisou, 1954
Aplanobacter nicholsi Brisou, 1954
Aplanobacter servanense (Kalantaria et Petrossian) Brisou, 1954
Achromobacter alcaligenes (Petruschky) Brisou et Prévot, 1954
Achromobacter chitinophilum (Hork) Brisou, 1954
Achromobacter echinodermis Brisou, 1954
Achromobacter grypheae (Moureau et Cougoureux) Brisou, 1953
Achromobacter litoralis (Russel) Bergey et coll.
Achromobacter phosphoricum (Migula) Bergey et coll.
Achromobacter pikowskyi Bergey et coll.
Achromobacter pinnatum (Ravenel) Bergey et coll.
Acinetobacter eurydice (White) Brisou et Prévot, 1954
Acinetobacter lwoffi (Audureau) Brisou et Prévot, 1954
Flavobacterium chitinochroma (Hork) Brisou, 1954
Flavobacterium halophilum Bergey et coll., 1930
Protaminobacter singulare (Humm, 1946) Brisou, 1954

Family Protobacteriaceae

Thiobacillus thiooxydans Waksman et Joffe, 1922

Order Spirillales Prévot, 1948

Family *Vibrionaceae* Prévot, 1948

Vibrio avidus Humm, 1946
Vibrio fortis Humm, 1946
Vibrio frequens Humm, 1946
Vibrio notus Humm, 1946
Vibrio stanieri Humm, 1946
Vibrio toulonnensis Defressine et Gazeneuve
Vibrio turbidus Humm, 1946

Family Spirillaceae

Cytophaga rosea Kadota, 1954
Spirillum itersonii Giesberger, 1936
Spirillum undula (Müller) Ehrenberg, 1832
Spirillum virginiarum Dimitroff, 1926

Order Bacillales

Family Bacillaceae

Bacteridium thermocellulolyticus Coolhas, 1928

Order Clostridiales

Family Clostridiaceae

Inflabilis sanguicole (Vaucher et Alt) Prévot, 1938
Inflabilis satellitis (Loris et Melikov) Prévot, 1938
Inflabilis setiensis Prévot et Raynaud, 1944
Clostridium balaenae (Nielsen) Prévot, 1890

Order Sporovibrionales Prévot, 1940

Family Sporovibrionaceae

Sporovibrio desulfuricans (Beijerinck, rev. Baars) Starkey, 1938

Table 4 (continued)

MYCOBACTERIA

CLASS Actinomycetales

Order Actinobacteriales

Family Spherophoraceae

Spherocillus cutirubra (Lochead) Brisou, 1954

Spherocillus salinaria (Harrison et Kennedy) Brisou, 1954

ALGOBACTERIA

CLASS Siderobacteriales

Order Chlamydobacteriales

Crenothrix polyspora

PROTOZOOBACTERIA

Order Spirochetales Buchanan

Treponema cotti Duboscq et Lebailly, 1912

Treponema hartmanni Gross, 1911

Treponema perexile Duboscq et Lebailly, 1912

Treponema triglae Duboscq et Lebailly, 1912

author has attempted to base his systematics on phylogenetic principles and has combined many species differing only minutely from one another.

Table 5 is a list of microorganism species taken from the depths of the Black Sea. As we know, even if all the criteria required by either of the keys are strictly observed in studying the morphological, cultural and biochemical characters needed for specific identification of a given strain, it is still very rarely possible to establish the identity of a particular strain with species described in the key. We are therefore somewhat tentative in assigning the Black Sea strains to the aggregate species listed by Krasil'nikov (1949).

Variants of these aggregate species are denoted by letters of the alphabet.

As can be seen from Table 5, the Black Sea species of microorganisms belong to the classes Actinomycetes Krasil'nikov and Eubacteriae Stanier et van Niel, the orders Actinomycetales Buchanan, Mycobacteriales Krasil'-nikov, Coccaceae Krasil'nikov and Eubacteriales Buchanan, the families Actinomycetaceae Buchanan, Mycobacteriaceae Chester, Coccaceae Zopf, Pseudomonadaceae Winslow et al., Bacteriaceae Cohn, Bacillaceae Fisher and the genera *Actinomyces* Harz, *Mycobacterium* Lehmann et Neumann, *Mycococcus* Krasil'nikov, *Pseudobacterium* Krasil'nikov, *Micrococcus* Cohn, *Sarcina* Goodsir, *Pseudomonas* Migula, *Bacterium* Ehrenberg, *Chromobacterium* Bergonzini, *Thiobacterium* Lehmann et Neumann, *Bacillus* Cohn.

There are 86 species in all and 239 variants. The relatively great variety, of microbial forms found in the Black Sea is explained by the large number of water and mud samples investigated and by the diversity of microbiological media used in isolating the cultures. It must be remembered, too, that the Black Sea is an intracontinental sea, where the influence of continental drainage bearing terrigenous organic matter is much more pronounced than in an open sea or in the ocean.

The Black Sea studies showed that many species and variants of microorganisms had extensive distribution areas. They were found in places

Table 5. Microorganism species isolated from various depths in the open part of the Black Sea

CLASS Actinomycetes Krasil'nikov, 1945

Order Actinomycetales Buchanan, 1918

Family Actinomycetaceae Buchanan, 1918

Actinomyces candidus Kras., 1941 – strain A
Actinomyces candidus Kras., 1941 – strain B
Actinomyces globisporus Kras., 1941 – strain A
Actinomyces globisporus Kras., 1941 – strain B
Actinomyces griseus Krainsky, 1914 – strain A
Actinomyces griseus Krainsky, 1914 – strain B
Actinomyces griseus Krainsky, 1914 – strain C

Order Mycobacteriales Krasil'nikov, 1949

Family Mycobacteriaceae Chester, 1901

Mycobacterium album Söhngen, 1913 – strain A
Mycobacterium album Söhngen, 1913 – strain B
Mycobacterium album Söhngen, 1913 – strain C
Mycobacterium album Söhngen, 1913 – strain D
Mycobacterium album Söhngen, 1913 – strain E
Mycobacterium album Söhngen, 1913 – strain F
Mycobacterium citreum Kras., 1941 – strain A
Mycobacterium citreum Kras., 1941 – strain B
Mycobacterium hyalinum Söhngen, 1913 – strain A
Mycobacterium hyalinum Söhngen, 1913 – strain B
Mycobacterium hyalinum Söhngen, 1913 – strain C
Mycobacterium hyalinum Söhngen, 1913 – strain D
Mycobacterium hyalinum Söhngen, 1913 – strain E
Mycobacterium hyalinum Söhngen, 1913 – strain F
Mycobacterium hyalinum Söhngen, 1913 – strain G
Mycobacterium lacticolum Lehmann et Neumann, 1889 – strain A
Mycobacterium lacticolum Lehmann et Neumann, 1889 – strain B
Mycobacterium lacticolum Lehmann et Neumann, 1889 – strain C
Mycobacterium lacticolum Lehmann et Neumann, 1889 – strain D
Mycobacterium lacticolum Lehmann et Neumann, 1889 – strain E
Mycobacterium nigrum Kras., 1941
Mycococcus albus Kras., 1941
Pseudobacterium alboflavum (Dooren Jong) Kras.
Pseudobacterium biforme (Eggerth) Kras. – strain A
Pseudobacterium biforme (Eggerth) Kras. – strain B
Pseudobacterium biforme (Eggerth) Kras. – strain C
Pseudobacterium biforme (Eggerth) Kras. – strain D
Pseudobacterium biforme (Eggerth) Kras. – strain E
Pseudobacterium castigatum (McBeth) Kras. – strain A
Pseudobacterium castigatum (McBeth) Kras. – strain B
Pseudobacterium cocciformis (Severin) Kras. – strain A
Pseudobacterium cocciformis (Severin) Kras. – strain B
Pseudobacterium cocciformis (Severin) Kras. – strain C
Pseudobacterium cocciformis (Severin) Kras. – strain D
Pseudobacterium decidiosum (Wright) Kras. – strain A
Pseudobacterium decidiosum (Wright) Kras. – strain B
Pseudobacterium furcosum (Veillon et Zuber) Kras. – strain A
Pseudobacterium furcosum (Veillon et Zuber) Kras. – strain B
Pseudobacterium furcosum (Veillon et Zuber) Kras. – strain C
Pseudobacterium furcosum (Veillon et Zuber) Kras. – strain D
Pseudobacterium furcosum (Veillon et Zuber) Kras. – strain E
Pseudobacterium furcosum (Veillon et Zuber) Kras. – strain F
Pseudobacterium furcosum (Veillon et Zuber) Kras. – strain G
Pseudobacterium furcosum (Veillon et Zuber) Kras. – strain H

Table 5 (continued)

Pseudobacterium furcosum (Veillon et Zuber) Kras.–strain I
Pseudobacterium furcosum (Veillon et Zuber) Kras.–strain K
Pseudobacterium furcosum (Veillon et Zuber) Kras.–strain L
Pseudobacterium furcosum (Veillon et Zuber) Kras.–strain M
Pseudobacterium furcosum (Veillon et Zuber) Kras.–strain N
Pseudobacterium lactis (Conn) Kras.
Pseudobacterium latericeum (Adametz) Kras.–strain A
Pseudobacterium latericeum (Adametz) Kras.–strain B
Pseudobacterium latericeum (Adametz) Kras.–strain C
Pseudobacterium latericeum (Adametz) Kras.–strain D
Pseudobacterium lutescens (Migula) Kras.
Pseudobacterium marinopiscosum (ZoBell et Upham) Kras.–strain A
Pseudobacterium marinopiscosum (ZoBell et Upham) Kras.–strain B
Pseudobacterium marinopiscosum (ZoBell et Upham) Kras.–strain C
Pseudobacterium marinopiscosum (ZoBell et Upham) Kras.–strain D
Pseudobacterium marinopiscosum (ZoBell et Upham) Kras.–strain E
Pseudobacterium marinopiscosum (ZoBell et Upham) Kras.–strain F
Pseudobacterium marinopiscosum (ZoBell et Upham) Kras.–strain G
Pseudobacterium maris (Harrison) Kras.–strain A
Pseudobacterium maris (Harrison) Kras.–strain B
Pseudobacterium opacum (Sack) Kras.–strain A
Pseudobacterium opacum (Sack) Kras.–strain B
Pseudobacterium ovatum (Egg. et Gagn.) Kras.–strain A
Pseudobacterium ovatum (Egg. et Gagn.) Kras.–strain B
Pseudobacterium ovatum (Egg. et Gagn.) Kras.–strain C
Pseudobacterium ovatum (Egg. et Gagn.) Kras.–strain D
Pseudobacterium ovatum (Egg. et Gagn.) Kras.–strain E
Pseudobacterium ovatum (Egg. et Gagn.) Kras.–strain F
Pseudobacterium qualis (Steinhaus) Kras.–strain A
Pseudobacterium qualis (Steinhaus) Kras.–strain B
Pseudobacterium subluteum (Dobrz) Kras.–strain A
Pseudobacterium subluteum (Dobrz) Kras.–strain B
Pseudobacterium variabilis (Distaso) Kras.

Order Coccaceae Krasil'nikov, 1945

Family Coccaceae Zopf, 1889
Micrococcus albicans Trevisan, 1889
Micrococcus albus (Rosenb.) Buchanan, 1911–strain A
Micrococcus albus (Rosenb.) Buchanan, 1911–strain B
Micrococcus albus (Rosenb.) Buchanan, 1911–strain C
Micrococcus albus (Rosenb.) Buchanan, 1911–strain D
Micrococcus albus (Rosenb.) Buchanan, 1911–strain E
Micrococcus albus (Rosenb.) Buchanan, 1911–strain F
Micrococcus albus (Rosenb.) Buchanan, 1911–strain G
Micrococcus albus (Rosenb.) Buchanan, 1911–strain H
Micrococcus aurantiacus (Schröter) Cohn, 1872–strain A
Micrococcus aurantiacus (Schröter) Cohn, 1872–strain B
Micrococcus aurantiacus (Schröter) Cohn, 1872–strain C
Micrococcus aurantiacus (Schröter) Cohn, 1872–strain D
Micrococcus aurantiacus (Schröter) Cohn, 1872–strain E
Micrococcus aureus (Rosenb.) Migula, 1900–strain A
Micrococcus aureus (Rosenb.) Migula, 1900–strain B
Micrococcus aureus (Rosenb.) Migula, 1900–strain C
Micrococcus aureus (Rosenb.) Migula, 1900–strain D
Micrococcus aureus (Rosenb.) Migula, 1900–strain E
Micrococcus aureus (Rosenb.) Migula, 1900–strain F
Micrococcus aureus (Rosenb.) Migula, 1900–strain G
Micrococcus candidus Cohn, 1872–strain A

Table 5 (continued)

Micrococcus candidus Cohn, 1872 – strain B
Micrococcus candidus Cohn, 1872 – strain C
Micrococcus candidus Cohn, 1872 – strain D
Micrococcus candidus Cohn, 1872 – strain E
Micrococcus candidus Cohn, 1872 – strain F
Micrococcus candidus Cohn, 1872 – strain G
Micrococcus candidus Cohn, 1872 – strain H
Micrococcus candidus Cohn, 1872 – strain I
Micrococcus candidus Cohn, 1872 – strain K
Micrococcus candidus Cohn, 1872 – strain L
Micrococcus candidus Cohn, 1872 – strain M
Micrococcus candidus Cohn, 1872 – strain N
Micrococcus candidus Cohn, 1872 – strain O
Micrococcus citreus Migula, 1900 – strain A
Micrococcus citreus Migula, 1900 – strain B
Micrococcus citreus Migula, 1900 – strain C
Micrococcus citreus Migula, 1900 – strain D
Micrococcus citreus Migula, 1900 – strain E
Micrococcus citreus Migula, 1900 – strain F
Micrococcus citreus Migula, 1900 – strain G
Micrococcus citreus Migula, 1900 – strain H
Micrococcus conglomeratus Migula, 1900
Micrococcus flavus (Flügge) Lehmann et Neumann, 1896
Micrococcus luteus (Schröter) Cohn, 1872
Micrococcus radiatus Flügge, 1886 – strain A
Micrococcus radiatus Flügge, 1886 – strain B
Micrococcus roseus Flügge, 1886 – strain A
Micrococcus roseus Flügge, 1886 – strain B
Micrococcus sulfureus Zimmermann, 1890 – strain A
Micrococcus sulfureus Zimmermann, 1890 – strain B
Micrococcus sulfureus Zimmermann, 1890 – strain C
Micrococcus ureae Cohn, 1872
Sarcina alba Zimmermann, 1890 – strain A
Sarcina alba Zimmermann, 1890 – strain B
Sarcina flava De Bary, 1887 – strain A
Sarcina flava De Bary, 1887 – strain B
Sarcina flava De Bary, 1887 – strain C
Sarcina flava De Bary, 1887 – strain D
Sarcina nivea Henrici, 1894

CLASS Eubacteriae Stanier et van Niel, 1941

Order Eubacteriales Buchanan, 1917

Family Pseudomonadaceae Winslow et al., 1917
Pseudomonas gracilis Migula, 1900
Pseudomonas longa (Zimm.) Migula, 1900 – strain A
Pseudomonas longa (Zimm.) Migula, 1900 – strain B

Family Bacteriaceae Cohn, 1872
Bacterium agile Jensen, 1898 – strain A
Bacterium agile Jensen, 1898 – strain B
Bacterium agile Jensen, 1898 – strain C
Bacterium agile Jensen, 1898 – strain D
Bacterium agile Jensen, 1898 – strain E
Bacterium agile Jensen, 1898 – strain F
Bacterium agile Jensen, 1898 – strain G
Bacterium agile Jensen, 1898 – strain H
Bacterium album (Copeland) Kras. – strain A
Bacterium album (Copeland) Kras. – strain B
Bacterium album (Copeland) Kras. – strain C
Bacterium album (Copeland) Kras. – strain D
Bacterium album (Copeland) Kras. – strain E
Bacterium album (Copeland) Kras. – strain F
Bacterium album (Copeland) Kras. – strain G
Bacterium album (Copeland) Kras. – strain H
Bacterium album (Copeland) Kras. – strain I

Table 5 (continued)

Bacterium album (Copeland) Kras. – strain K
Bacterium album (Copeland) Kras. – strain L
Bacterium album (Copeland) Kras. – strain M
Bacterium album (Copeland) Kras. – strain N
Bacterium album (Copeland) Kras. – strain O
Bacterium album (Copeland) Kras. – strain P
Bacterium album (Copeland) Kras. – strain R
Bacterium album (Copeland) Kras. – strain S
Bacterium album (Copeland) Kras. – strain T
Bacterium candicans (G. et P. Frankl.) Migula, 1900 – strain A
Bacterium candicans (G. et P. Frankl.) Migula, 1900 – strain B
Bacterium candicans (G. et P. Frankl.) Migula, 1900 – strain C
Bacterium halophilum (Bergey et al.) Kras.
Bacterium liquefaciens (Eisenberg) Kras. – strain A
Bacterium liquefaciens (Eisenberg) Kras. – strain B
Bacterium liquefaciens (Eisenberg) Kras. – strain C
Bacterium liquefaciens (Eisenberg) Kras. – strain D
Bacterium liquefaciens (Eisenberg) Kras. – strain E
Bacterium liquefaciens (Eisenberg) Kras.–strain F
Bacterium liquefaciens (Eisenberg) Kras. – strain G
Bacterium liquefaciens (Eisenberg) Kras. – strain H
Bacterium liquefaciens (Eisenberg) Kras. – strain I
Bacterium liquefaciens (Eisenberg) Kras. – strain K
Bacterium liquefaciens (Eisenberg) Kras. – strain L
Bacterium nitrificans (Chester) Kras. – strain A
Bacterium nitrificans (Chester) Kras. – strain B
Bacterium nitrificans (Chester) Kras. – strain C
Bacterium nitrificans (Chester) Kras. – strain D
Bacterium proteus (Hauser) Kras.
Chromobacterium aquatile (G. et P. Frankl.) Kras. – strain A
Chromobacterium aquatile (G. et P. Frankl.) Kras. – strain B
Chromobacterium aquatile (G. et P. Frankl.) Kras. – strain C
Chromobacterium aquatile (G. et P. Frankl.) Kras. – strain D
Chromobacterium aurantiacum (G. et P. Frankl.) Topley et Wilson, 1931
Chromobacterium chlorinum (Migula) Kras. – strain A
Chromobacterium chlorinum (Migula) Kras. – strain B
Chromobacterium citricum (Kerm) Kras. – strain A
Chromobacterium citricum (Kerm) Kras. – strain B
Chromobacterium citricum (Kerm) Kras. – strain C
Chromobacterium denitrificans Topley et Wilson
Chromobacterium flavum (Fuhrmann) Kras.
Chromobacterium miniaceum (Zimmermann) Kras.
Thiobacterium beijerinckii Issachenko et Salimovskaja, 1928 – strain A
Thiobacterium beijerinckii Issachenko et Salimovskaja, 1928– strain B
Thiobacterium beijerinckii Issachenko et Salimovskaja, 1928 – strain C

Family Bacillaceae Fischer, 1895
Bacillus amarus Hammer, 1919
Bacillus amylozyma Perdrix, 1891
Bacillus angulans (Burchard) Kras. – strain A
Bacillus angulans (Burchard) Kras. – strain B
Bacillus angulans (Burchard) Kras. – strain C
Bacillus angulans (Burchard) Kras. – strain D
Bacillus angulans (Burchard) Kras. – strain E
Bacillus angulans (Burchard) Kras. – strain F
Bacillus angulans (Burchard) Kras. – strain G

Table 5 (continued)

Bacillus angulans (Burchard) Kras. – strain H
Bacillus angulans (Burchard) Kras. – strain I
Bacillus anthracoides Huppe et Wood, 1889 – strain A
Bacillus anthracoides Huppe et Wood, 1889 – strain B
Bacillus anthracoides Huppe et Wood, 1889 – strain C
Bacillus aurantius (Sack) Bergey et al., 1930 – strain A
Bacillus aurantius (Sack) Bergey et al., 1930 – strain B
Bacillus cohaerens Gottheil, 1901 – strain A
Bacillus cohaerens Gottheil, 1901 – strain B
Bacillus cohaerens Gottheil, 1901 – strain C
Bacillus cohaerens Gottheil, 1901 – strain D
Bacillus cohaerens Gottheil, 1901 – strain E
Bacillus coprogenes (Flügge) Kras.
Bacillus danicus Löhnis et Westermann, 1908 – strain A
Bacillus danicus Löhnis et Westermann, 1908 – strain B
Bacillus danicus Löhnis et Westermann, 1908 – strain C
Bacillus disciformis Gräfenhann, 1891
Bacillus disciformis nonliquefaciens nova subsp.
Bacillus foliaceus Migula, 1900 – strain A
Bacillus foliaceus Migula, 1900 – strain B
Bacillus foliaceus Migula, 1900 – strain C
Bacillus formosus Bredemann et Heigener, 1935
Bacillus goniosporus Burchard, 1897 – strain A
Bacillus goniosporus Burchard, 1897 – strain B
Bacillus goniosporus Burchard, 1897 – strain C
Bacillus goniosporus Burchard, 1897 – strain D
Bacillus limbatus (Klecki) Migula, 1900
Bacillus lubinskii Migula, 1900
Bacillus luteus Garbowski, 1907
Bacillus mediosporus Migula, 1900
Bacillus mesentericus Trevisan, 1886 – strain A
Bacillus mesentericus Trevisan, 1886 – strain B
Bacillus mycoides Flügge, 1886 – strain A
Bacillus mycoides Flügge, 1886 – strain B
Bacillus natans Kern, 1901 – strain A
Bacillus natans Kern, 1901 – strain B
Bacillus natans Kern, 1901 – strain C
Bacillus natans Kern, 1901 – strain D
Bacillus natans Kern, 1901 – strain E
Bacillus nigricans Kern, 1897
Bacillus rusticus (Kern) Kras. – strain A
Bacillus rusticus (Kern) Kras. – strain B
Bacillus salinus Nadson, 1914
Bacillus solidus Lüderitz, 1889 – strain A
Bacillus solidus Lüderitz, 1889 – strain B
Bacillus solidus Lüderitz, 1889 – strain C
Bacillus solidus Lüderitz, 1889 – strain D
Bacillus subtilis (Ehrenberg) Cohn, 1872
Bacillus thermoliquefaciens Bergey et al., 1923
Bacillus thermotranslucens Bergey et al., 1923
Bacillus virgatus Kern, 1897
Bacillus vitreus Migula, 1900 – strain A
Bacillus vitreus Migula, 1900 – strain B
Bacillus vitreus Migula, 1900 – strain C

far apart and at various depths of the water column. The range of these species and varieties was not restricted to the zone of gyral currents; they were no less frequently found in regions of chemical stratification. In most cases incubation in nutrient media yielded more than one colony of a species or variety from a given sample, and often tens or even hundreds of colonies. This showed that the microbial forms in question were multiplying at the site from which they were isolated.

We have not touched on the species composition of the fungus population of the sea and ocean. Although this question has been covered in detail in a monograph by Johnson and Sparrow (1961), it will be in place

Table 6. Species of yeast organisms of marine origin

Species	Occurrence	Authors
Candida intermedia (Cif. et Ashf.) Langeron et Guerra	Biscayne Bay mud	Fell, Ahearn, Meyers, Roth, 1960
	Atlantic Ocean, coast of Portugal, surface layer of water	Taysi and van Uden, 1964
	Seaweeds	Suehiro and Tomiyasu, 1962
	Mud from tide land.	Suehiro, 1963
C. boidinii	Biscayne Bay mud	Fell, Ahearn, Meyers, Roth, 1960
	Atlantic Ocean, coast of Portugal, surface layer of water	Taysi and van Uden, 1964
C. melinii Diddens et Lodder	Biscayne Bay mud	Fell, Ahearn, Meyers, Roth, 1960
C. tenuis Diddens et Lodder	Biscayne Bay mud	Fell, Ahearn, Meyers, Roth, 1960
	Mud near Cat Cay, Bahamas Atlantic Ocean, Gulf Stream, near Bahamas	Fell and van Uden, 1963
	Seaweeds	Suehiro and Tomiyasu, 1962
C. curvata (Diddens et Lod.) n. comb.	Biscayne Bay mud	Fell, Ahearn, Meyers, Roth, 1960
	Mud near Cat Cay, Bahamas	Fell and van Uden, 1963
C. pulcherrima (Lindner) Windisch	Black Sea, in water from surface to 1250 m deep Sea of Okhotsk and north-west Pacific, in water from surface to 2500 m deep	Kriss, Rukina and Tikhonenko, 1952; Kriss and Novozhilova, 1954; Novozhilova, 1955
	Atlantic Ocean, coast of Portugal, surface layer of water	Taysi and van Uden, 1964
C. guilliermondii (Cast.) Langeron et Guerra	Indian Ocean, in water 2-6 miles from Bombay	Bhat and Kachwalla, 1955; Bhat, Kachwalla and Mody, 1955

Table 6 (continued)

Species	Occurrence	Authors
C. guilliermondii (Cast.) Langeron et Guerra	Surface of shrimps caught in the Gulf of Mexico	Phaff, Mrak and Williams, 1952
	Atlantic Ocean, mud near Cat Cay, Bahamas; Gulf Stream near Bahamas; from water and fishes of Biscayne Bay	Fell and van Uden, 1963
	Mud from tide land	Suehiro, 1963
	Atlantic Ocean, coast of Portugal, surface layer of water	Taysi and van Uden, 1964
C. melibiosi n. spec.	Indian Ocean, in water 2-6 miles from Bombay	Bhat and Kachwalla, 1955; Bhat, Kachwalla and Mody, 1955
C. tropicalis (Cast.) Berkhout	Indian Ocean, in water 2-6 miles from Bombay	Bhat and Kachwalla, 1955; Bhat, Kachwalla and Mody, 1955
	Biscayne Bay mud	Fell, Ahearn, Meyers, Roth, 1960
	Algae on south and north coasts of Florida	Capriotti, 1962
	Sea fishes near Bahamas Biscayne Bay water	Fell and van Uden, 1963
	Seaweeds	Suehiro and Tomiyasu, 1962
	Sea plankton	Suehiro, Tomiyasu and Tanaka, 1962
	Mud from tide land	Suehiro, 1963
C. parapsilosis (Ashf.) Langeron et Jalice	*Surface of shrimps caught in the Gulf of Mexico	Phaff, Mrak and Williams, 1952
	Atlantic Ocean, Gulf Stream near Bahamas. From water, mud and sea fishes of Biscayne Bay; mud near Cat Cay, Bahamas From fishes, Bahamas	Fell and van Uden, 1963

Table 6 (continued)

Species	Occurrence	Authors
C. parapsilosis (Ashf.) Langeron et Jalice	Atlantic Ocean, coast of Portugal, surface layer of water	Taysi and van Uden, 1964
	Gulf Stream, in 200-300 m water layer	Capriotti, 1962
C. parapsilosis (Ashf.) Langeron et Jalice, var. *intermedia* van Rij et Verona	Gulf Stream, in 200-300 m water layer	Capriotti, 1962
	Sea plankton	Suehiro, Tomiyasu and Tanaka, 1962
	Seaweeds	Suehiro, 1960; Suehiro and Tomiyasu, 1962.
C. humicola (Daszewska) Diddens et Lodder	Internal parts of sea molluscs	Kobayasi, Tsubaki and Soneda, 1953
C. pelliculosa Redaelli	Internal parts of sea molluscs	Kobayasi, Tsubaki and Soneda, 1953; Nakasima, 1954, 1955, 1957
C. reukaufii (Grüss) Diddens et Lodder	In coral epibiotics	van Uden and ZoBell, 1962
C. albicans (Robin) Berkhout	Islands off Florida, near the sea surface	Capriotti, 1962
	Mud from Biscayne Bay	Fell and van Uden, 1963
	Seaweeds	Suehiro, 1960
C. marina n. spec.	In coral epibiotics	van Uden and ZoBell, 1962
C. lipolytica (Harrison) Diddens et Lodder	Seaweeds	Suehiro, 1962
	Atlantic Ocean, coast of Portugal, surface layer of water	Taysi and van Uden, 1964
C. solanii nov. spec.	Sea plankton	Suehiro, Tomiyasu and Tanaka, 1962
C. krusei (Cast.) Berkhout	Biscayne Bay water	Fell and van Uden, 1964

Table 6 (continued)

Species	Occurrence	Authors
C. brumptii Langeron et Guerra	Atlantic Ocean, coast of Portugal, surface layer of water	Taysi and van Uden, 1964
	Seaweeds	Suehiro and Tomiyasu, 1962
	Sea plankton	Suehiro, Tomiyasu and Tanaka, 1962
	Mud from tide land	Suehiro, 1963
C. catenulata Diddens et Lodder	Atlantic Ocean, coast of Portugal, surface layer of water	Taysi and van Uden, 1964
C. lusitaniae	Atlantic Ocean, coast of Portugal, surface layer of water	Taysi and van Uden, 1964
C. mycoderma (Reess) nov. comb.	Atlantic Ocean, coast of Portugal, surface layer of water	Taysi and van Uden, 1964
	North sea, fish skin	Ross and Morris, 1962
	Mud from tide land	Suehiro, 1963
C. rugosa var. *elegans*	Pacific Ocean, near south California, in water from 50 m depth	van Uden and Castelo-Branco, 1963
Debaryomyces hansenii (Zopf) nov. comb.	Indian Ocean, in water 2-6 miles from Bombay	Bhat and Kachwalla, 1955, Bhat, Kachwalla and Mody 1955
D. subglobosus (Zach.) n. comb.	Indian Ocean, in water 2-6 miles from Bombay	Bhat and Kachwalla, 1955; Bhat, Kachwalla and Mody, 1955
	Internal parts of marine animals	Capriotti, 1962
	North Atlantic, muddy water 2200, 3340, 3725m deep, shrimp eggs, internal parts of starfish, of sea cucumber, sponges, fish scales and skin, sea perch roe	Siepmann and Höhnk, 1962
D. kloeckeri Guill. et Péju	Indian Ocean, in water 2-6 miles from Bombay	Bhat and Kachwalla, 1955; Bhat, Kachwalla and Mody, 1955

Table 6 (continued)

Species	Occurrence	Authors
D. kloeckeri Guill. et Péju	Biscayne Bay mud	Fell, Ahearn, Meyers, Roth, 1960
	Internal parts of sea molluscs	Nakasima, 1955, 1957
	Internal parts of red ocean perch, fish scales, sponge	Siepmann and Höhnk, 1962
	Mud near High Cay, Andros Sea fishes, Biscayne Bay, Atlantic Ocean, Gulf Stream near Bahamas	Fell and van Uden, 1963
D. nicotianae Giovannozzi	Indian Ocean, in water 2-6 miles from Bombay	Bhat and Kachwalla, 1955; Bhat, Kachwalla and Mody, 1955
D. minuta	Sea fishes, Biscayne Bay	Fell and van Uden, 1963
Hansenula californica (Lodder) Wickerham	Surface of shrimps caught in the Gulf of Mexico	Phaff, Mrak and Williams, 1952
	Internal parts of fishes	Siepmann and Höhnk, 1962
H. anomala (Hansen) H. et P. Sydow	Biscayne Bay mud	Fell, Ahearn, Meyers, Roth, 1960
	Internal parts of sea molluscs	Nakasima, 1955, 1957
	Sea fishes, Biscayne Bay	Fell and van Uden, 1963
	Mud from tide land	Suehiro, 1963
Hanseniaspora apiculata(Rees)*Kudryavtsev*	Black Sea, 50 miles from coast, in water 250 m deep	Kriss, Rukina and Tikhonenko, 1952
H. valbyensis Klöcker	Sea fishes, Biscayne Bay	Fell and van Uden, 1963
Saccharomyces ellipsoideus II (Hansen) Dekker	Skagerrak	Fischer, 1894
	Islands of Florida, near surface; algae on north coast of Florida	Capriotti, 1962

Table 6 (continued)

Species	Occurrence	Authors
S. pasteurianum Hansen	Skagerrak	Fischer, 1894
S. fructuum n. spec.	Indian Ocean, in water 2-6 miles from Bombay	Bhat and Kachwalla, 1955; Bhat, Kachwalla and Mody, 1955
	Mud from Biscayne Bay	Fell and van Uden, 1963
S. rosei (Guilliermond) n. comb.	Indian Ocean, in water 2-6 miles from Bombay	Bhat and Kachwalla, 1955; Bhat, Kachwalla and Mody, 1955
S. steineri n. spec.	Indian Ocean, in water 2-6 miles from Bombay	Bhat and Kachwalla, 1955; Bhat, Kachwalla and Mody, 1955
S. estuarii	In coral epibiotics	van Uden and ZoBell, 1962
	Mud from Biscayne Bay	Fell and van Uden, 1963
S. delbrueckii Lindner	Mud from tide land	Suehiro, 1963
S. exiguus Hausen	Mud from tide land	Suehiro, 1963
S. cerevisiae Hansen	Atlantic Ocean, coast of Portugal, surface layer of water	Taysi and van Uden, 1964
	Mud from tide land	Suehiro, 1963
S. fragilis Jörgensen	Pacific Ocean, near south California, in water from 100 m	van Uden and Castelo-Branco, 1963
Sporobolomyces salmonicolor Kluyver et van Niel	Black Sea, in water from surface to a depth of 1750 m	Kriss and Novozhilova, 1954; Novozhilova, 1955
	Sea of Okhotsk and north-west Pacific, in water from surface to a depth of 1000 m	
Nadsoniella nigra Issachenko	Barents Sea, in water 5-10 m deep in Yekaterina Harbour	Issachenko, 1914
Nadsoniomyces sphenoides Kudryavtsev	Sea of Japan, surface of algae *Laminaria japonica*	Kudryavtsev, 1932

Table 6 (continued)

Species	Occurrence	Authors
Torulopsis denitrificans Gräf	South China Sea, 110 miles from coast, surface layer of water	Gräf, 1909
T. candida Saito	Indian Ocean, in water 2-6 miles from Bombay	Bhat and Kachwalla, 1955; Bhat, Kachwalla and Mody, 1955
	Black Sea, in water from surface to 1500 m deep	Kriss, Rukina and Tikhonenko, 1952; Novozhilova, 1955
	Sea of Okhotsk and north-west Pacific, in water from surface to bottom	
	North Atlantic, muddy water at 2200 and 3725 m; shrimp eggs, fish scales, internal parts of sponge	Siepmann and Höhnk, 1962
T. famata (Harrison) n. comb.	Indian Ocean, in water 2-6 miles from Bombay	Bhat and Kachwalla, 1955; Bhat, Kachwalla and Mody, 1955
	Black Sea, in water from surface to 300 m deep Sea of Okhotsk and north-west Pacific, in water from surface and from 25 m	Kriss, Rukina and Tikhonenko, 1952; Novozhilova, 1955
	Seaweeds	Suehiro, 1960; Suehiro and Tomiyasu, 1962
	Mud near Cat Cay, Bahamas Mud near High Cay, Andros	Fell and van Uden, 1963
T. glabrata (Anderson) Lodder et de Vries	Indian Ocean, in water 2-6 miles from Bombay	Bhat and Kachwalla, 1955; Bhat, Kachwalla and Mody, 1955
	Surface of shrimps caught in the Gulf of Mexico	Phaff, Mrak and Williams, 1952
T. aeria (Saito) Lodder	Surface of shrimps caught in the Gulf of Mexico	Phaff, Mrak and Williams, 1952
	Internal parts of sea molluscs	Kobayasi, Tsubaki and Soneda, 1953

Table 6 (continued)

Species	Occurrence	Authors
T. aeria (Saito) Lodder	Black Sea, in water from surface to 300 m deep Sea of Okhotsk in water from surface and from 25 m	Kriss, Rukina and Tikhonenko, 1952; Novozhilova, 1955
T. lipofera Dooren de Jong	Sea of Okhotsk, in 0-10 m water layer	Kriss and Novozhilova, 1954; Novozhilova, 1955
T. haemulonii n. spec.	From water of Biscayne Bay and from water near the coast of Portugal	van Uden and Kolipinski 1962
T. torresii n. spec.	In coral epibiotics	van Uden and ZoBell, 1962
T. maris n. spec.	In coral epibiotics	van Uden and ZoBell, 1962
T. inconspicua n. spec.	Sea plankton	Suehiro, Tomiyasu and Tanaka, 1962
	North Sea, fish skin	Ross and Morris, 1962
	Seaweeds	Suehiro, 1962
Trichosporon cutaneum (de Beurm, Gougerot et Vaucher) Ota	Surface of shrimps caught in the Gulf of Mexico	Phaff, Mrak and Williams, 1952
	From algae on the north coast of Florida	Capriotti, 1962
	Shrimp eggs, internal parts of sponge, scales and internal parts of fishes	Siepmann and Höhnk, 1962
	From water, mud, sea fishes of Biscayne Bay, From sea fishes near Bahamas	Fell and van Uden, 1963
	Seaweeds	Suehiro, 1960; Suehiro and Tomiyasu, 1962
	Sea plankton	Suehiro, Tomiyasu and Tanaka, 1962
	Mud from tide land	Suehiro, 1963

Table 6 (continued)

Species	Occurrence	Authors
Trichosporon cutaneum (de Beurm, Gougerot et Vaucher) Ota	Atlantic Ocean, coast of Portugal, surface layer of water	Taysi and van Uden, 1964
Tr. maritimum Siepmann n. spec.	North Atlantic, muddy water from 3340 and 3725 m and from shrimp eggs	Siepmann and Höhnk, 1962
Tr. atlanticum Siepmann n. spec.	Shrimp eggs	Siepmann and Höhnk, 1962
Tr. piscium Siepmann n. spec.	Fish skin	Siepmann and Höhnk, 1962
Tr. diddensii Phaff, Mrak et Williams	Surface of shrimps caught in the Gulf of Mexico	Phaff, Mrak and Williams, 1952
Tr. pullulans (Lindner) Diddens et Lodder	Mud from tide land	Suehiro, 1963
Tr. behrendii n. spec.	Seaweeds	Suehiro, 1960
Tr. infestans (Moses et Vianna) Ciferri et Redaelli	Seaweeds	Suehiro, 1960; Suehiro and Tomiyasu, 1962
Rhodotorula mucilaginosa (Jörg.) Harrison	Indian Ocean, in water 2-6 miles from Bombay	Bhat, Kachwalla and Mody,
	Surface of shrimps caught in the Gulf of Mexico	Phaff, Mrak and Williams, 1952
	Biscayne Bay mud	Fell, Ahearn, Meyers, Roth, 1960
	Internal parts of sea molluscs	Kobayasi, Tsubaki and Soneda, 1953
	Black Sea, in water from surface to 300 m deep	Kriss, Rukina and Tikhonenko, 1952
	Bahamas, near surface and in 100-200 m water layer	Capriotti, 1962
	Okhotsk Sea and N.W. Pacific, in water from surface to 2500 m; from mud layer surface	Kriss and Novozhilova, 1954; Novozhilova, 1955

Table 6 (continued)

Species	Occurrence	Authors
Rhodotorula mucilaginosa (Jörg.) Harrison	Fish skin and scales	Siepmann and Höhnk, 1962
	Mud near High Cay, Andros From water and sea fishes of Biscayne Bay; Atlantic Ocean, Gulf Stream near Bahamas	Fell and van Uden, 1963
	Seaweeds	Suehiro, 1962; Suehiro and Tomiyasu, 1962
	Mud from tide land	Suehiro, 1963
	Sea plankton	Suehiro, Tomiyasu and Tanaka, 1962.
Rh. pallida Lodder	Indian Ocean, in water 2-6 miles from Bombay	Bhat, Kachwalla and Mody, 1955
	Black Sea, in water from surface to 50 m deep	Kriss and Novozhilova, 1954; Novozhilova, 1955
Rh. glutinis (Fres.) Harrison	Surface of shrimps caught in the Gulf of Mexico	Phaff, Mrak and Williams, 1952
	Biscayne Bay mud	Fell, Ahearn, Meyers, Roth, 1960
	Black Sea, in water from surface to 300 m deep Sea of Okhotsk, in water from surface to 2500 m deep	Kriss, Rukina and Tikhonenko, 1952; Kriss and Novozhilova, 1954; Novozhilova, 1955
	Scales and internal parts of fishes	Siepmann and Höhnk, 1962
	Gulf Stream, in 200-300 m water layer	Capriotti, 1962
	Atlantic Ocean, coast of Portugal, surface layer of water	Taysi and van Uden, 1964
	Mud near High Cay, Andros Atlantic Ocean, Gulf Stream near Bahamas, sea fishes, Bahamas, Biscayne Bay water	Fell and van Uden, 1963

Table 6 (continued)

Species	Occurrence	Authors
Rh. glutinis (Fres.) Harrison	Pacific Ocean, near south California, surface layer of water and in water from 25,50, 100, 250 and 500 m	van Uden and Castelo-Branco, 1963
	Sea plankton	Suehiro, Tomiyasu and Tanaka, 1962
Rh. glutinis var. *rubescens* (Saito) Lodder	Black Sea, in water from 75m and 100 m layers Sea of Okhotsk, in water from 10-2500 m depth	Novozhilova, 1955
Rh. minuta (Saito) Harrison	Internal parts of sea molluscs	Kobayasi, Tsubaki and Soneda, 1953
	Biscayne Bay mud	Fell, Ahearn, Meyers, Roth, 1960
	Bahamas, in 200-300 m water layer	Capriotti, 1962
	Sea fishes near Bahamas	Fell and van Uden, 1963
	Sea plankton	Suehiro, Tomiyasu and Tanaka, 1962
Rh. graminis	Biscayne Bay mud	Fell, Ahearn, Meyers, Roth, 1960
	Biscayne Bay water	Fell and van Uden, 1963
Rh. graminis	Pacific Ocean, near south California, surface layer of water	van Uden and Castelo-Branco, 1963
Rh. rubra (Demme) Lodder	Internal parts of sea molluscs	Kobayasi, Tsubaki and Soneda, 1953
	Shrimp eggs	Siepmann and Höhnk, 1962
	Atlantic Ocean, coast of Portugal, surface layer of water	Taysi and van Uden, 1964
Rh. marina Phaff, Mrak et Williams	Surface of shrimps caught in the Gulf of Mexico	Phaff, Mrak and Williams, 1952

Table 6 (continued)

Species	Occurrence	Authors
Rh. marina Phaff, Mrak et Williams	Bahamas, in mud from 828 m depth	Fell, Ahearn,Meyers, Roth, 1960
Rh. peneaus Phaff, Mrak et Williams	Surface of shrimps caught in the Gulf of Mexico	Phaff, Mrak and Williams, 1952
Rh. texensis Phaff, Mrak et Williams	Surface of shrimps caught in the Gulf of Mexico	Phaff, Mrak and Williams, 1952
	Biscayne Bay mud	Fell, Ahearn,Meyers, Roth, 1960
	North Atlantic, muddy water from 2200 m deep; internal parts of a sea urchin	Siepmann and Höhnk, 1962
	Gulf Stream, in 200-300 m water layer. Bahamas, in 100-200 m and 200-300 m layers	Capriotti, 1962
Rh. aurantiaca (Saito) Lodder	Black Sea, in water from surface to 200 m deep Sea of Okhotsk and north-west Pacific, in water from surface to 2500 m deep	Kriss and Novozhilova, 1954; Novozhilova, 1955
	Atlantic Ocean, Gulf Stream near Bahamas	Fell and van Uden, 1963
Rh. flava(Saito) Lodder	Sea plankton	Suehiro, Tomiyasu and Tanaka, 1962.
Cryptococcus laurentii (Kuff.) Skinner	Indian Ocean, in water 2-6 miles from Bombay	Bhat, Kachwalla and Mody, 1955
	Biscayne Bay mud	Fell, Ahearn,Meyers, Roth, 1960
	Black Sea, in water from surface to 1000 m deep Sea of Okhotsk and north-west Pacific, in water from surface to 2500 m deep	Kriss, Rukina and Tikhonenko, 1952; Kriss and Novozhilova, 1954; Novozhilova, 1955
	Mud near High Cay, Andros Atlantic Ocean, Gulf stream near Bahamas	Fell and van Uden, 1963

Table 6 (continued)

Species	Occurrence	Authors
Cryptococcus laurentii (Kuff.) Skinner	Seaweeds	Suehiro, 1962; Suehiro and Tomiyasu, 1962
	Pacific Ocean, near south California, surface layer of water	van Uden and Castelo-Branco, 1963
	Mud from tide land	Suehiro, 1963
	Sea plankton	Suehiro, Tomiyasu and Tanaka, 1962
Cr. neoformans (Sanf.) Vuillemin	Black Sea, in water from surface to 70 m deep	Kriss and Novozhilova, 1954; Novozhilova, 1955
	Sea plankton	Suehiro, Tomiyasu and Tanaka, 1962
	Seaweeds	Suehiro and Tomiyasu, 1962
Cr. luteolus (Saito) Skinner	Black Sea, in 25-50 m water layer Sea of Okhotsk and north-west Pacific, in water from surface to 2500 m deep	Kriss and Novozhilova, 1954; Novozhilova, 1955
	Sea plankton	Suehiro, Tomiyasu and Tanaka, 1962
Cr. albidus (Saito) Skinner	Biscayne Bay mud	Fell, Ahearn, Meyers, Roth, 1960
	Gulf Stream, in 50-100 m water layer; internal parts of marine animals	Capriotti, 1962
	Atlantic Ocean, coast of Portugal, surface layer of water	Taysi and van Uden, 1964
	Mud near Cat Cay, Bahamas	Fell and van Uden, 1963.
	Seaweeds	Suehiro and Tomiyasu, 1962
	Sea plankton	Suehiro, Tomiyasu and Tanaka, 1962

Table 6 (continued)

Species	Occurrence	Authors
Cr. albidus (Saito) Skinner	Pacific Ocean, near south California, surface layer of water and in water from 100 and 500 m	van Uden and Castelo-Branco, 1963
Cr. neoformans (Sanf.) Vuillemin var. *uniguttulatus* (Zach.) n. var	Biscayne Bay mud	Fell, Ahearn, Meyers, Roth, 1960
	Mud near Cat Cay, Bahamas	Fell and van Uden, 1963
Cr. diffluens (Zach.) n. comb.	Biscayne Bay mud	Fell, Ahearn, Meyers, Roth, 1960
	Mud near High Cay, Andros	Fell and van Uden, 1963
	Seaweeds	Suehiro and Tomiyasu, 1962
	Sea plankton	Suehiro, Tomiyasu and Tanaka, 1962
Cr. terreus	Pacific Ocean, near south California, surface layer of water	van Uden and Castelo-Branco, 1963
Cr. terricolus	Pacific Ocean, near south California, surface layer of water	van Uden and Castelo-Branco, 1963
Metschnikowiella zobellii van Uden et Castelo-Branco	Pacific Ocean near south California, surface water layer, and internal parts of fishes	van Uden and Castelo-Branco, 1963
M. krissii van Uden et Castelo-Branco	Pacific Ocean, near south California, surface water layer	van Uden and Castelo-Branco, 1963
Pichia farinosa (Lindner) Hansen	In coral epibiotics	van Uden and ZoBell, 1962
P. fermentans Lodder	Algae on south and north coasts of Florida	Capriotti, 1962

Table 6 (continued)

Species	Occurrence	Authors
Pichia bovis	Atlantic Ocean, coast of Portugal, surface layer of water	Taysi and van Uden, 1964
P. membranaefaciens Hansen	Atlantic Ocean, coast of Portugal, surface layer of water	Taysi and van Uden, 1964
	North sea, internal parts of fishes	Ross and Morris, 1962
Kloeckera apiculata (Reess emend. Klöcker) Janke	Atlantic Ocean, coast of Portugal, surface layer of water	Taysi and van Uden, 1964
	Pacific Ocean, near south California, surface layer of water and internal parts of fishes	van Uden and Castelo-Branco, 1963
	Mud from tide land	Suehiro, 1963
Geotrichum candidum Link	Mud from tide land	Suehiro, 1963

here to give data on the species of yeast organisms found in the sea.

Table 6 gives a list of such species. As can be seen, they belong to the genera *Candida* (species *C. guilliermondii*, *C. melibiosi*, *C. tropicalis*, *C. parapsilosis*, *C. parapsilosis*, var. *intermedia*, *C. intermedia*, *C. boidinii*, *C. melinii*, *C. tenuis*, *C. curvata*, *C. marina*, *C. reukaufii*, *C. albicans*, *C. pulcherrima*, *C. humicola*, *C. pelliculosa*, *C. catenulata*, *C. brumptii*, *C. krusei*, *C. lypolytica*, *C. lusitaniae*, *C. mycoderma*, *C. rugosa* var. *elegans*, *C. solanii* n. spec.), *Torulopsis* (species *T. candida*, *T. denitrificans*, *T. famata*, *T. glabrata*, *T. aeria*, *T. lipofera*, *T. haemulonii*, *T. torresii*, *T. maris*, *T. inconspicua* n. spec.), *Rhodotorula* (species *Rh. mucilaginosa*, *Rh. glutinis*, *Rh. pallida*, *Rh. glutinis* var. *rubescens*, *Rh. minuta*, *Rh. graminis*, *Rh. rubra*, *Rh. aurantiaca*, *Rh. marina*, *Rh. peneaus*, *Rh. texensis*, *Rh. flava*), *Cryptococcus* (species *Cr. laurentii*, *Cr. neoformans*, *Cr. neoformans*, var. *uniquttulatus*, *Cr. luteolus*, *Cr. albidus*, *Cr. diffluens*, *Cr. terreus*, *Cr. terricolus*), *Sporobolomyces* (species *S. salmonicolor*), *Trichosporon* (species *Tr. cutaneum*, *Tr. piscium*, *Tr. diddensii*, *Tr. maritimum*, *Tr. atlanticum*, *Tr. pullulans*, *Tr. behrendii*, *Tr. infestans*). *Metschnikowiella* (species *M. zobellii* and *M. krissii*), *Saccharomyces* (species *S. ellipsoideus*, *S. pasteurianum*, *S. fructuum*, *S. rosei*, *S. steineri*, *S. estuarii*, *S. cerevisiae*, *S. delbrueckii*, *S. fragilis*, *S. exiguus*), *Hansenula*

Table 7. Species of Actinomyces and Proactinomyces found in seas and oceans

Species	Occurrence	Authors
Actinomyces albus (Rossi-Doria) Gasperini	Mud from Mogil'noye Lake and Yekaterina Harbour	Issachenko, 1914
	Chukchi Sea (shallow areas), from water at 25 m, from bottom layer of water and from bottom mud	Kriss, 1952
A. candidus Krasil'nikov	Chukchi Sea (shallow areas), from bottom layer of water	Kriss, 1952
	Black Sea (deep areas well away from land), from water at 500 and 1750 m	Kriss, Markianovich and Rukina, 1951
A. globisporus Krasil'nikov	Black Sea (deep areas well away from land), from water at 50, 75, 100, 175, 250 and 750 m and from bottom mud	Kriss, Markianovich and Rukina, 1951
A. griseus Krainsky	Chukchi Sea (shallow areas), from water at 25 m and from bottom mud; Bering Strait, from bottom layer of water	Kriss, 1952
	Black Sea (deep areas well away from land), from water at all levels from surface to 1000 m	Kriss, Markianovich and Rukina, 1951
A. halotrichis ZoBell et Upham	Pacific Ocean, along Californian coast, from mud	ZoBell and Upham, 1944
A. marinolimnosus ZoBell et Upham	Pacific Ocean, along Californian coast, from mud	ZoBell and Upham, 1944
A. marinus Humm et Shepard	Atlantic coast of USA, coastal sands	Humm and Shepard, 1946
A. pelogenes	Black Sea mud, limans	Sawjalov, 1913
A. ruber (Krainsky) Kriss	Chukchi Sea (shallow areas), from bottom layer of water and bottom mud	Kriss, 1952

Table 7 (continued)

Species	Occurrence	Authors
A. sterilis ruber Krasil'nikov	Bering Strait, from bottom layer of water and bottom	Kriss, 1952
Nocardia cuniculi Snyders	Marine mud deposits mixed with algae and gypsum	Siebert and Schwartz, 1956
Proactinomyces actinomorphus (Gray et Thornton) Jensen	Chukchi Sea (shallow areas), from bottom layer of water	Kriss, 1952
P. albus Krasil'nikov	Chukchi Sea (shallow areas), from bottom	Kriss, 1952
P. atlanticus Humm et Shepard	Atlantic coast of USA, from marine algae	Humm and Shepard, 1946
P. flavus Humm et Shepard	Atlantic coast of USA, from mud	Humm and Shepard, 1946

(species *H. californica, H. anomala*), *Hanseniaspora* (species *H. apiculata, H. valbyensis*), *Nadsoniella* (species *N. nigra*), *Nadsoniomyces* (species *N. sphenoides*), *Debaryomyces* (species *D. hansenii, D. subglobosus, D. kloeckeri, D. nicotianae, D. minuta*), *Pichia* (species *P. farinosa, P. fermentans, P. bovis, P. membranaefaciens*), *Kloeckera* (species *K. apiculata*). *Geotrichum* (species *G. candidum*).

Gasperini, *A. candidus* Krasil'nikov, *A. globisporus* Krasil'nikov, *A. griseus* Krainsky, *A. halotrichis* ZoBell et Upham, *A. marinolimnosus* ZoBell et Upham, *A. marinus* Humm et Shepard, *A. pelogenes, A. ruber* (Krainsky) Kriss, *A. sterilis ruber* Krasil'nikov, *Nocardia cunicula* Synders, *Proactinomyces actinomorphus* (Gray et Thornton) Jensen, *P. albus* Krasil'nikov, *P. atlanticus* Humm et Shepard, *P. flavus* Humm et Shepard (Table 7).

All but three of the Actinomycetes were found in coastal waters. The three exceptions, *A. candidus* Krasil'nikov, *A. globisporus* Krasil'nikov and *A. griseus* Krainsky, were isolated from Black Sea water, taken from considerable depths (500 – 1750 m), by Kriss, Rukina and Markianovich (1951).

This completes our account of the species composition of microorganisms found in the sea. It is based on published data and it does not include microorganisms which have been given only a figure or letter symbol or have been determined only as far as genus.

We have already mentioned that the great majority of the species named refer to microbial forms found not only in the sea but also in soil and other natural substrates. This shows that investigators have been anxious to identify microorganisms isolated from a marine milieu with known soil-dwelling and other land species. This tendency can be justified on the grounds that a number of microbial forms are capable of adapting to environmental change from land to sea or *vice versa*. There is, however, the further consideration that in the course of laboratory study cultures of numerous generations of both marine and soil-dwelling species are produced in artificial nutrient media and under conditions very remote from the ecological environment of their habitat. Prolonged laboratory culture will inevitably smooth out, to some extent, biological differences between microbial forms due to specific features in their ecology. As a result of adaption to standard conditions created by the investigator in order to determine the species affinity of the cultures under study, microbial forms from different habitats can become similar.

Unfortunately, modern methods of microbial species diagnostics do not enable us to differentiate between species which live and multiply in the sea, on the one hand, and, on the other, forms which, though found in the sea, are really land species, not adapted to marine life, but which have merely remained viable up to the moment of their discovery. Butkevich (1932), ZoBell (1946) and others suggested that the criterion for distinguishing marine species should be the sensitivity of microorganisms to salt concentration and composition in a nutrient medium with the mean salt content of ocean water. This cannot be accepted as a sufficient criterion. The salinity of the water is not the sole determinant of the specificity of sea and ocean as a habitat for microorganisms. Further, the salt tolerance, both of land and of marine microorganisms, fluctuates widely and in many microbial forms is a readily variable character. A further consideration to be borne in mind is that salinity of soil is not so rare a phenomenon and that there are plenty of inland salt waters (limans, lakes) where conditions are suitable for the generation of land microbial forms similar to marine species in regard to salt tolerance.

The most reliable criterion for deciding whether a given microbial form is a marine microorganism is obviously its ability to multiply in the sea — but, explicitly in the sea, not in isolated samples of water, where conditions are completely different from those of the natural habitat. An index of this capacity is the frequency of occurrence of a particular form, especially if it is observed in parts of the sea or ocean far apart from one another. ZoBell and Upham (1944) rightly note that the range of certain species of bacteria found by them in the Pacific, up to 600 m from land, proved that those species were marine microorganisms. A still more important indication of multiplication in the sea is the occurrence of a particular microbial form not singly but in numbers in the water sample. If, when the sample is seeded on dense nutrient media, several colonies of one species develop, then there can be no doubt, provided the sample was taken from an open part of the sea at a considerable distance from land, that the species in question is a marine form, particularly if it is found in numbers elsewhere in the sea or ocean.

The presence of a large number of individuals belonging to the same microbial form in a sample taken from coastal waters is by no means a sure indication that the form in question is a marine species. The fact that a sample contains a considerable concentration of cells belonging to a particular species may not be due to multiplication of that species but to the presence of numerous individual microbes of the species, carried from land into the coastal waters with runoff.

It is equally obvious that isolated individual microorganisms found in samples taken from open water well away from the land will, in the great majority of cases, be sea-dwelling species. Here a reliable criterion is the frequency of occurrence of forms represented by single cells. In the Arctic, in the seas of Antarctica and in water masses drawn by the currents from high to low latitudes, the heterotrophic microbial population is so scattered that only single colonies of any particular microbial form can be found in a 40–50 ml sample (Kriss, 1963). To judge from the frequency of their occurrence at great distances from the mainland or from islands, these are marine species which, owing to inadequate concentration of the readily assimilable organic matter essential for their vital activity, do not easily multiply.

For microorganisms, the sea is a specialized environment. ZoBell (1946) quotes published data and his own observations showing that conditions in the sea are unfavourable to the existence of many forms of microorganisms transported there from the land. Our investigations have shown that there is no such diversity of microbial species in open areas of the sea and ocean as in the soil. It can now be taken as established that such microorganisms as Actinomycetes, which occur extensively in soil, are not indigenous to the sea. Not once have the branching mycelial filaments of Actinomyces been detected on any of the many hundreds of membrane filters through which samples from various horizons of the water column in the Black Sea, the Caspian Sea, the Sea of Okhotsk, the north-west Pacific and the polar region of the Arctic Ocean have been passed, or on slides exposed at depth in the sea for periods ranging from a few hours to several days. The Actinomycetes occasionally isolated from sea-water samples on organic and mineral media are obviously random occurrence of forms not adapted to marine life.

The fact that large numbers of microorganisms transported from land to sea perish, does not, of course, mean that all microorganisms living in the sea are strictly marine species. It could well be that heterotrophic marine microorganisms which multiply on protein media in the laboratory are merely variants of species which inhabit both land and sea.

It is for these reasons that we have been reluctant (Kriss, 1963) to allocate new specific names to microbial forms isolated from the water and mud of the Black Sea, the Sea of Okhotsk and the north-west Pacific.

For these species we have drawn on the names of soil-dwelling or other land species found to resemble them in regard to the morphological, cultural and biochemical characters used as criteria in accordance with Krasil'nikov's key (1949). This is no way implies doubt that the great majority, at any rate, of the microbial forms in our collection are sea dwellers and not random land species which happened to have remained viable; but we should not have been justified in regarding them as new species since they may be species capable of multiplying either in the sea or in land habitats, as has been shown (Kriss, 1945, 1952) in respect of a number of microbial forms found in coastal waters of the Chukchi Sea and east Siberian seas.

Although we can speak of strictly land species and even of large systematic groups of microorganisms, such as the Actinomycetes, for which the seas and oceans are not a suitable habitat, there is still no complete proof of the existence of strictly marine species, genera or larger taxonomic units. There are no sufficient grounds for assuming that microbial species and genera at present regarded as strictly marine will not in fact be found in the soil and other land environments. It must be remembered that hardly any attempt has been made to look for them there.

At present, the Krasil'nikoviae, a new class of microorganisms (Kriss, Mitskevich, 1957) widely distributed in the ocean depths, can fairly confidently be regarded as a group of strictly marine organisms. These peculiar, filamentous, non-branching microorganisms, bearing at one end a head consisting of round bodies, have been found at various depths in the Arctic, Pacific and Atlantic oceans and in all geographical zones, from the North Pole to the Equator, at the deepest levels of the Black Sea, where the hydrogen sulphide concentration is very high, but not in the depths of Lake Baykal or the Caspian, although the mean salinity of the latter is 12.85% (Knipovich, 1963).

Other views concerning the Krasil'nikoviae have now emerged. Some authors regard these filamentous-botryose microorganisms not as a class, but as an order, Calamobotryocidales (Zavarzin, 1961); others believe they may possibly be primitive fungoid organisms (Johnson, Sparrow, 1961); still others suggest that they may be Protozoa or parts of the bodies of marine invertebrates.

In illustrations given by Chun (1880), Lankester (1900), Taku Komai (1922) and Kükenthal-Krumbach (1923–1925) the colloblasts of the ctenophores resemble filamentous-botryose microorganisms, but it is impossible to identify them from these drawings. The colloblasts do not possess the characteristic flabellate or umbellate type of structure often observed in Krasil'nikoviae heads. The growth cycle of the colloblasts, according to Samassa's histological investigations (1892), is complex and does not fit our observations on Krasil'nikoviae. The hypothesis that the round bodies making up the head cluster of the filamentous-botryose microorganisms are identical with the granules whereby the ctenophore's food sticks to the surface of the colloblasts is invalidated by the fact that the round bodies of the Krasil'nikoviae are easily detached from the filaments bearing them and can be found on the slides in large numbers, lying free or attached to fragments of the filaments.

Investigators may well have mistaken filamentous-botryose microorganisms, settling on the tentacles of ctenophores, for the structures known as colloblasts.

The microbial cells of unusual morphology which have been detected by direct microscopy techniques in the depths of the seas and oceans deserve attention (Kriss, Biryuzova, Lebedeva, 1958). The great majority of these forms will not grow on artificial nutrient media in the laboratory. Some of them seem to be obligate periphyton, since they have been found only on overgrowth slides.

It is now obvious that the published lists of species of microorganisms isolated from a marine medium do not, even in regard to morphology, reflect the full diversity of microbial forms living in the depths of the sea. The reason is that microbiology has not advanced far in devising methods of culturing microorganisms which live in natural habitats. Only with the development of the ecological-physiological trend in the study of microbial life is the possibility of obtaining a detailed picture of microorganic biocenoses in the seas and oceans becoming feasible.

At the present level of microbial systematics we cannot overcome the difficulties encountered in attempting species diagnosis of sea-dwelling microorganisms. To describe these forms as new species, merely on the grounds that they inhabit the sea, is no solution. The only criterion for erecting a new species is the totality of characters revealing the biological configuration of the form under consideration.

Unfortunately, because of our inadequate knowledge, it is rarely open to the investigator to use this criterion and we therefore find it more reasonable to compare with land species those marine microorganisms which, in their characteristics, are not distinguished from species occurring on land, and to regard such marine forms as variants of the latter, ecotypes or races, adapted to life under the specific conditions of the sea.

2

Microbiological material collected from open areas of the world ocean

In order to obtain cultures of microorganisms living in the water of seas and oceans we used the technique of culturing on ultrafilters (Kriss, 1963).

Water for the microbiological investigations was collected in Nansen sampling bottles from the standard hydrographical levels of 0, 10, 25, 50, 75, 100, 150, 200, 250, 300, 400, 500, 600, 800, 1000, 1500, 2000, 2500, 3000 m and deeper at 1000 m intervals and in certain cases from intermediate levels as well. In the Central Arctic, the Greenland and Norwegian Seas and the Atlantic and Indian Oceans, with few exceptions, the whole water column from surface to bottom was investigated at these levels. In the Pacific Ocean at roughly half the number of stations water was taken from depths down to 2000–2500 m only. The total number of samples investigated was about 4000.

The suitability of the Nansen bottle for purposes of marine microbiological research has lately been the subject of controversy and experimentation. The microbiological sampler devised by ZoBell (1941) having proved unsuitable for deep-sea use (ZoBell, 1954; Sieburth et al., 1963), several new devices have been designed for this purpose (Sorokin, 1962; Niskin, 1962; Lewis et al., 1963; Sieburth et al., 1963), since a number of the authors named believe the Nansen bottle to be unsuitable for microbiological work, despite its reliability as a device for taking serial water samples from the ocean depths. It is therefore essential to examine in detail the experience accumulated in using the latter instrument for microbiological study of marine basins.

In selecting any sample for microbiological analysis, the main objective is to create conditions precluding the introduction of bacteria from without. Non-sterile apparatus is sometimes used, when the risk of contamination by incidental microflora can be confidently excluded. In oil-well drilling, for example, non-sterile instruments are used for the actual drilling and the oil or sheet water brought up comes into contact with all the layers of rock and soil through which the well passes. Again, the various bottle-type sampling instruments, as well as the ground pipes, before they reach

Table 8. Number of live bacteria in sea water left for various periods in brass Nansen samplers and glass jars at 22°C (expressed as a percentage of the original number) (ZoBell, 1946)

Time (min)	Nansen sampler			Glass jars
	No. 13	No. 18	No. 19	
0	100	100	100	100
5	94	85	69	103
10	82	74	62	95
30	78	56	40	96
60	70	51	36	92
120	52	37	29	91
300	28	14	7	93
1440	19	3	6	543

the sample intake, are in contact with layers of water or mud containing bacteria. Sterilized scalpels, knives and various other instruments used in selecting microbiological samples of soil, deposits and frozen ground will remain sterile until their first contact with the object in question, after which they will function as non-sterile instruments. Nevertheless. in oil, water, soil and geological microbiology, practice has shown that samples and specimens in the required sterile condition can be obtained as a result of the flushing in wells and the flowage through open instruments, or by taking cores, subsoil columns and intact portions of soil, deposits or frozen ground in sufficient thickness.

In its open form the Nansen sampler is a metal tube. The walls of the tube are subject to intense friction by the water as the instrument is lowered, since the speed at which it is let down on the cable is usually greater than 1 m per second. This friction inevitably prevents bacteria from settling on the walls and so being carried down into the deeper layers of water. Nor does the external construction of the Nansen sampler entail any greater risk of introducing microorganisms from the surface to the deep layers than occurs if microbiological samplers are used.

After the water sample has been taken, the surplus water is poured off, and only droplets, in process of drying out remain in the sample bottle. During the brief period before the walls of the sample dry out completely, any bacteria which have remained on them are subject to the bactericidal action of the metal, the sterilizing effect of which should not be underrated, as can be seen from ZoBell's data (1946) (Table 8).

As can be seen from the table, after one hour 36 – 70% of the original number of live bacteria remained in the Nansen sampler; after two hours, 29 – 52% and after 24 hours only a few per cent. In the glass jars, on the other hand, not only did the bacteria survive during these time intervals, but even began to multiply during the first few hours of storage. Drew (1914) and Bedford (1931), who investigated the influence of different

Table. 9. Number of heterotrophic bacteria in water samples from a metal sampler and a sterile, glass Issachenko sampler (Gurfeyn, 1935)

Sample No.	No. of bacteria per cm³		Difference, %
	Metal sampler	Glass sampler	
1	19	18	5.4
2	7	7	0
3	17	16	6
4	9	10	10.5
5	21	27	25
6	120	130	8
7	114	120	5
8	133	155	15.2
Mean difference, %			8.6

metals on the bacterial population of sea water, also noted the fairly rapid onset of the sterilizing action of metals on bacteria, the only exception being platinum. This important circumstance – the bactericidal effect of the walls of metal bottles – should be taken into account when such bottles are used for taking water samples from the depths of the sea. It is essential to transfer the water into a sterile, glass vessel and begin investigating the samples immediately the sampler is brought up.

If these conditions are observed, there is no perceptible difference in the quantity and composition of microorganisms between sea-water samples taken with the metal bottle and those taken with a sterile, glass Issachenko sampler. According to Gurfeyn's data (1935), the discrepancy in the number of colonies grown from samples taken with both types of instrument, in eight experiments performed on water from the Golden Horn (Table 9), did not exceed 9%. Similar results were obtained in determining the titre of ammonia-producing and dentrifying microorganisms (Table 10) and in studying the morphological composition of the microflora in water samples from metal and from sterile glass bottles. Not more than five minutes elapsed between the submergence of the instruments compared, which were lowered to the same depths.

Lebedeva and Tsiban (1966) carried out comparative microbiological studies of water samples collected with Nansen bottles and with sterilized and stoppered bottles to determine the extent of contamination of the former either from air or residual drops of water while on deck or during passage through the surface layers of the sea. These investigations were made in the shallow, highly-productive, north-western zone of the Black Sea and in its open deep-sea area. In the summer and autumn of 1963 and the winter of 1964 at 29 stations – in estuarine, coastal and open waters – water samples were taken from 0, 5, 10, 15, 20, 25 and 30 m with Nansen

Table 10. Titre of saprophytic, ammonia-producing and denitrifying bacteria in water samples from a metal sampler and a sterile, glass Issachenko sampler (Gurfeyn, 1935)

Depth, m	Metal sampler									Issachenko sampler								
	0.5 cm^3			0.1 cm^3			0.01 cm^3			0.5 cm^3			0.1 cm^3			0.01 cm^3		
	H_2S	NH_3	NO_2	H_2S	NH_3	NO_2	H_2S	NH_3	NO_2	H_2S	NH_3	NO_2	H_2S	NH_3	NO_2	H_2S	NH_3	NO_2
3	+++	+++	++	++	++	++	−	++	−	+++	+++	++	++	++	++	−	++	−
7	++	++	++	++	+	+	−	− +	traces	++	++	++	++	++	++	−	+	+
13	+	+	++	−	+	+	−	+	−	+	+	++	−	+	++	−	+	+

Note: H_2S – decomposition; NH_3 – ammonia production; NO_2 – denitrification; + – slight, ++ – good, +++ – vigorous

and Sorokin bottles (1960). The Nansen bottles were not sterilized; the Sorokin bottles were autoclaved for 40 min at 120°C. Both types of bottle were lowered simultaneously, the distance between them being about 1 m. Eighty-one samples were examined.

In the open sea, work was done in 1962 at stations 20 to 30 miles off the south Crimean coast. Water samples were collected with Nansen bottles, both non-sterilized and sterilized (with 96% alcohol or by autoclaving for an hour at 1.5 atm.) at 0, 25, 50, 100, 150, 200, 250, 500, 750, 1000, 1250, 1400, 1500 and 1650 m. Parallel samples were taken with Rodina's microbiological bottles (1956) from the 5 m layer. Immediately the bottles were brought up the samples were transferred, with every microbiological precaution, into sterile glass flasks and filtered, 40 ml at a time, through membrane filters (pore diameter 0.5 μ). The filters were then placed in Petri dishes, on nutrient agar made up from a dry powder, consisting 60% of tryptic hydrolysate of fish meal and 40% of agar, dissolved in sea water (50 g of powder per litre) and autoclaved for 20 minutes at 120°C (pH 7.2). The filters were incubated for 2 to 4 days at 22°–24°C. The colonies were then counted. Sterile water was passed through control filters for each experiment. As a rule, no colonies appeared on the control filters.

For the first series of experiments six Nansen bottles were used. These were left open on deck for 12 hours, then filled with 200 ml of sterile water and repeatedly agitated, so that the water washed the walls of the bottles; 40 ml were then taken from each bottle and incubated on membrane ultrafilters. The number of colonies counted per 40 ml sample varied from 0 to 6.

The point at issue is whether the results obtained from microbiological investigation of the surface layer of the sea are affected by atmospheric contamination of the sampling bottles. Experiment showed that the number

Table 11. Number of saprophytic bacteria in 40 ml samples taken simultaneously with sterilized and non-sterilized Nansen bottles from various depths of the Black Sea (average data from three simultaneous filtrations of each sample)

Depth, m	Non-sterilized bottles	Alcohol-sterilized bottles
0	80	35
50	39	17
100	9	6
250	49	94
500	10	14
750	2	8
	$\bar{X}_I = 32$	$\bar{X}_{II} = 29$

of bacteria in samples of sea water from the surface layer taken simultaneously with non-sterilized and sterilized (by autoclaving or with alcohol) Nansen bottles and with microbiological sampling bottles was almost identical (Tables 11, 12, 13, 14, 16).

Near the ship the surface layer of the water is heavily contaminated by refuse and bottom fouling. It is therefore generally assumed that an open Nansen bottle which has passed through this contaminated layer must infect the layers below. Tables 13 and 14, however, show that the number of bacteria in samples collected from the 5 m level is practically the same irrespective of whether Nansen bottles or closed microbiological bottles are used. The friction of the water as the Nansen bottle is lowered evidently prevents bacteria from settling on its walls and from contaminating not only samples from the deeper layers but even those from nearest the surface.

Comparative experiments in the open part of the Black Sea showed that samples taken with Nansen bottles (Table 14) contained a slightly smaller number of bacteria than those taken with glass microbiological sampling bottles. As a great many samples were taken almost simultaneously, there was a delay of half an hour to four hours in treating the Nansen-bottle samples. Such samples should obviously be treated with the minimum of delay in order to obviate the bactericidal action of metal ions escaping from the walls of the bottle into the water sample. Samples taken with Nansen bottles and immediately subjected to microbiological investigation were found to yield results identical with those obtained from samples taken with microbiological bottles (Table 13).

We found no confirmation of Sorokin's data (1962, a and b) indicating that the number of bacteria in water samples taken with Nansen bottles sterilized in alcohol was very low in comparison with the number in non-sterilized bottles. Table 11 shows that whether the samples were taken with alcohol-sterilized or with non-sterilized Nansen bottles, the bacterial count was the same, even though the former had been washed with 96% alcohol thoroughly agitated for 5 minutes.

Even at the $p = 99\%$ level ($t = 0.47$) the mean values for the bacterial count are not statistically different according to the Student-Fischer test (Ashmarin, Vorob'yev, 1962). Nor is there essentially any statistically significant difference in the average values of the bacterial count between non-sterilized and autoclave-sterilized Nansen bottles (Table 12), even if we take the 99% probability level ($t = 0.41$). These comparative studies thus show that the Nansen-type bottle can be relied on to provide aseptic samples from various depths of the sea.

Our experience has shown that the risk of contamination or of possible transport of microorganisms from surface to deep layers entailed by use of the Nansen sampler can be completely discounted. That the samplers will be in a condition of high microbiological purity at the moment of intake, whether at the surface or from various depths of the ocean, is evident, for example, from the absence of bacteria in the majority of water samples taken at nine stations in the Kuril-Kamchatka depression area, even though considerable volumes of water (35–40 ml) were investigated, and the negligibly small number in the other samples (Kriss, 1963, Table 11). The

Table 12. Number of saprophytic bacteria in 40 ml samples taken simultaneously with autoclave sterilized and non-sterilized Nansen bottles from various depths of the Black Sea (average data from three simultaneous filtrations of each sample)

Depth, m	Exp. 1 (June 1962)		Exp. 2 (September 1962)	
	Sterilized	Non-sterilized	Sterilized	Non-sterilized
0	27	16	60	81
25	–	–	34	43
50	11	12	27	6
100	73	76	40	28
150	–	–	63	1
200	–	–	37	39
250	15	3	18	15
500	3	4	28	28
750	3	6	–	–
1000	11	20	7	1
1250	9	30	–	–
1400	1	5	–	–
1500	–	–	5	5
1650	1	4	–	–
	For two experiments:		$\bar{X}_I = 24$	$\bar{X}_{II} = 21$

Table 13. Number of saprophytic bacteria in 40 ml samples taken
ogical sampler (MS) from various depths in

Station no.	1		2		3		4		5		6		9		11	
Levels, (m)	NB	MS	NB	MS	NB	MS	NB	MS	NB	MS	NB	MS	NB	MS	NB	MS
Summer																
0															88	84
5															284	168
9																
10																
15																
20																
25																
30																
Autumn																
0	328	380	320	280	168	96	128	160	260	168	244	176				
5											60	100				
9	320	168														
10			168	124	88	72	20	12	12	4						
15											40	28				
20			280	354	54	60	146	140	164	204						
25											28	12				
30									144	148						
Winter																
0	340	240	640	528	16	4							16	48		
5	316	312	520	488												
9																
10	540	600		8	12											
15				28	48	48										
20																
25																
30																

$\bar{X}_{NB} = 176$ $\bar{X}_{MS} = 181$

small percentage of samples which yielded several tens of colonies came mainly from deep-layer samples taken at stations where the photic zone contained smaller numbers of heterotrophic bacteria, so that the introduction of microorganisms from the top layer of ocean was impossible.

Investigation of many hundreds of Nansen-bottle samples, taken at high and middle latitudes in the Indian, Pacific and Atlantic Oceans, gave a similar picture (Kriss et al., 1958; Kriss et al., 1960).

Water samples in which only single heterotrophic organisms or none at all were found in 40 – 50 ml made up 60% of the total in the Indian Ocean, to 99% in the Atlantic.

simultaneously with Nansen bottles (NB) and Sorokin's microbiol-
the north-western area of the Black Sea

12	13	14	15	16	17	18	19
NB MS	NB MS	NB MS	NB MS	NB MS	NB MS	NB MS	NB MS
92 88	440 496	96 92	284 224	160 154	40 208	36 192	200 280
104 100		20 12	320 360	168 180	164 224	408 288	60 40
	232 244						
		128 104					
				188 224	288 280	464 640	54 244
			158 168				
		52 80					
				160 174	480 400	184 204	224 216
				168 200		160 240	168 160
				192 120	424 412	52 104	
							116 180
						240 172	
					160 128		
4 8	84 100	64 116			120 100	48 104	208 280
4 0							
	4 24	8 460			0 28	60 60	
					24 8		
		120 60					

Toward the lower latitudes the heterotrophic microbial population of the water column increases, giving an increasing percentage of samples from which tens and hundreds of colonies can be grown after filtration of 40-50 ml of water, In high and middle latitudes such rich samples are a rarity, but in low latitudes samples containing only small quantities of heterotrophic bacteria (0-9 colonies from 40-50 ml of water) were obtained only from particular levels. It should be remembered that the high and middle latitude areas of the seas are considerably more prolific than the equatorial and tropical areas. This shows the weakness of the proposition—that bacterial contamination of sample bottles does not occur in the highly prolific areas

Table 14. Number of saprophytic bacteria in 40 ml samples taken simultaneously with Nansen bottles and Sorokin's microbiological sampler at various depths in the north-western area of the Black Sea

Nansen bottles	Sterile bottles
354	564
160	281
311	296
260	470
474	312
72	90
176	309
67	272
37	502
148	411
192	545
127	516
90	298
356	230
	400
	278
	284
	400
	259
$\bar{X}_I = 202 \pm 76$	$\bar{X}_{II} = 354 \pm 59$

of the Indian, Pacific and Atlantic Oceans and does occur at latitudes where the fecundity of the water is very low.

The unexpectedly large numbers of heterotrophic bacteria found at certain levels of the ocean column in regions remote from the equatorial-tropical zone are due to the currents which draw water from that zone northwards and southwards, just as the high-latitude water penetrating tropical areas and crossing the equator determines the low content of heterotrophic organisms at corresponding depths in the low-latitude sea areas.

The theory that these effects are due to the transport of bacteria into the deep layers from the top layers of the ocean by Nansen samplers is invalidated by the frequent occurrence of smaller numbers of heterotrophic organisms at the surface levels than at depths; moreover, depth samples taken in the equatorial-tropical zone have proved sterile, even though the Nansen samplers passed through hundreds of metres and kilometres of water column rich in heterotrophic microorganisms before these sterile probes were taken in (Kriss et al., 1958, Figs. 5 and 8).

Nevertheless, Bogoyavlenskiy, a hydrochemist, considers the Nansen sampler unsuitable for taking microbiological water samples (1962). He says that the samples collected with two samplers, each of which was lowered to different depths in the Indian Ocean, contained similar numbers of heterotrophic microorganisms. But he ignores the important circumstance that eighteen other samplers used in the same hydrological series and lowered to various depths gave directly opposite results (Lebedeva, 1962). It is an elementary rule of scientific procedure that an author cannot, however attached he may be to his own point of view, base a conclusion on two experiments when the results of eighteen other experiments do not tally with that conclusion. All the facts adduced indicate that the bactericidal action of the Nansen samplers' metal walls and the violent friction of the water on them while the sampler is being lowered to the required depths guarantee the sterility of the instrument before the sample is taken in and consequently the complete suitability of this instrument for obtaining microbiological water samples from the sea.

Sorokin's work (1962, a and b) aimed at disproving this assertion, calls for further comment. Sorokin designed two glass samplers which he used in sterile condition to take water samples from the mid-Pacific. At some stations he performed comparative investigations on samples taken with his own and with Nansen samplers at various depths of the ocean. From a few levels, samples were taken also with Nansen samplers which had previously been washed with alcohol. According to Sorokin's data the number of heterotrophic bacteria in the samples taken with a Nansen sampler contained tens, hundreds and even thousands of times more heterotrophic organisms than the samplers taken with sterile glass samplers from the same depths. The sterile glass bottle samplers yielded only tens of colonies, single colonies or, in some cases, none at all per 10 ml of water, yet those taken with the Nansen samplers often yielded thousands of heterotrophs from the same quantity of water.

Examination of these data, however, reveals an interesting point. Of

Table 15. Change in number of saprophytic bacteria in water taken from various depths in the open area of the Black Sea and stored in litre glass vessels at 18 to 20°C (average data from 2 or 3 simultaneous filtrations of 40 ml of water from each sample)

Depth, m	Initial no.	Number after			
		6 h	12 h	18 h	24 h
0	34	29	25	59	356
50	1	1	1	1	10
100	1	1	1	5	153
250	20	25	23	99	380
500	181	218	402	1736	2900
750	30	41	36	43	162
1000	1	4	2	2	1
1250	12	18	18	32	93
1500	13	8	7	7	12
1650	592	370	441	753	2080

Table 16. Comparative results of microbiological analysis of water samples collected from the surface layer and the 5–30 m layer of the north-western area of the Black Sea with Nansen bottles (NB) and Sorokin's microbiological samplers (MS)

Layer of water column, m	Sampling device	Total no. of samples	No. of samples containing			
			0	1–9	10–99	100–640
			bacteria			
0 – 1	NB	29	0	1	10	18
	MS	29	0	2	5	22
5 – 30	NB	38	1	3	10	24
	MS	38	1	3	9	25

1026 samples taken by Abyzov with Nansen samplers in the same areas of the Pacific, not a single one was found to contain thousands of heterotrophic bacteria per 10 ml of water (Kriss et al., 1958; Kriss, 1959, Tables 112–118; Kriss 1963). Moreover out of this huge number of samples only two yielded 500 colonies on filtration of 50 ml of water (100 bacteria per 10 ml of water); 1024 samples from the Nansen samplers contained tens of heterotrophs or fewer per 10 ml of water.

Comparing our data (Table 17) with those of Sorokin (1962b, Table 3) we find that his figures for the number of heterotrophic organisms in samples taken by him with Nansen samplers are greater, by a factor of a thousand, a hundred, or at least some tens, then those obtained by Abyzov, using Nansen samplers in the same areas of the Pacific and using the same count method (culturing on ultrafilters).

The explanation may be that the samples taken by Sorokin were kept back during processing, after being transferred from the samplers to glass vessels. The intensive multiplication of heterotrophic bacteria, which sets in very rapidly in isolated water samples from lakes, seas and oceans, has repeatedly been described in the literature. This phenomenon obviously played a considerable part in causing Sorokin's samples to yield such large numbers of heterotrophic bacteria, greater than those in the samples taken by Abyzov from the same parts of the Pacific by a factor of tens, a hundred or even a thousand.

There is further evidence to show that Sorokin's data are exaggerated for it would be practically impossible to count such a large number of colonies (many thousands) as he shows in his tables on the No. 2 membrane filters which he used, since the diameter of the filter surface is only 3 cm (Sorokin, 1962, a and b). He passed 20–40 ml of water through these filters and consequently the figures given in his table must be at least doubled.

It is obvious also, if Sorokin's Nansen samplers had been fouled by microflora in the photic zone, and so had carried that microflora down to the deep levels, the fact that he had washed the Nansen bottles with alcohol could not have determined the coincidence between the number of heterotrophic bacteria in the water samples taken from great depths with samplers washed in alcohol and the number in the sterile, closed glass jars lowered by him to the same depths.

The failure of the attempt to present the Nansen sampler as unsuitable for taking microbiological water samples from the sea is particularly clear if we compare our data (Table 17) on the mid-Pacific samples with Sorokin's figures (1962b, Table 1) relating to samples taken by him with sterile, glass samplers in the same areas of the Pacific and investigated by the same count method as was used by Abysov. In both cases the concentration of heterotrophic bacteria is of the same order of magnitude and is measured in single or double figures per 10 ml of water.

It is remarkable that in the photic zone (0 – 200 m), where, according to Sorokin, the degree of bacterial contamination of the samplers is due to the fecundity of the water, the concentration in almost 40% of the Nansen samples (155 out of 410, Table 17) was lower by an order than in the samples obtained by Sorokin with sterile, glass bottles. In the remaining Nansen samples (255 out of 410) the order of magnitude was expressed in tens per 10 ml of water, just as in the samples taken by Sorokin with glass bottles.

One gets the impression that the design of Sorokin's glass sampler was not perfect. It can be seen from Table 17 that, despite individual fluctuations in micro-distribution of labile forms of organic matter and to hydrological phenomena, the concentration of heterotrophic bacteria diminishes with depth in the mid-Pacific (but by no means to zero, as Sorokin indicates). This is seen in the increased percentage of samples containing

Table 17. Quantitative distribution of heterotrophic microorganisms growing on protein media in various layers of water in the mid-Pacific

Water layer	Total no. of water samples	No. and % age of water samples and no. of bacteria per 10 ml of water					
		0–9 bacteria		10–90 bacteria		100 bacteria	
		No. of water samples	%	No. of water samples	%	No. of water samples	%
0	53	23	43.3	28	52.9	2	3.8
1–50	149	69	46.3	80	53.7		
51–200	208	63	30.3	145	69.7		
201–300	105	55	52.4	50	47.6		
301–600	163	82	50.3	81	49.7		
601–1500	167	102	61.0	65	39.0		
1501–2500	101	62	61.3	39	38.7		
2501–4500	48	26	54.2	22	45.8		
4501–Bottom	32	21	65.7	11	34.3		

from 0 – 9 heterotrophic organisms in 10 ml of water and the reduced percentage of samples in which these organisms are counted in tens in the same volume of water.

Further evidence of the unsuitability of Sorokin's depth sampler can be found in the results of Japanese microbiological investigations in the Pacific (Taga Nobuo, Seki Fumitaka, 1962):

Depth, m	No. of heterotrophic bacteria per 100 ml of water			Depth, m	No. of heterotrophic bacteria per 100 ml of water		
	st. E_4	st. E_5	st. E_6		st. E_4	st. E_5	st. E_6
0	390	480	40	600	30	8	23
20	20	90	390	800	210	5	13
50	50	830	35	1000	8	5	5
100	10	110	330	1500	<3	10	63
200	25	15	280	2000	8	18	3
400	55	58	38	3000	–	–	22
				4000	–	42	4

These results, obtained from microbiological study of water samples taken with ZoBell's sterile bacteriological sampler (ZoBell, 1946), point to the erroneousness of Sorokin's contention (1962, a and b) that below a few hundred metres there are practically no saprophytic bacteria in the ocean. As can be seen from the Japanese table, below 1000 m saprophytes were counted in units and in tens per 10 ml of water. The occurrence of micro- and macrozonality in the horizontal and vertical distribution of the heterotrophic bacteria also clearly emerges.

It is noteworthy that the order of magnitude of the concentration of heterotrophic bacteria found in the Pacific water column by the Japanese expedition turned out to be the same as in our investigations with Nansen samplers – namely, units, tens and in some cases hundreds per 10 ml of water.

The suitability of the Nansen sampler for obtaining aseptically microbiological water samples from the sea is thus once again confirmed by microbiological investigations of deep-water samples taken with sterile ZoBell samplers (Taga Nobuo, Seki Fumitaka, 1962) and by Sorokin's investigations (1962, a and b) with sterile glass samplers in the top layers of the ocean. The advantage of the Nansen sampler over existing bacteriological samplers lies in its reliability for obtaining batch samples from the required depths in deep-water investigations.

In selecting water samples for analysis we used every microbiological precaution, in laboratories constructed on board ship or on scientific drifting stations. Immediately after the samples were taken they were passed through membrane filters at the rate of 35 – 40 – 50 ml per filter. The filters were then placed upside down in Petri dishes on the surface of nutrient agar (tryptic hydrolysate of fish meal) for culturing the microbial cells seeded on the filter. This nutrient medium was prepared in ocean water. Suspensions in a 10% dilution of mud taken from the surface layer of the bottom were seeded on the same medium.

After three to seven days incubation at 18 – 35° the colonies produced were counted and members of differentiated colonies were transferred on to agar slopes of the same composition in test tubes. The test tubes were kept in the laboratory until visible growth appeared and then kept at 2 – 4°C until the end of the expedition. In the Indian Ocean the subcultures were started on board at monthly intervals.

In all, more than 4000 strains were cultivated, obtained from various positions at sea, from the North Pole to Antarctica, and from different levels of the water column, from the surface to maximum depth.

Species diagnosis of the cultures was based on the criteria used by Krasil'nikov (1949), Lodder and Kreger van Rij (1952) and Kudryavtsev (1954) in their keys. The morphology, cultural characteristics and biochemical properties of these cultures were studied on a series of media.*

The morphological and cultural characters were investigated on nutrient agar of the above-mentioned composition and the Gram reaction was determined on cells of one or two day old cultures in the same medium.

The shape of the cells, the occurrence of internal structures and filaments, the arrangement of the cells relative to one another and the motility were observed under the microscope.

Attention was paid to the character of growth on solid media and to the colour, shape, surface and margins of the colonies. In addition, in order to show up the pigment more clearly, the cultures were seeded into test tubes containing slants of starch (10g), asparagine (1g), K_2HPO_4 (1g), $CaCO_3$ (2 g), sea salt (30 g), tap water (1000 ml) and agar-agar (20 g).

Once the cultures had been identified and separated into groups, specimens of each group were inspected at various intervals to establish the growth cycle.

The cells were measured on the first to third days of growth.

The following media were used for diagnosing the spore-forming bacteria.

1. Meat-peptone agar + wort agar – before being poured into the Petri dishes the meat–peptone agar extract was mixed with equal proportions of wort agar. The medium was allowed to dry a little and a drop of spore suspension was then placed on its surface.
2. Meat-peptone agar with 1% glucose was poured into test tubes to a column height of 7 cm and inoculated by puncture.
3. A potato medium was prepared in the following way. Tap water was poured over pieces of very thinly sliced potato, so that the water

*The following took part in this work: S. S. Abyzov, V. A. Alimkina, L. V. Bazaitova, M. D. Yevdokimova, N. N. Kirikova, M. N. Lebedeva, Ye. M. Markianovich, Ye. I. Smirnova and L. N. Khadzhi-Murat.

column in the test tube was about 5 cm high; the medium was sterilized at 1 atm.

The proteolytic activity was investigated on meat-peptone gelatine, meat-peptone broth and milk. The liquefaction of the gelatine, the curdling and peptonization of the milk and the formation of ammonia and hydrogen sulphide in the broth were recorded for 15 days. Strips of litmus paper and of paper wetted with a solution of lead acetate, attached to a plug of cotton wool inside the test tube, turned respectively blue in the presence of ammonia and black in the presence of hydrogen sulphide. Fermentation capacity was estimated by colouring the peptone water with azolitmine (1% peptone and 0.02% azolitmine) to which was added 1% of one of the following carbohydrates: glucose, sucrose, maltose, lactose or mannitol. A colourless area round a streak on the potato agar after treatment with Lugol's solution indicated that the strains isolated were capable of breaking down starch. Ability of the strains to use inorganic sources of nitrogen and reduce nitrates to nitrites was determined on synthetic Czapek's medium of the following composition: K_2HPO_4 – 0.5 g; $MgSO_4$ – 0.5 g; NaCl – 0.5 g; KNO_3 – 1.0 g; chalk – 2.0 g; sucrose – 20.0 g, agar-agar – 20.0 g; $FeSO_4$ – trace, distilled water 1000.0 ml. Griess reagent was used to detect the appearance of nitrites.

In the absence of growth, sea salt was added to the meat-peptone gelatine, milk, carbohydrate peptone water, potato agar and synthetic medium containing an inorganic source of nitrogen, at the rate of 3 parts of sea salt to 100 parts of the medium. All cultures of marine yeasts were inoculated into Gorodkova's medium, gypsum blocks and a meat-peptone agar slope to determine spore-forming ability. Morphological and cultural characteristics of the yeast were studied on wort agar. The wort used was 7° Ball. Cells from the wort agar cultures were inspected under the microscope on the first, third, fifth and fifteenth days of growth. Cultures three days old on the wort agar were used to measure the cell sizes.

The fermentative powers of the yeasts were determined in yeast extract containing 2% of one of the following carbohydrates: glucose, sucrose, maltose, galactose, lactose (for asporogenous yeasts). For sporogenous yeasts raffinose was added instead of lactose. The fermentation tests were performed in Dunbar's tubes filled with the above-mentioned media.

In accordance with the requirements of the Lodder and Kreger van Rij key the auxanographic method was used to determine the capacity of the yeast cultures to assimilate various sources of nitrogen and carbon. The nitrogen assimilation capacity of asporogenous yeasts was tested in relation to peptone, urea, asparagine, ammonium sulphate and potassium nitrate and the carbohydrate assimilation was tested in respect of glucose, sucrose, maltose, galactose and lactose.

The medium for the nitrogen assimilation tests was 1.0 g of potassium monophosphate, 0.5 g of magnesium sulphate, 20.0 g of glucose and 20.0 g of washed agar-agar dissolved in 1 litre of distilled water. To determine carbohydrate assimilation 5 g of ammonium sulphate was added to this medium instead of glucose. To the melted medium 2% of the nitrogen and carbohydrate sources were added; the medium was poured into test tubes and sterilized at 0.5 atm.

In order to obtain comparable results inoculations of yeasts of the same strain were made simultaneously into the whole series of carbohydrate or nitrogen sources under investigation. The inoculation was performed with a loop of yeast suspension in water, prepared from a two day old culture in the following manner. A small amount of wort agar culture was transferred with a small platinum loop into a test tube containing 10 ml of sterile tap water. As the loop came into contact with the inner wall of the test tube a small amount of culture was left above the level of the water in the form of a barely perceptible trace; the loop was then flamed and again introduced into the test tube containing the water, a drop of water was captured in the loop and in it the material already introduced was rubbed against the wall of the tube. The suspension obtained was washed off into the water from which the inoculum was transferred to the agar surface by means of the platinum loop.

The capacity of spore-forming yeasts to assimilate various sources of carbohydrate was tested on solid Reader medium: $MgSO_4$ – 0.7 g; NaCl – 0.5 g; Ca $(NO_3)_2$ – 0.4 g; KH_2PO_4 – 1.0 g; K_2HPO_4 – 0.1 g; yeast extract – 50 ml; yeast autolysate – 50 ml; the test carbohydrate – 60.0g; agar-agar – 20.0 g; tap water – 1 litre.

Glucose, sucrose, maltose, galactose, lactose, xylose, arabinose and raffinose were used as carbohydrate sources.

Ethyl alcohol was tested as a source of carbohydrate for the growth of the yeast cultures isolated. To a mineral medium (distilled water – 1000 cm^3, ammonium sulphate – 1.0 g; potassium monophosphate – 1.0 g; magnesium sulphate – 0.5 g), distributed in 20 ml amounts in 100 ml flasks, 3% of ethyl alcohol were added. The results were recorded after six days.

Nutrient media were used also for Actinomycetes cultures: potato agar (1000.0 g of potato extract; 1.0 g of chalk; 20.0 g of agar-agar); Krasil'nikov's synthetic medium (1938) consisting of 1000.0 g of distilled water with 0.5 g K_2HPO_4, 0.5 g $MgCO_3$, 0.5 g NaCl, 1.0 g KNO_3, 0.001 g Fe_2SO_4 and excess of chalk. As a source of nutrient carbohydrate 2 – 3% of sucrose were added.

The structure of substrate and aerial mycelium was studied on potato agar, wort agar, nutrient agar and synthetic agar on the third, fifth, tenth and fifteenth days of culturing.

As the morphological and cultural characteristics and the biochemical properties of all the microorganisms were studied, it became progressively possible to compare them and identify them within each systematic group. This procedure of identifying the material while it was being studied, instead on the basis of descriptions, made it possible to group together cultures which did not differ from one another and so build up a picture of the distribution of these microorganisms in the sea.

Species determination of these forms presented considerable difficulties. With rare exceptions, the forms studied could not be identified with the species described in the keys, since they differed in a number of respects; but to start describing all microbial forms differing from one another as new species would only further confuse the already far from perfect systematics of microorganisms.

With some reservations, therefore, we have treated such forms as variants of those species in the Krasil'nikov (1949), Lodder and Kreger van Rij (1952), and Kudryavtsev (1954) keys to which they bore the strongest resemblance, distinguishing them by letters of the alphabet.

3

Salt tolerance of marine microorganisms

There is a considerable literature on the problem of bacterial salt tolerance. In regard to microorganisms isolated from the sea, however, it is obvious that their preference will be for nutrient media prepared in sea water (ZoBell, 1946). Butkevich (1932) suggests that microbial forms from the sea which flourish equally well in salt-free media and in media containing 3% of common salt evidently belong to the freshwater bacteria.

Vargues, in an important recent work (1962), considers in detail the problem of halophilia in marine bacteria. Taking as examples eight cultures of non-sporing rods isolated from the sea, he studied their capacity to reproduce in a salt-free medium and at various concentrations of NaCl, determined the influence of different ions on them, measured the respiratory activity as a function of the salinity of the substrate and so forth.

All these studies were made on microorganisms found in coastal waters. It was therefore of interest to discover the salt tolerance of forms inhabiting the depths of the high seas.

For this purpose about 2500 strains from our collection were simultaneously inoculated into two series of test tubes containing nutrient agar slants (tryptic hydrolysate of fish meal). To one series 3% of sea salt was added; the other series contained no salt. Three to five days after inoculation the cultures which had developed and those which had grown poorly or not at all were counted.

As can be seen from Table 18 all the strains except five grew well on the nutrient agar containing sea salt; more than half (63.4%) proved halophilous, that is, unable to grow or growing poorly on the nutrient agar to which no sea salt had been added.

We are not inclined to regard the remaining 36.6% of the strains as freshwater bacteria, but rather as salt-tolerant forms suited by the degree of salinity present in the nutrient agar without sea salt.

The figures in Table 19 indicate the proportion of halophilous microorganisms among those isolated from Pacific Ocean water. The percentage fluctuates between 56.5 and 88 in the various geographical zones.

Table 18. Salt tolerance of microorganisms isolated from various ocean areas

Ocean area	Cultures growing in medium with 3 % sea salt*	Cultures not growing in medium without sea salt**	Total no. of cultures growing poorly or not at all in medium without sea salt***
Pacific	1053/1054 99.9%	416/1054 39.5%	680/1054 64.5%
Indian Ocean and Antarctic seas	804/805 99.9%	399/805 49.5%	600/805 74.5%
Atlantic; Greenland and Norwegian Seas	612/615 99.5%	107/615 17.3%	289/615 46.9%
Total for all seas	2469/2474 99.8%	922/2474 37.3%	1569/2474 63.4%

* Number of cultures growing in medium containing sea salt as fraction and percentage of number of cultures studied
** Number of cultures not growing in medium without sea salt as fraction and percentage of number of cultures studied
*** Number of cultures not growing or growing poorly in medium without sea salt as fraction and percentage of number of cultures studied

In the Indian Ocean and the seas of Antarctica the percentage of halophilous microorganisms fluctuates between 53 and 91 (Table 20); the percentage in the Norwegian Sea, in the north subtropical zone and the equatorial-tropical region of the Atlantic turned out to be roughly the same (Table 21).

The comparatively small percentage of halophilous microorganisms (21 – 23%) in the North Atlantic and the Greenland Sea is striking. The reason may lie in the influence of the East Greenland current, which brings slightly freshened water from the Arctic Ocean. The Norwegian Sea is affected by the Gulf Stream and this is evidently why the proportion of halophilous organisms in it is similar to that in the tropical parts of the Atlantic.

It is interesting that the salt tolerance of the microorganisms isolated varied little in the course of culturing under laboratory conditions. Cultures obtained from the Greenland Sea displayed the same percentage of halophilous microorganisms (Table 21) a year, and even four and a half years later.

In studying the biochemical activity of marine microorganisms we found that some cultures, which had not developed or had displayed no biochemical activity on a given medium, started growing and actively modifying the

Table 19. Salt tolerance of microorganisms isolated from various parts of the Pacific

Latitude	Section 172°E		Section 174°W		Pacific as a whole	
	Cultures growing in medium containing 3% sea salt*	Cultures growing poorly or not at all in medium without sea salt**	Cultures growing in medium containing 3% sea salt*	Cultures growing poorly or not at all in medium without sea salt**	Cultures growing in medium containing 3% sea salt*	Cultures growing poorly or not at all in medium without sea salt**
23—40° N	$\frac{65}{65}$ 100%	$\frac{39}{65}$ 60.0%	$\frac{37}{37}$ 100%	$\frac{26}{37}$ 70.2%	$\frac{102}{102}$ 100%	$\frac{65}{102}$ 63.7%
10—23° N	$\frac{129}{129}$ 100%	$\frac{84}{129}$ 65.1%	$\frac{51}{51}$ 100%	$\frac{45}{51}$ 88.2%	$\frac{180}{180}$ 100%	$\frac{129}{180}$ 71.7%
10°N.—10° S	$\frac{198}{198}$ 100%	$\frac{121}{198}$ 61.1%	$\frac{127}{127}$ 100%	$\frac{92}{127}$ 72.4%	$\frac{325}{325}$ 100%	$\frac{213}{325}$ 65.5%
23—10° S	$\frac{124}{124}$ 100%	$\frac{70}{124}$ 56.5%	$\frac{93}{93}$ 100%	$\frac{60}{93}$ 64.5%	$\frac{217}{217}$ 100%	$\frac{130}{217}$ 59.9%
40—23° S	$\frac{125}{125}$ 100%	$\frac{75}{125}$ 60.0%	$\frac{104}{105}$ 99.0%	$\frac{68}{105}$ 64.8%	$\frac{229}{230}$ 99.6%	$\frac{143}{230}$ 62.2%
Total . . .	$\frac{641}{641}$ 100%	$\frac{389}{641}$ 60.7%	$\frac{412}{413}$ 99.8%	$\frac{291}{413}$ 70.5%	$\frac{1053}{1054}$ 99.9%	$\frac{680}{1054}$ 64.5%

*No. of cultures growing in medium containing sea salt as fraction and % of no. of cultures studied

**No. of cultures growing poorly or not at all in medium without sea salt as fraction and % of no. of cultures studied

Table 20. Salt tolerance of microorganisms from various parts of the Indian Ocean and Antarctic seas

Latitude	Section 20°E		Section 88-98°W		Stations between 20° and 88-98°E		Ocean as a whole	
	Cultures growing in medium containing 3% sea salt*	Cultures growing poorly or not at all in medium without sea salt**	Cultures growing in medium containing 3% sea salt*	Cultures growing poorly or not at all in medium without sea salt**	Cultures growing in medium containing 3% sea salt*	Cultures growing poorly or not at all in medium without sea salt**	Cultures growing in medium containing 3% sea salt*	Cultures growing poorly or not at all in medium without sea salt**
10—23° N			$\frac{76}{76}$ 100%	$\frac{60}{76}$ 78.9%			$\frac{76}{76}$ 100%	$\frac{60}{76}$ 78.9%
10° N — —10° S			$\frac{129}{129}$ 100%	$\frac{110}{129}$ 85.3%			$\frac{129}{129}$ 100%	$\frac{110}{129}$ 85.3%
23°—10° S			$\frac{131}{131}$ 100%	$\frac{112}{131}$ 85.5%			$\frac{131}{131}$ 100%	$\frac{112}{131}$ 85.5%
40—23° S	$\frac{37}{37}$ 100%	$\frac{24}{37}$ 64.9%	$\frac{107}{107}$ 100%	$\frac{79}{107}$ 73.8%			$\frac{144}{144}$ 100%	$\frac{103}{144}$ 71.5%
50—40° S	$\frac{32}{32}$ 100%	$\frac{17}{32}$ 53.1%	$\frac{39}{39}$ 100%	$\frac{24}{39}$ 61.6%	$\frac{20}{20}$ 100%	$\frac{14}{20}$ 70%	$\frac{91}{91}$ 100%	$\frac{55}{91}$ 60.5%
60—50° S	$\frac{42}{42}$ 100%	$\frac{23}{42}$ 54.8%	$\frac{34}{34}$ 100%	$\frac{28}{34}$ 82.3%	$\frac{53}{54}$ 98.1%	$\frac{37}{54}$ 68.5%	$\frac{129}{130}$ 99.2%	$\frac{88}{130}$ 67.7%
70—60° S	$\frac{39}{39}$ 100%	$\frac{22}{39}$ 56.4%	$\frac{23}{23}$ 100%	$\frac{21}{23}$ 91.3%	$\frac{42}{42}$ 100%	$\frac{29}{42}$ 69%	$\frac{104}{104}$ 100%	$\frac{72}{104}$ 69.3%
Total . . .	$\frac{150}{150}$ 100%	$\frac{86}{150}$ 57.3%	$\frac{539}{539}$ 100%	$\frac{434}{539}$ 80.5%	$\frac{115}{116}$ 99.1%	$\frac{80}{116}$ 69%	$\frac{804}{805}$ 99,9%	$\frac{600}{805}$ 74,5%

*No. of cultures growing in medium containing sea salt as fraction and % of no. of cultures studied

**No. of cultures growing poorly or not at all in medium without sea salt as fraction and % of no. of cultures studied

Table 21. Salt tolerance of microorganisms isolated from various parts of the Atlantic Ocean and the Greenland and Norwegian Seas

Sea area		Dec. 1961 expt.		March 1958 expt.	
		Cultures growing in medium containing 3% sea salt*	Cultures growing poorly or not at all in medium without sea salt**	Cultures growing in medium containing 3% sea salt*	Cultures growing poorly or not at all in medium without sea salt**
Greenland Sea		159/159 100%	37/159 23.3%	343/356 96.3%	77/356 21.6%
Norwegian Sea		68/69 98.5%	35/69 50.7%	—	—
Atlantic Ocean	40° N and further north	31/33 93.9%	7/33 21.2%	—	—
	23—40° N	45/45 100%	33/45 73.3%	—	—
	10—23° N	96/96 100%	55/96 57.3%	—	—
	10° N —10° S	131/131 100%	72/131 54.9%	—	—
	23—10° S	82/82 100%	50/82 61%	—	—
Total		612/615 99.5 %	289/615 46.9%	—	—

*Number of cultures growing in medium containing sea salt as fraction and percentage of number of cultures studied

**Number of cultures growing poorly or not at all in medium without sea salt as fraction and percentage of number of cultures studied

Table 22. Variation in biochemical activity of cultures after addition of sea salt

Sea area	Peptone water with					Potato agar
	mannitol	glucose	sucrose	maltose	lactose	
Pacific Ocean	8/58 (1155)	33/146 (1169)	6/99 (1142)	21/115 (1158)	13/70 (1145)	705/808 (1180)
Indian Ocean and Antarctic seas	10/126 (875)	7/161 (869)	7/139 (860)	17/140 (844)	0/60 (845)	516/563 (781)
Atlantic Ocean and Greenland and Norwegian Seas	18/197 (957)	69/294 (955)	18/262 (1076)	12/206 (1048)	3/104 (1060)	348/457 (1080)

The fractions show the numbei of biochemically active cultures after addition of sea salt over the total number of biochemically active cultures; the figures in parentheses represent the total number of cultures studied.

medium after the addition of 3% of sea salt. In media which already contained salt (peptone water with carbohydrates) the addition of sea salt elicited up to 24% increase in the number of biochemically active cultures, whereas on starch agar not otherwise containing salt the number of cultures hydrolysing starch increased by 75–90% on addition of salt (Table 22).

No connection was detected between the influence of salinity on the biochemical activity of the cultures isolated and the latitude of the areas where they were collected.

4

Viability of heterotrophic marine microorganisms in laboratory cultures

More than 4000 strains of heterotrophic microorganisms have been isolated from various parts of the ocean, from the North Pole to Antarctica, and from various levels of the water column, from the surface to maximum depth, as well as from the bottom. The viability of these strains in the process of culturing under laboratory conditions was the subject of special observations, the results of which are given below.

It was pointed out earlier (Kriss, 1963) that the membrane-filter method of growing microorganisms yielded an underestimate of the microbial population in a sample of water if the concentration of microorganisms in the sample was high. In the small area of the filter, antagonisms are more sharply expressed than under conditions in which growth is scattered. Moreover, it must be remembered that rapidly-multiplying forms, provided they are present in sufficient number, will take possesion of the entire filter surface until such time as slower-growing species can develop. This means that in inoculating the water sample we must allow for some percentage, difficult to determine, of marine microorganisms which will not be able to multiply in the given nutrient medium or will not survive competition with other microbial species.*

Samples from colonics incubated on a filter or in dishes containing suspensions of mud were transferred to an agar slant after three to five days growth on membrane filters. Yet despite this comparatively short period of incubation and although the composition of the nutrient medium was the same, from 1.5 to 9% of the microorganisms failed to survive (Table 23). The forms which perished were obviously highly sensitive to metabolic products accumulated in the growing colony.

*(Editor's footnote). It should also be noted that the use of media containing relatively high concentrations of organic substances and incubation at temperatures different from those which the organisms would encounter in their natural habitat may have resulted in the selection of particular kinds of bacteria and the suppression of others.

Table 23. Viability of heterotrophic marine microorganisms under laboratory culturing

Sea area	No. of microorganisms isolated	Transfer from filters to agar slant		Reinoculation on nutrient agar containing sea salt; % age loss of strains from cultures kept on board on cold storage for different periods										After 1st yr. culturing in Moscow		After 2nd yr. culturing in Moscow		After 3rd yr. culturing in Moscow		Total	
		No. of surviving strains	% age loss	15 days	1 month	1 ½ months	2 months	2 ½ months	3 months	3 ½ months	4 months	Total: No. of surviving strains	Total: % age loss	No. of surviving strains	% age loss	No. of surviving strains	% age loss	No. of surviving strains	% age loss	No. of surviving strains	% age loss
Pacific Ocean	1898	1800	5.2	—	4.2	15.8	20.6	20.9	17.9	9.7	53.7	1498	15.9	1213	15.0	1102	5.8	—	—	1102	41.9
Indian Ocean and Antarctic seas	1286	1268	1.4	—	3.3	—	4.1*	—	13.4*	—	17.8*	1168	7.8	975	15.0	870	8.1	848	1.7	848	34.0
Atlantic Ocean	481	474	1.5	—	—	0.0	0.4	7.8	—	—	—	465	1.9	391	15.3	—	—	—	—	391	18.7
Greenland Sea	583	558	4.3	20.0	4.8	—	—	—	—	—	—	510	8.2	419	15.6	343	13.0	249	16.1	249	57.2
Norwegian Sea	430	391	9.1	—	—	14.4	—	—	—	—	—	329	14.4	123	47.9	—	—	—	—	123	71.4

*Cultures reinoculated on board at monthly intervals

On arrival in Moscow all the cultures obtained during the expedition were transferred to the same nutrient agar, prepared this time not in ocean water but in tap water, to which 3% of sea salt had been added. The time that elapsed between the isolation of the colonies incubated from water and mud samples and the subculturing in Moscow of the microorganisms which had been kept in cold storage on board varied from two weeks to four months, except for the cultures from the Indian Ocean, which were subcultured on nutrient agar containing sea salt a month after reinoculation on board.

As can be seen from Table 23, some of the cultures did not grow after the first reinoculation in Moscow. The percentage of strains which developed on nutrient agar containing sea salt was comparatively high (79–100%); the only considerable loss occurred in cultures from the subtropical zone of the Pacific. We cannot be sure that this isolated case of wholesale death of strains was the result of keeping them for four months before reinoculation in Moscow; of the group of strains taken from the Pacific and kept for three and a half months, only about 10% perished and the survival rate was roughly the same in strains from the Indian Ocean and the Antarctic Seas, which had been reinoculated on board at monthly intervals.

After each successive reinoculation the number of cultures diminished, although they were kept in cold storage at temperatures of 3–8°C. The highest losses occurred during the first year of culturing. In the second and third years losses were smaller (Table 23). All in all, the proportion of marine heterotrophic microorganisms surviving the whole period of culturing varied from a third (Norwegian Sea) to two-thirds (Indian Ocean) of the

Table 24. Viability of marine heterotrophic organisms from different geographical zones after one year's culturing in Moscow

Provenance (latitude)	Atlantic Ocean, Norwegian and Greenland Seas			Indian Ocean and Antarctic seas			Pacific Ocean		
	No. of strains isolated	No. of strains perishing	% age loss	No. of strains isolated	No. of strains perishing	% age loss	No. of strains isolated	No. of strains perishing	% age loss
70—50° S	—	—	—	479	142	29.6	—	—	—
50—40° S	—	—	—	165	57	34.5	—	—	—
40—23° S	—	—	—	269	95	35.7	538	248	46.6
23—10° S	89	4	4.5	146	12	8.2	330	112	34.0
10° S — 10° N	148	5	3.4	137	2	1.5	469	97	20.7
10—23° N	109	3	2.8	90	2	2.2	300	95	31.6
23—40° N	73	9	12.3	—	—	—	261	141	54.0
40—60° N	61	18	29.5	—	—	—	—	—	—
60—80° N	1013	471	46.5	—	—	—	—	—	—

total. The only exception was the collection of Atlantic cultures, in which 90 strains perished; but this may have been due to the shorter period of observations on the viability of the Atlantic strains.

In order to find out why so large a percentage of the marine heterotroph cultures perished we investigated the relationship between viability and frequency of reinoculation. The majority of the strains was reinoculated at intervals of 3–4 months; those which were growing badly were reinoculated every two months. It was found that for a certain number of strains frequent reinoculations improved the chances of survival. In most cases, however, three to four monthly intervals between inoculations did not lead to higher losses, particularly in the second and third years of culturing. A long interval (six months) reduced the percentage of surviving cultures in the Pacific Ocean collection.

The individual characteristics of the strains are obviously the most important factor in determining their sensitivity to the products of their own metabolism accumulated in the medium before the next inoculation. It must be remembered that the whole collection was reinoculated on a nutrient medium of unchanged composition; nor were there any abrupt variations in the conditions under which the cultures were kept between reinoculations.

There was a strikingly clear relationship between the survival of the marine heterotrophs under laboratory conditions and the geographical provenance of the cultures. Table 24 shows data on the viability of cultures of heterotrophic microorganisms obtained from various geographical zones of the Atlantic, Pacific and Indian Oceans. Since the duration of laboratory culturing varied according to the provenance of the strains only data relating to the first year of culturing have been used for comparison.

As can be seen from Table 24 the percentage loss among strains from high latitudes was several times greater than among those from the equatorial-tropical zones. In the Atlantic collection the percentage loss in cultures from the sub-Arctic and Arctic regions (Norwegian and Greenland Seas) was 6 to 15 times greater than among cultures from low latitudes. Approximately the same ratios of percentage loss are observed if we compare strains from the equatorial-tropical zone of the Indian Ocean with those from the Antarctic seas. In regard to the Pacific, the percentage loss from the equatorial zone is half as great as from the subtropical areas.

In view of the fact that the collections of marine heterotrophs from different parts of the world consisted largely of microorganisms inhabiting deep waters, where the temperature is roughly the same in all geographical zones, it is hard to believe that the greater viability of the low-latitude strains is due to better adaptation to laboratory temperatures.

It seems rather that the comparatively high percentage of loss among strains from the high latitudes was due to the accumulation of metabolic products in the cultures, as a result of the manifold enzymatic activity (see below) of these heterotrophs. Perhaps cells from such cultures were more susceptible to toxic by-products because of their weaker biochemical activity.

5

Distribution of stable and labile forms of organic matter in the water column of the sea and ocean

We can take it that organic matter is fairly evenly distributed in the depths of the open sea. Its concentration is not high; Krogh (1934) gives it as 5 mg/l and Skopintsev, (1950) gives the still lower figure of 2 mg/1.

The bulk of the organic matter in the ocean is autochthonous, produced by the vital activity and death of the animal, plant and bacterial population of the water column and mud. This accounts for the variety of organic compounds suspended or dissolved in ocean water. They have been found to include such biologically active substances as enzymes, vitamins and antibiotics.*

Through the processes of decomposition and conversion the organic matter in the ocean is mineralized or otherwise altered. Microorganisms play the main role in its decay and transformation. Stable and labile forms of organic matter are distinguished, according to degree of resistance to the action of microbial enzymes. It should be noted that such organic substances as carbohydrates, organic acids, amino acids and peptones, which are readily assimilable by microorganisms, are among those resistant to the action of potassium permanganate (Dzyadzio, 1938; Skopintsev, Mikhaylovskaya, 1948).

Most of these organic substances are oxidized by potassium permanganate in an acid or alkaline medium to a small percentage of the theoretical values, whereas the humic acids, phenol and others, which are resistant to microorganisms, show high values of permanganate oxidizability. This accounts for the discrepancy between the figures obtained by the oxidation method, which is the most widespread method of determining the concentration of organic matter in bodies of water, and the figures for the concentration of heterotrophic microorganisms in the same samples of ocean water.

*(Editor's footnote). It may be noted here that the greater part of the organic matter in ocean water is in dissolved form, its quantity being up to 4000 times that of the organic matter present in the living organisms in the water. For a recent review on the subject of dissolved organic matter in sea water see E. K. Duursma in *Chemical Oceanography,* 1, edited by J. P. Riley and G. Skirrow, Academic Press, London and New York, 1965, pp. 433 –75.

Lebedeva (1959) points out that many samples of Indian Ocean water which were negative by the oxidation test contained large quantities of saprophytic microorganisms growing on peptone media; on the other hand, samples of water showing high oxidizability were found to contain only small amounts of saprophytic bacteria or none at all. In the former case, obviously, the concentration of labile organic matter was high, whereas in the latter case it was low.

At their present level of development of methods for determining organic matter in natural waters, the sole criterion of the relative content of labile forms of organic matter in sea or ocean water is the quantity of heterotrophic microorganisms in it which will grow on protein media.* The biochemical oxygen demand (BOD) method essentially reflects the activity of heterotrophic bacteria which multiply rapidly in flasks containing isolated water samples; on the quantity and activity of these bacteria depend the rate and degree of oxidation of labile organic matter in the sample.

Information on the quantitative range of heterotrophic bacteria (developed on laboratory media) in the depths of the ocean can therefore give us a picture of the distribution of labile forms of organic matter, which will consequently undergo comparatively rapid mineralization, in the oceanic water column.

We collected such data during the Arctic, Indian, Pacific and Atlantic expeditions of 1954–59.

Distribution of labile forms of organic matter in the ocean depths

The Arctic, sub-Arctic, Antarctic and sub-Antarctic regions of the ocean differ sharply from the equatorial-tropical zone in regard to the quantity of heterotrophic microorganisms assimilating labile forms of organic matter, while the subtropical areas occupy an intermediate position in this respect. Our data on the distribution of heterotrophic microorganisms are therefore grouped accordingly, by geographical regions. Data relating to the vertical section of the water column are grouped by layers, distinguished from one another by their productivity or by the provenance, polar or tropical, of the water passing through them.

Table 25 shows data on the quantitative distribution of heterotrophic microorganisms owing their development to readily assimilable forms of organic matter in various layers of the water in high latitudes. These figures are indicative of the quantity of organic matter in the water column,

*(Editor's footnote). A promising approach to the solution of this problem has been made by R. T. Wright and J. E. Hobbie (1965, *Limnol. Oceanogr.*, 10, pp. 22–28), using substrates labelled with radiocarbon and a method similar to that used in studying enzyme kinetics.

Table 25. Quantitative distribution of microorganisms assimilating labile forms of organic matter in high-latitude (Arctic, sub-Arctic, Antarctic and sub-Antarctic) regions of the ocean

Water layer, m	No. of samples	% age of samples with various nos. of colonies per 40 – 50 ml		
		0 – 9	10 – 99	>100
0	48	62.6	16.6	20.8
1—50	123	62.7	9.8	27.5
51—200	197	83.2	8.7	8.1
201—300	80	86.2	12.5	1.3
301—600	109	81.6	15.7	2.7
601—1500	108	85.2	10.2	4.6
1501—2500	69	71.0	5.8	23.2
2501—4500	80	87.5	10.0	2.5
4501—bottom	6	100.0		

according to vertical distribution from surface to bottom, in the Arctic, sub-Arctic, Antarctic and sub-Antarctic regions.

As can be seen from Table 25, the oceanic water column in high latitudes is very poor in labile forms ot organic matter. Even at the surface and in the zones of active photosynthesis, 60% of the water samples contained such small quantities of heterotrophic microorganisms that after filtration of 40 – 50 ml of water not more than nine colonies developed on the membrane filters. The percentage of such samples gradually increases with depth, so that the picture is one of steadily increasing impoverishment of the oceanic water column in labile organic matter as the bottom is approached.

Water samples from which more than a hundred colonies incubated after filtration of 40 – 50 ml made up about 21 to 27% of the samples from the surface layers. Further down, a relatively high content in labile organic matter was observed only in the 1500 – 2500 m layer, through which passes water of equatorial-tropical origin.

In the equatorial-tropical zone of the ocean the whole water column is far richer in organic matter readily assimilable by microorganisms than are the high-latitude water masses. We suggest (see below) that this may be because tropical waters, which are much less productive than high-latitude waters, are enriched in labile allochthonous organic matter, readily assimilable by microorganisms, discharged from the shore.

That the concentration* of the labile forms of organic matter in tropical seas is tens of times greater than in areas near the Poles is evident from the high percentage of equatorial-tropical samples from which more than a hundred colonies incubated on fish-peptone media. In the entire oceanic

* (Editor's footnote). There should be a distinction here between *concentration* and *rate of supply*. A low concentration of substrate might support a large population of bacteria if its rate of turn-over were high.

Table 26. Quantitative distribution of microorganisms assimilating labile forms of organic matter in the equatorial-tropical zone of the ocean

Water layer, m	No. of samples	% age of samples with various nos. of colonies per 40 – 50 ml		
		0 – 9	10 – 99	>100
0	63	4.8	14.3	80.9
1—50	175	7.4	26.4	66.2
51—200	260	5.4	25.0	69.5
201—300	102	4.9	43.2	51.9
301—600	179	10.1	28.5	61.4
601—1500	192	11.9	31.3	56.8
1501—2500	116	14.6	23.3	62.1
2501—4500	103	16.5	21.4	62.1
4501 – bottom	34	20.5	41.2	38.3

water column except only the bottom layers, such samples made up more than 50% of the total (Table 26). The highest percentage of samples with a very low concentration of heterotrophs (0 – 9 colonies from 40 – 50 ml of water) was taken near the bottom, but did not exceed 20% of the total.

In the subtropical zones the mixing of equatorial-tropical water with water from high latitudes leads to a higher concentration of labile organic matter than in the polar regions and to a lower concentration than in the equatorial-tropical regions. This is evident from the ratio of samples containing small numbers of heterotrophic microorganisms to samples containing large numbers (Table 27).

Characteristic of all three regions of the world's seas and oceans – high latitude, subtropical and tropical – was a regular increase, in proportion to distance from the ocean surface and proximity to the bottom, in the percentage of water samples poor in heterotrophs and a regular decrease in the percentage of samples from which more than a hundred colonies

Table 27. Quantitative distribution of microorganisms assimilating labile forms of organic matter in subtropical parts of the ocean

Water layer, m	No. of samples	% age of samples with various nos. of colonies per 40 – 50 ml		
		0 – 9	10—99	>100
0	44	22.7	50.1	27.2
1—50	123	37.4	39.8	22.8
51—200	166	37.3	43.4	19.3
201—300	75	46.7	44.0	9.3
301—600	123	54,5	30.9	14.6
601—1500	124	58.1	30.0	11.9
1501—2500	81	59.3	26.0	14.7
2501—4500	48	54.1	25.0	20.9
4501— bottom	25	52.0	36.0	12.0

developed (Tables 25 and 27). Only in certain layers were deviations observed, associated with the passage either of high-latitude or of equatorial-tropical water in these layers.

A rise in the concentration of labile forms with distance from the polar regions towards the Equator is thus the characteristic feature of the horizontal distribution of organic matter and a reduction in the content of labile forms with depth is equally characteristic of its vertical distribution. On the global scale these patterns are disturbed in certain places and at certain depth by powerful currents which draw water of equatorial-tropical origin towards the north and south, and polar water towards the low latitudes. These local disturbances, however, do not alter the general picture of the distribution of labile forms of organic matter, readily assimilable by microorganisms, in the seas and oceans in general.

Distribution of stable forms of organic matter in the seas and oceans

Labile forms make up only a small part of the organic matter occurring in sea water. Even in samples with a very high content of heterotrophic microorganisms, the quantities detected fall far short of the actual concentration of organic matter in the sample (2–5 mg/l). It is sufficient to seal a sample of sea water in a flask and keep it for 2–5 days to find vigorous multiplication, at the rate of tens and hundreds of thousands per ml of water, of microorganisms utilizing labile organic compounds. This shows how little organic matter had been used by the heterotrophs in the sample before it was poured off into the flasks.

The phenomenon of sudden, rapid increase in the population of heterotrophic microorganisms in isolated samples from a body of water is of great interest. There is already a considerable literature on the intensive multiplication of microorganisms assimilating labile forms of organic matter. in flasks containing water taken from lakes, seas and oceans (Whipple, 1901; Fred et al., 1924; Gee, 1932; Waksman, Carey, 1935; Zobell et al., 1934, 1936, 1943; Voroshilova, Dianova, 1937; Lloyd, 1937; Kriss, Markianovich, 1959 and others). The quantity of bacterial heterotrophs in isolated water samples increases hundreds and thousands of times within a few days and can rise even to several millions per ml. Fred, Wilson and Dav enport (1924), for example, observed an increase in the concentration of heterotrophic bacteria from 126 to 7 400 000 per ml after the water had been kept in flasks. ZoBell and Anderson (1936) described a similar increase in the heterotroph population of sea water kept for a few days in isolated samples.

It is important to emphasize that the immense increase in the bacterial biomass in flasks containing samples from natural bodies of water is due mainly to that part of the microbial biocoenosis which uses labile organic matter as a substrate. This drastically alters the ratio, in the flasks, between bacterial forms capable of multiplying on peptone media and species lacking that ability. Evidence for this can be found in the results of comparative determinations of the quantity of bacteria in flasks containing sample water by the meat-peptone agar inoculation method, on the one hand, and the direct count method, on the other. According to the data of Voroshilova and Dianova (1937), the number of bacteria growing on MPA increased hundreds, thousands and tens of thousands of times, whereas the number counted by direct microscopy was only a few times greater than at the start.

Throughout the literature on microbiological processes in flasks containing samples taken from various types of bodies of water there is complete unanimity concerning the rapid multiplication of heterotrophic bacteria in such flasks. There are no grounds for assuming that when carbonate containing the radioactive isotope of carbon (C^{14}) is added to isolated samples of water or mud the increase in bacterial mass will be due to multiplication of chemosynthetic bacteria. Kuznetsov (1955) and Sorokin (1955, 1957), who erroneously maintain that this is the case, base their assertion on the appearance of radioactive carbon in the bacterial cells; but now that there is a large amount of evidence on the role of heterotrophic assimilation of carbon dioxide in the processes of biosynthesis, direct proof is essential before we can assert that the radioactive carbon in the flasks was assimilated not by heterotrophs multiplying in isolated water samples but by chemosynthetic bacteria.

Sorokin (1955, 1957) assumes that the growth of the bacterial biomass in the experimental flasks was due to chemosynthesis, on the grounds that in the control flasks, to which sodium azide had been added along with the carbonate, assimilation of radioactive carbon was many times lower or did not occur at all. It must be remembered, however, that sodium azide is a poison, acting not only on oxidizing enzymes, but also on other enzymatic systems contributing to biosynthesis, and that therefore its addition must inevitably have hindered the multiplication of heterotrophic microorganisms.

Nor can any value be placed on such indirect proof as Sorokin offers (1957), in showing that more carbon was assimilated in flasks with water to which methane and hydrogen had been added, since it is well known that bacteria oxidizing methane and hydrogen are by no means obligate autotrophs, but will multiply on organic media and, moreover, are capable, while decomposing organic matter, of simultaneously oxidizing, for example, hydrogen (Wilson et al., 1953). The possible connection between these oxidizing processes and the processes of heterotrophic assimilation of carbon dioxide must not be underestimated. Further, it should be noted that the results of these experiments of Sorokin were not corroborated by the results of Zharova's investigations (1963).

The fact that fixation of radioactive carbon by bacteria multiplying in flasks containing sample water occurs mainly through heterotrophic assimilation of carbon dioxide is shown by the experiments of Sorokin (1958) and Zharova (1963) in which glucose, calcium lactate or sodium formate were added to isolated samples of mud or water. In the samples to which these readily assimilable organic substances were added the amount of radioactive carbon absorbed by the bacteria was several times higher than at the start.

The radiocarbon method suggested by Steemann-Nielsen (1952) for determining photosynthesis production is unfortunately unsuitable for determining rates of chemosynthesis in bodies of water. With the negligible modifications described by Kuznetsov (1955) and Sorokin (1955, 1957) this method gives no more than a rough idea of the activity of the process of heterotrophic carbon dioxide assimilation in flasks containing water or mud samples. In this connection Sorokin's data (1961), showing that 30% of the cell carbon in heterotrophic bacteria may derive from carbon dioxide in the process of heterotrophic carbon dioxide assimilation, are worth noting.

According to ZoBell (1946) the vigorous multiplication of heterotrophic microorganisms in sample flasks is the result of adsorption of organic matter, distributed in the water, on the walls of the flasks. It is suggested that part of the labile forms in natural bodies of water occurs in such small concentrations that only accumulation due to adsorption on the inner surface of the flasks makes these substances accessible to heterotrophs.

Our view (Kriss, Markianovich, 1959) is that not only does concentration of organic matter on the glass-water interface occur, but also the transformation of stable forms into forms assimilable by heterotrophic microorganisms. Pchelin (1951) points out that denaturation of proteinaceous matter sets in on the phase boundary and, as we know, denatured proteins are more readily hydrolysed by bacterial enzymes.

Such ideas are supported by comparative experiments with water samples from the Bay of Sevastopol and from various depths out to sea (120 miles from the shore). The concentration of heterotrophic microorganisms is considerably lower in the deep parts of the Black Sea than in the Bay of Sevastopol (Kriss, 1963; Tables 40 and 41); this indicates that the water column in the open parts of the Black Sea is poorer in labile forms of organic matter than the water in the Bay.

Yet the rate of increase in the heterotroph population and in the size of the heterotroph biomass in the flasks containing water from various depths in the open part of the Black Sea was no different from that observed in the flasks containing water from the Bay of Sevastopol. After the deep-water samples had been kept for two days the concentration of heterotrophs in them ran into thousands and tens of thousands per ml. This shows that there was a sharp increase in the amount of nutrient material – that is, labile forms of organic matter – in the water flasks, obviously due to conversion of stable organic matter into forms readily susceptible to the action of bacterial enzymes.

The fact that the number of heterotrophs in the flasks could increase to several tens and hundreds of thousands per ml, even when the number of heterotrophic microorganisms in the experimental sea-water sample was small (that is, even when there was a low concentration of labile forms of organic matter) suggests that while the water was stored in the flasks the main source of material enabling the microorganisms to multiply was organic matter not readily accessible to the microorganisms until transformed at the boundary between the solid and liquid phases into forms which they could use.

Here we must say a little about the method known as BOD (biological oxygen demand) by which, it is suggested, the amount of organic matter in natural waters can be determined from the oxygen demand. The method consists in agitating a water sample in order to saturate it with atmospheric oxygen and then pouring it into two or more oxygen flasks. The amount of oxygen in the flasks before the start of the experiment is compared with the amount in flasks containing water kept for 5, 10, 20 days, one month or longer periods; the oxygen loss due to oxidation of organic matter in the flasks, in other words the BOD, is thereby determined, in mg of oxygen per litre.

For the first few days the rate of oxygen consumption is usually very high; it then diminishes, but does not fall to zero even if the experiment is prolonged for several months. It is quite obvious that there is a close connection between the dynamics of the oxygen consumption process and the dynamics of the process of bacterial multiplication in the isolated water samples – vigorous multiplication of bacteria in the flasks during the first few days, followed by a reduction in their numbers. No such immense growth of the bacterial biomass as occurs when the water is kept in flasks is observed in natural bodies of water; Skopintsev (1950) is therefore perfectly correct in pointing out that the results of conventional BOD determinations (over periods of five or ten days) cannot possibly be used to estimate the value or rate of oxygen demand in the sea itself.

We may add that even BOD data based on longer periods of storage of sea-water samples tell us nothing about the oxygen demand under natural conditions. Even after samples have been kept in flasks for six months the quantity of heterotrophic bacteria found in the flasks is hundreds or thousands of times greater than in similar volumes of water in the sea itself (Kriss, 1963; Table 38). The BOD values in these cases merely show that the process of biochemical oxygen utilization in the flasks continues at the expense of stable organic matter transformed at the interface between the solid and liquid phases into forms that can be broken down by the enzymes of heterotrophic bacteria.

The stable organic matter in the sea is inhomogeneous in regard to the degree of its resistance to microbial enzymes. Those forms of it which, owing to a series of conversions, are still not capable of being utilized by heterotrophic microorganisms growing on peptone media, but are accessible to microbial species not capable of multiplying on ordinary microbiological media, are for the most part found in the surface layers of the water column in the sea.

The distribution of such forms of organic matter can be estimated from the distribution of microorganisms detectable only by direct microscopy. The biomass of these microorganisms is highest in the photic zone and sharply declines, except in the Black Sea, at depths below 500 m (Kriss, 1956). Because of their large population, heterotrophic microorganisms determined by direct microscopy play the principal role in the processes of organic matter mineralization in the seas and oceans.

The depths of the ocean are rich in aquatic humus, if by this we understand forms of organic matter which cannot easily be broken down by microorganisms. But even at great depths – 1000, 2000, 3000 m – where organic matter, to judge from the small size of the microbial population, consists almost exclusively of aquatic humus, such matter can, at a solid-liquid interface, turn into food for heterotrophic microorganisms assimilating labile organic compounds.

In the light of experiments in which sea water has been stored in flasks, it appears that the transformation of aquatic humus into forms assimilable by microorganisms invariably occurs at the contact boundaries between suspended particles and the water. Particles settling on their way to the bottom of the sea can create microzones, where accumulation and transformation of aquatic humus occur, resulting in the development of heterotrophic microorganisms which in turn bring out its partial or complete mineralization.

II

SPECIES COMPOSITION OF MICROORGANISMS FROM THE HIGH SEAS

Introduction

The following numbers of cultures survived: non-sporing rods – 2200; coccal forms – 266; spore-forming bacteria – 113; mycobacteria – 15; proactinomycetes – 3; actinomycetes – 4; yeast organisms – 62.

On the basis of Krasil'nikov's *Key* (1949) we assigned the bacteria and actinomycetes in this collection to the classes Actinomycetes Krasil'nikov and Eubacteriae Stanier et van Niel, n. comb., and to the families, genera, species and variants listed below: families. Actinomycetaceae Buchanan, Mycobacteriaceae Chester, Coccaceae Zopf, Bacteriaceae Cohn, Pseudomonadaceae Winslow et al., Bacillaceae Fisher, Spirillaceae Migula; genera, *Pseudobacterium* Krasil'nikov, *Pseudomonas* Migula, *Bacterium* Ehrenberg, *Vibrio* Müller, Bacillus Cohn, *Micrococcus* Cohn, *Sarcina* Goodsir, *Mycobacterium* Lehmann et Neumann, *Actinomyces* Harz, *Proactinomyces* Jensen; species *Bacterium agile* Jensen, variants A, B, C, D, E, F, G, H, I, K, L, *Bact. candicans* (G. et P. Frankland) Migula, variants A, B, C, D, E, F, G, H, I, *Bact. parvulum* Conn, variants A, B, C, D, E, F, *Bact. imperiale* Steinhaus, variants A, B, *Bact. zopfii* Kurth, *Bact. stearophilum* Weinzirl, *Pseudomonas sinuosa* Wright, variants A, B, C, D, E, F, G, *Ps. caudatus* (Wright) Conn, variants A, B, C, D, *Ps. fluorescens* Migula, variants A, B, C, D, *Ps. liquida* G. et. P. Frankland, n. comb., variants A, B, *Vibrio nigricans* Weibel, variants A, B, *Pseudobacterium rosea-album* Sack, variants A, B, *Pseudob. biforme* Eggerth, *Pseudob. cocciformis* Severin, variants A, B, *Pseudob. opacum* Sack, variants A, B, *Pseudob. marinopiscosum* ZoBell et Upham, *Pseudob. variabilis* Distaso, n. comb., variants A, B, C, D, E, F, *Pseudob. vulgatum* (Egg. et Gagn.), n, comb., *Bacillus catenula* (Duclaux) Migula, variants A, B, C, D, E, F, G, H, I, *Bac. idosus* Burchard, variants A, B, C, D, E, F, *Bac. filaris* Migula, variants A, B, C, D, E, F, G, H, I, J, *Bac. virgulus* Duclaux, *Bac. glutinosus* Kern, variants A, B, C, *Bac. mycoides* Flügge, *Bac. cereus* Frankland, *Bac. solidus* Lüderitz, *Bac. brevis* Migula, *Bac. circulans* Jordan, *Bac. lubinskii* Migula, *Bac. sphaericus* Neide, *Micrococcus radiatus* Flügge, variants A, B, C, D, E, F, G, H, I, J, K, L,

M. albus (Rosenb.) Buchanan, variants A, B, C, D, E, F, *M. viticulosus* Flügge, variants A, B, C, D, E, *M. albicans* Trevisan, variants A, B, C, D, E, F, G, H, *M. tetragenus* Gaffky, *M. albescens* Henrici, *M. chlorinus* Cohn, *M. granulosus* Kern, *M. subflavus* (Bumm) Migula, variants A, B, C, E, F, *M. conglomeratus* Migula, variants A, B, *M. citreus* Migula, variants A, B, *M. luteolus* Henrici, variants A, B, C, D, *M. pallidus* Henrici, *M. rugatus* (Weichs.) Migula, variants A, B, *M. luteus* (Schröter) Cohn, variants A, B, C, D, *M. ochraceus* Rosenthal, variants A, B, C, D, E, *M. sulfureus* Zimmermann, *M. roseus* Flügge, variants A, B, C, D, E, F, G, H, *M. aurantiacus* (Schröter) Cohn, variants A, B, C, D, E, F, G, *M. cinnabareus* Flügge, variants A, B, C, D, E, F, G, H, I, *Sarcina subflava* Ravenel, variants A, B, *S. luteola* Gruber, *Mycobacterium filiforme* Krasil'nikov, variants A, B, *Mycob. lacticolum* Lehmann et Neumann, *Mycob. mucosum* Krasil'nikov, variants A, B, C, D, E, *Mycob. luteum* (Söhngen) Krasil'nikov, variants A, B, C, *Mycob. album* Söhngen, *Actinomyces globisporus* Krasil'nikov, *Proactinomyces albus* Krasil'nikov.

For the yeast organisms the keys of Lodder and Kreger van Rij (1952) and Kudryavtsev (1954) were used. The yeasts were assigned to the orders Cryptococcales Lodder and Kreger van Rij and Unicellomycetales nov. cohors Kudryavtsev (Kudryavtsev); to the families Cryptococcaceae Lodder and Kreger van Rij, Sporobolomycetaceae Lodder and Kreger van Rij and Saccharomycetaceae; to the genera *Torulopsis* Berlese, *Rhodotorula* Harrison, *Sporobolomyces* Kluyver et van Niel and *Debaryomyces* Klöcker; and to the species *Torulopsis aeria* (Saito) Lodder, variants A, B, C, *T. dattila* (Kluyver) Lodder, *T. famata* (Harrison) n. comb., *T. holmii* (Jörg.) Lodder, *Rhodotorula mucilaginosa* (Jörg.) Harrison, *Rh. glutinis* (Fres.) Harrison, *Rh. glutinis* (Fres.) Harrison var. *rubescens* (Saito) Lodder, *Rh. rubra* (Demme) Lodder, *Sporobolomyces roseus* Kluyver et van Niel, variants A, B, *Debaryomyces rosei* Kudryavtsev, n. comb., *Debar. globosus* Klöcker, *Debar. guilliermondii* Dekker.

6

Species of non-sporing bacteria

Non-sporing rods, 1.7 – 4.3 × 0.4 – 1.0 μ, with rounded ends, single or paired; filaments also occur (Fig. 21). Motile. Peritrichous. Gram-negative.

On nutrient agar containing sea salt the streak is a greyish-creamy colour, sometimes with a pinkish tinge (in young cultures), with scalloped edges and smooth surface (Figs. 22 and 22a). Single strains produce a wrinkled, dry film.

On starch agar with asparagine the streak is white with yellowish spots, mat and with scalloped edges.

On potato – no growth; some strains form a pinkish-creamy slime and the potato turns brown.

On meat-peptone broth – turbidity, ring, sediment.

Gelatine not liquefied. Milk not peptonized. No acid in peptone water containing mannitol, glucose, sucrose, maltose or lactose. In peptone water containing glucose and sucrose several of the strains sometimes form a greenish pigment. Starch hydrolysed. Mineral nitrogen assimilated. Nitrates reduced to nitrites.

From: Atlantic Ocean, (st. **345**), 76, 95 m; (st. **364**), 305, 2975 m; (st. **366**), 998, 2002, 3999, 5200 m; (st. **367**), 30, 50, 100, 300, 600, 800, 1970, 2888 m; (st. **368**), 48, 77, 97, 147, 197, 497, 2490, 3962 m; (st. **369**), 10, 31, 102, 199, 296, 393, 966, 4210 m; (st. **370**), 0, 28, 137, 274, 543 m; (st. **372**), 39, 90, 291, 1445, 3946 m; (st. **374**), 10, 28, 49, 1050, 3086, 3691 m; (st. **376**), 27, 86, 213 m; (st. **378**), 0, 49, 58, 195, 388, 2490, 2971 m; (st. **380**), 29, 147, 398, 794, 992, 2045, 3945, 4930 m; (st. **383**), 27, 45, 200, 708, 886, 1442, 2190, 3607 m; (st. **387**), 73, 92, 185, 724, 907, 1980, 2540, 3078, 4152, 4748 m; (st. **389**), 0, 23, 64, 139, 332, 647, 820, 2482, 3024, 3935, 4715 m;

Greenland Sea, (st. **17**), 200 m; (st. **23**), 1000, 2000 m;

Indian Ocean, (st. **259**), 49 m; (st. **261**), 25 m; (st. **269**), 100 m; (st. **271**), 0 m; (st. **276**), 1222 m; (st. **274**), 1469 m; (st. **278**), 425 m; (st. **280**), 100 m; (st. **285**), 0, 103, 1400, 1840, 4290 m; (st. **287**), 0 m;

(st. **289**), 1025, 2470 m; (st. **291**), 2080 m; (st. **295**), 0, 1030 m; (st. **297**), 0, 1970 m; (st. **303**), 10, 51 m; (st. **305**), 192, 245, 700, 1590 m; (st. **307**), 155, 300, 400, 500, 745, 1000, 4300, 5050 m; (st. **309**), 0, 100, 200, 400, 984, 1455, 1950, 3790, 4710, 5180, 5370 m; (st. **311**), 173, 210, 246, 330, 1293, 3750 m; (st. **312**), 98, 350, 1490, 4190 m; (st. **314**), 0, 180, 400, 1850, 2320, 4700 m; (st. **316**), 0, 75, 150, 195, 240, 288, 1000, 1413 m; (st. **318**), 0, 100, 150, 158, 198, 231, 310, 386, 590, 1470, 1880 m; (st. **320**), 0, 153, 496, 3279 m; (st. **322**), 50, 101, 152, 196, 250, 304, 408, 515, 1959, 2428, 3354, 3447 m; (st. **324**), 0, 50, 75, 100, 150, 200, 250 m; (st. **326**), 1450 m; (st. **327**), 200, 730, 1500, 2000 m; (st. **328**), 21 m; and also from mud (st. **274**);

Pacific Ocean, (st. **3780**), 115, 229 m; (st. **3786**), 45 m; (st. **3788**), 493 m; (st. **3791**), 170 m; (st. **3795**), 272, 329 m; (st. **3801**), 204, 272, 625 m; (st. **3802**), 50 m; (st. **3805**), 582 m; (st. **3812**), 4840 m; (st. **3814**), 0, 146, 300, 1945 m; (st. **3818**), 258, 4914 m; (st. **3823**), 163, 327, 775 m; (st. **3827**), 8500 m; (st. **3834**), 22 m; (st. **3837**), 10, 788 m; (st. **3839**), 95, 295, 590 m; (st. **3840**), 10, 963 m; (st. **3842**), 189 m; (st. **3843**), 98, 470 m; (st. **3844**), 375 m; (st. **3845**), 115, 209 m; (st, **3846**), 10, 100, 198, 247 m; (st. **3853**), 10, 146, 244, 918, 2124 m; (st. **3854**), 10, 152, 298, 496 m; (st. **3855**), 513, 1014 m; (st. **3856**), 50, 1510 m; (st. **3859**), 101, 407, 2036 m; (st. **3860**), 918 m; (st. **3862**), 150 m; (st. **3863**), 161, 2596, 3311 m; (st. **3864**), 77, 105, 1620 m; (st. **3866**), 204, 309, 1996 m; (st. **3868**), 107, 425, 533, 2212 m; (st. **3869**), 10, 498, 790, 1452, 1956 m; (st. **3871**), 313, 2290 m; (st. **3873**), 10, 192, 722 m; (st. **3874**), 10, 74, 112 m; (st. **3875**), 25, 153, 205 m; (st. **3876**), 151 m; (st. **3877**), 205, 800, 2017, 2544 m; (st. **3879**), 0, 9, 22, 65, 171, 250, 594 m; (st. **3880**), 22, 110, 2135 m; (st. **3881**), 164, 1785 m; and also from mud (st. **3834**).

Assigned to aggregate species *Bacterium agile* Jensen, 1898, var. A.

The non-sporing rods are distinguished from var. A in that they do not reduce nitrates.

From: Greenland Sea, (st. 22), 1500 m;

Atlantic Ocean, (st. **360**), 481, 575 m; (st. **362**), 802 m; (st. **364**), 10, 101, 153, 1507, 3937 m; (st. **366**), 50, 100, 150, 175, 200, 300, 399, 499, 599, 798 m; (st. **367**), 10, 50, 400, 500, 600, 2426, 3884 m; (st. **368**), 122, 147, 398, 598, 1993 m; (st. **369**), 49, 82, 102, 150, 199, 488, 585, 780, 1420, 1855, 2358, 5081 m; (st. **370**), 10, 73, 91, 183, 365, 457, 896, 1977, 2566, 3204, 4487, 5420 m; (st. **372**), 0, 20, 39, 71, 90, 139, 189, 291, 390, 494, 789, 984, 1445, 3946, 5137 m; (st. **374**), 10, 79, 99, 148, 198, 314, 421, 850, 2098, 2598 m; (st. **376**), 0, 9, 69, 120, 154, 422, 1066, 1260 m; (st. **378**), 30, 195, 388, 580, 2490, 2971 m; (st. **380**), 49, 98, 201, 1483 m; (st. **383**), 10, 134, 886,

1442, 2670, 4757 m; (st. **387**), 10, 280, 457, 1980, 3078 m; (st. **389**), 10, 40, 165, 252, 490, 1260, 3935 m;

Indian Ocean, (st. **242**), 26 m; (st. **243**), 26 m; (st. **246**), 25 m; (st. **248**), 36 m; (st. **249**), 25, 1930 m; (st. **251**), 23, 141 m; (st. **252**), 0, 25, 1862 m; (st. **256**), 25, 49, 1536, 2668 m; (st. **259**), 1305 m; (st. **260**), 0, 25, 218, 348, 856 m; (st. **261**), 0, 25 m; (st. **265**), 0, 26, 52 m; (st. **266**), 25 m; (st. **267**), 25, 415, 1488, 1958, 2856 m; (st. **271**), 25, 100, 2442 m; (st. **272**), 0, 11, 25, 340, 432, 1464 m; (st. **274**), 0, 23, 88, 1944 m; (st. **276**), 0, 25 m; (st. **278**), 26, 319 m; (st. **280**), 0, 25, 50, 75, 230, 310, 380 m; (st. **281**), 10, 23, 97, 282, 1422, 1812, 2256, 3095 m; (st. **282**), 27, 55, 108, 317 m; (st. **283**), 0, 25, 102, 481, 1544 m; (st. **285**), 26, 77, 402, 505, 2390 m; (st. **287**), 25, 75, 100, 578, 862, 1026, 2020, 3410, 3876 m; (st. **289**), 0, 25, 100, 425, 547, 2000, m; (st. **291**), 0, 25, 75, 100, 800, 1600, 3040 m; (st. 293), 0, 25, 75, 800, 1300, 1800 m; (st. **295**), 0, 75, 91, 410, 1550, 2050 m; (st. **297**), 25, 75, 91, 230, 275, 370, 1500, 2440 m; (st. **299**), 0, 10, 25, 77, 103, 147, 400, 503, 762, 1050, 1563, 2072, 2567, 3000, 3450, 3930 m; (st. **301**), 0, 10, 25, 50, 75, 565, 1158, 1750, 2300 m; (st. **303**), 0, 25, 51, 75, 150, 419, 1026, 1576, 2030, 2500, 2680, 2864 m; (st. **305**), 0, 25, 50, 75, 100, 150, 425, 552, 700, 1150, 1590, 2014, 2890 m; (st. **307**), 0, 10, 25, 50, 100, 205, 300, 400, 500, 745, 1400, 1890, 2350, 3300, 4300, 4820 m; (st. **309**), 10, 25, 50, 75, 150, 250, 300, 400, 500, 740, 2440, 2930, 3300, 4240, 4710, 5180 m; (st. **311**), 10, 25, 50, 75, 100, 150, 246, 330, 412, 830, 2250, 3240, 3750 m; (st. **312**), 0, 10, 25, 50, 72, 98, 147, 174, 350, 445, 680, 893, 1490, 1980, 2450, 3760 m; (st. **314**), 11, 53, 79, 106, 158, 180, 230, 287, 511, 785, 1029, 1390, 1850, 3750, 4700 m; (st. **316**), 10, 25, 50, 75, 100, 195, 288, 390, 495, 750, 1413, 1900, 2400, 2870, 3900, 4800 m; (st. **318**), 0, 10, 25, 50, 75, 794, 1034, 1470, 2620 m; (st. **320**), 10, 25, 51, 76, 102, 153, 198, 230, 273, 397, 1007, 1433, 1903, 2360, 3647, 3741 m; (st. **322**), 10, 25, 76, 2887 m; (st, **324**), 10, 25, 65, 300, 400, 500, 746, 990, 1480, 1930, 2375, 2840, 2930 m; (st. **326**), 0, 10, 50, 65, 75, 100, 150, 177, 220, 255, 414, 512, 776, 1100, 1680 m; (st. **327**), 88, 100, 150, 200, 250, 296, 390, 486, 974, 1500 m; (st. **328**), 0, 10, 54, 62, 125, 135, 197, 255, 320, 490, 600 m; (st. **329**), 0, 10, 25 m; and also from mud (st. **272**, **274**);

Pacific Ocean, (st. **3778**), 150, 948 m; (st. **3780**), 192 m; (st. **3781**), 72, 192, 390 m; (st. **3782**), 591, 2010 m; (st. **3786**), 0, 10, 195, 382 m; (st. **3788**), 202, 254, 304, 493, 590, 2034, 2259 m; (st. **3791**), 424, 529, 640, 1429, 1846, 2079 m; (st. **3795**), 10, 41, 422, 518, 613, 2048, 2986, 5158 m; (st. **3801**), 0, 14, 35, 69, 103, 136, 272, 340, 625, 1235, 1783 m; (st. **3802**), 50, 75, 200, 248, 596, 2024, 3077, 4006, 4492 m; (st. **3805**), 10, 24, 49, 74, 236, 287, 582, 773, 974, 1950, 2380, 3824, 4800, 5190 m; (st. **3808**), 0, 11, 44, 95, 241, 290, 627, 1029, 1554 m; (st. **3812**), 2456, 6578 m; (st. **3814**), 10, 25, 73, 146, 194, 400, 1472 m;

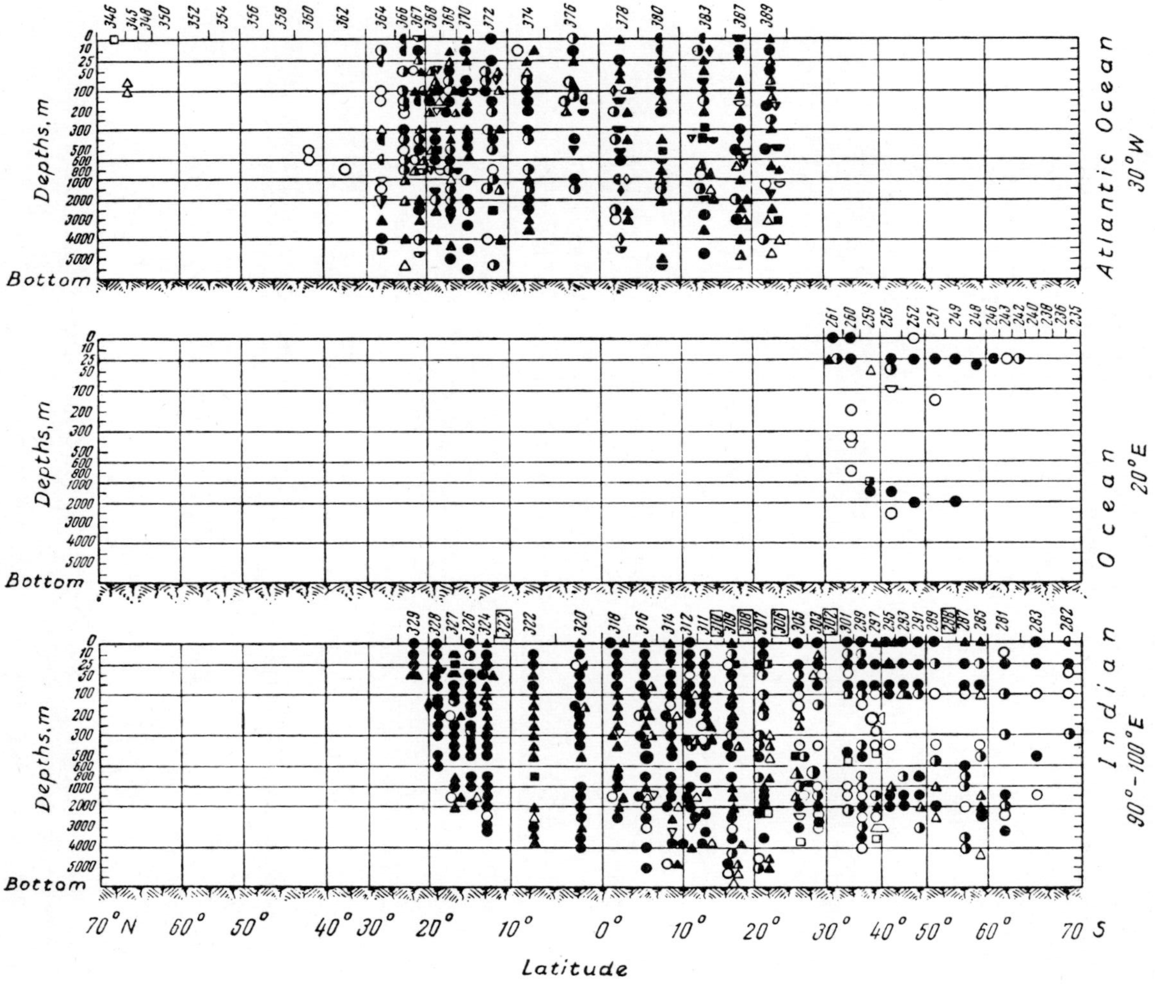

Atlantic Ocean
30°W
Ocean
20°E
Indian
90°-100°E
Depths, m
Bottom
0
10
25
50
100
200
300
500
600
800
1000
2000
3000
4000
5000
70° N
60°
50°
40°
30°
20°
10°
0°
10°
20°
30°
40°
50°
60°
70 S
Latitude

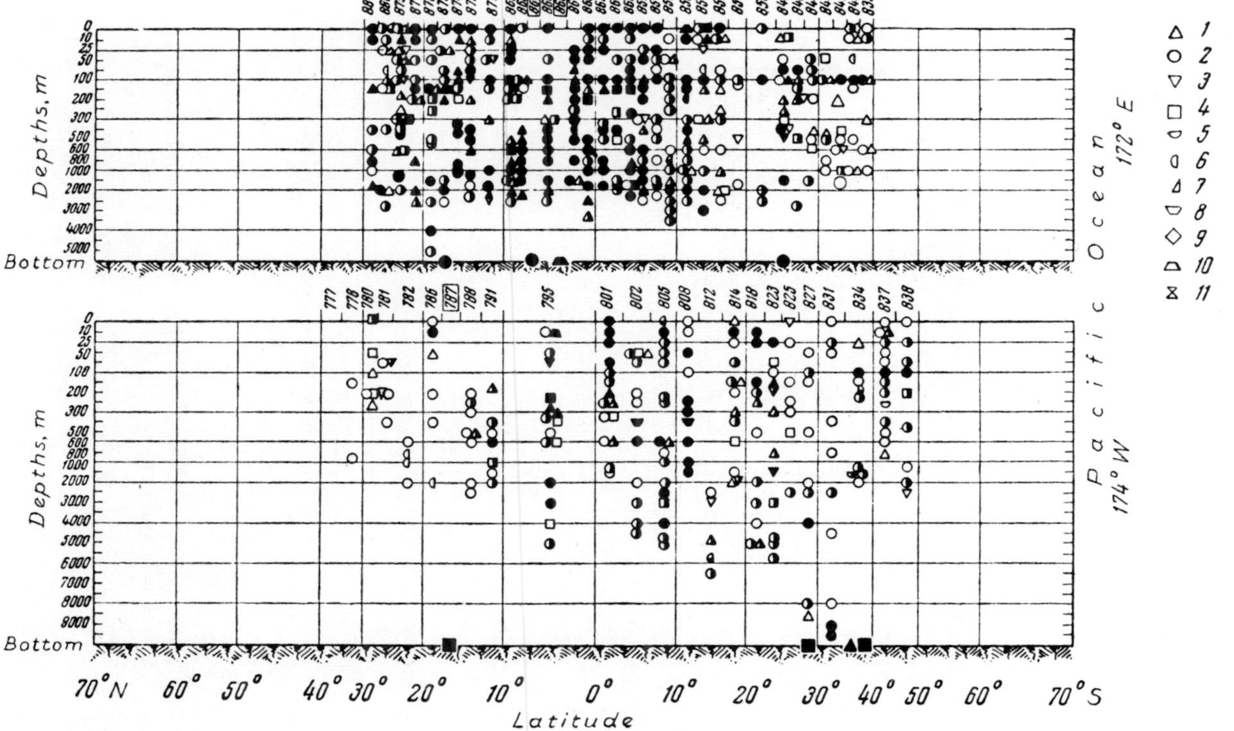

1 - *Bacterium agile*, var. A; 2 - *Bact. agile*, var. B; 3 - *Bact. agile*, var. C; 4 - *Bact. agile*, var. D; 5 - *Bact. agile*, var. E; 6 - *Bact. agile*, var. F; 7 - *Bact. agile*, var. G; 8 - *Bact. agile*, var. H; 9 - *Bact. agile*, var. I; 10 - *Bact. agile*, var. K; 11 - *Bact. agile*, var. L

In Figs. 2-16 the blacked-in symbols indicate more than 100 bacteria of the species or variant per 40-50 ml of water; the half blacked-in symbols indicate 10 to 100 and the open symbols 1 to 10 bacteria in the same volume of water. Only mud samples were investigated at stations indicated by a number enclosed in a box. In Figs. 2-16, owing to lack of space, the stations are shown in the following way: in the Pacific Ocean the recurrent first figure is 3 and in the Norwegian Sea the recurrent first figure is 1

Fig. 2 Distribution of non-sporing bacteria in seas and oceans

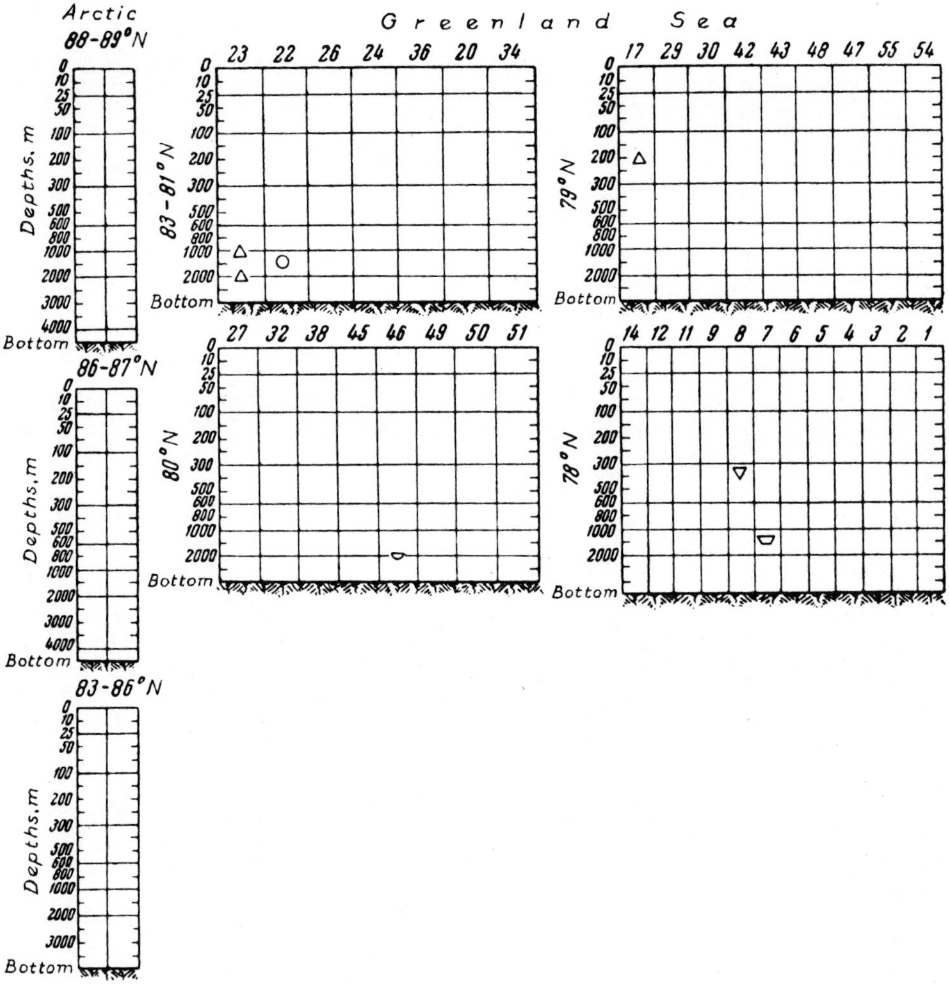

1 - *Bacterium agile*, var. A; 2 - *Bact. agile*, var. B; 3 - *Bact. agile*, var. C; 4 - *Bact. agile*, var. D; 5 - *Bact. agile*, var. E; 6 - *Bact. agile*, var. F; 7 - *Bact. agile*, var. G; 8 - *Bact. agile*, var. H; 9 - *Bact. agile*, var. I; 10 - *Bact. agile*, var. K 11 - *Bact. agile*, var. L

Fig. 2a Distribution of non-sporing bacteria in seas and oceans

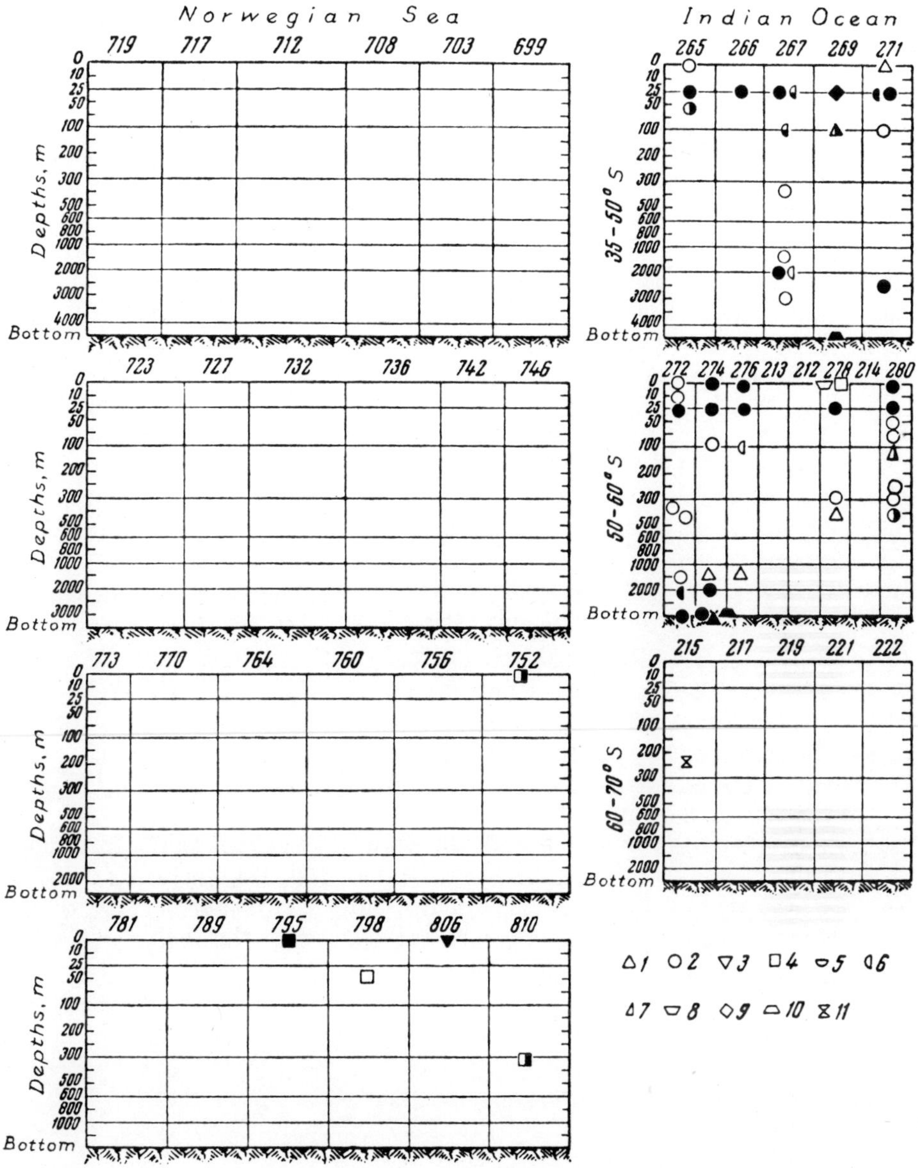
Norwegian Sea
Indian Ocean
719 717 712 708 703 699
723 727 732 736 742 746
773 770 764 760 756 752
781 789 795 798 806 810
265 266 267 269 271
272 274 276 213 212 278 214 280
215 217 219 221 222
Depths, m
Bottom
0 10 25 50 100 200 300 500 600 800 1000 2000 3000 4000
35–50° S
50–60° S
60–70° S
1 2 3 4 5 6 7 8 9 10 11

(st. **3818**), 11, 26, 151, 205, 526, 2026, 2900, 3926, 4914 m; (st. **3823**), 27, 110, 4759, 5036, 5782 m; (st. **3825**), 23, 141, 239, 290, 2582 m; (st. **3827**), 50, 100, 152, 507, 1988, 2470, 4295, 8045 m; (st. **3831**), 0, 23, 45, 383, 800, 2627, 4515, 7900, 8860, 9330 m; (st. **3834**), 90, 136, 225, 1370, 1752, 2024 m; (st. **3837**), 0, 10, 25, 50, 75, 100, 150, 199, 394, 493, 591 m; (st. **3838**), 10, 25, 72, 95, 465, 1368, 2171 m; (st. **3839**), 0, 10, 95, 590, 990 m; (st. **3840**), 0, 10, 95, 141, 470, 1142 m; (st. **3842**), 95, 476, 572, 1881 m; (st. **3843**), 98, 563, 744, 929 m; (st. **3844**), 47, 70, 92, 234, 467, 1886 m; (st. **3845**), 70, 160, 2776 m; (st. **3846**), 50, 75, 100, 400, 1854 m; (st. **3850**), 0, 105, 1983, 2518 m; (st. **3851**), 91, 136, 1712 m; (st. **3853**), 0, 10, 75, 98, 293, 630, 2531 m; (st. **3854**), 0, 10, 98, 595, 962, 1927, 2865 m; (st. **3855**), 10, 102, 154, 310, 412, 615, 814, 1014, 1585, 2090, 2518 m; (st. **3856**), 10, 50, 99, 150, 200, 250, 606, 1015, 2000, 2480, 2960, 3500 m; (st. **3857**), 0, 25, 49, 73, 98, 315, 415, 522, 790, 1236, 1802, 2222 m; (st. **3859**), 0, 26, 51, 152, 203, 305, 611, 814, 1018, 1523, 2541 m; (st. **3860**), 0, 10, 52, 80, 107, 272, 553, 677, 1158, 1717, 2270 m; (st. **3861**), 0, 50, 100, 374, 392, 1433, 1794, 2122 m; (st. **3862**), 0, 13, 29, 104, 343, 425, 534, 721, 880, 1794 m; (st. **3863**), 0, 11, 26, 54, 107, 514, 582, 826, 1095, 1836 m; (st. **3864**), 26, 53, 169, 206, 253, 308, 478, 821, 1620 m; (st. **3866**), 0, 50, 100, 410, 512, 615, 815, 1487, 2549 m; (st. **3868**), 0, 107, 161, 645, 864, 1085, 1649 m; (st. **3869**), 0, 50, 97, 145, 194, 978, 1452, 2476 m; (st. **3871**), 0, 10, 50, 100, 150, 950, 1748 m; (st. **3873**), 0, 22, 58, 77, 441, 530, 1312, 1800, 2292 m; (st. **3874**), 0, 150, 357, 424, 872, 1116, 1352 m; (st. **3875**), 0, 25, 75, 100, 1519, 2042, 2601 m; (st. **3876**), 0, 10, 50, 151, 497, 532, 1666, 2490, 3950, 4930 m; (st. **3877**), 0, 10, 50, 100, 148, 205 m; (st. **3879**), 0, 44, 88, 130, 322, 390, 460, 1360, 1940 m; (st. **3880**), 0, 11, 22, 165, 432, 2135, 2793 m; (st. **3881**), 0, 10, 408, 590, 750, 940 m; and also from mud (st. **3846**, **3867**, **3875**).

Assigned to the aggregate species *Bacterium agile* Jensen, 1898, var. B.

The non-sporing rods are distinguished from var. A in that they do not hydrolyse starch.

From: Greenland Sea, (st. **8**), 345 m;

Norwegian Sea, (st. **1806**), 0 m;

Atlantic Ocean, (st. **364**), 1985 m; (st. **368**), 48, 197, 800 m; (st. **369**), 2990 m; (st. **372**), 71 m; (st. **376**), 548 m; (st. **383**), 358 m; (st. **387**), 26, 724 m; (st. **389**), 165, 1970 m;

Indian Ocean, (st. **312**), 2900 m; (st. **314**), 26, 3270 m; (st. **316**), 1413 m; (st. **318**), 310 m;

Pacific Ocean, (st. **3780**), 192 m; (st. **3781**), 72 m; (st. **3795**), 66 m; (st. **3812**), 2938 m; (st. **3814**), 1945 m; (st. **3823**), 214, 1448 m; (st. **3825**), 0 m; (st. **3838**), 2645 m; (st. **3842**), 572 m; (st. **3845**), 209 m;

(st. **3846**), 400, 487 m; (st. **3851**), 490 m; (st. **3854**), 25 m; (st. **3859**), 305 m; (st. **3869**), 145 m; (st. **3871**), 53, 2782 m; (st. **3873**), 117 m; (st. **3879**), 22, 130 m.

Assigned to the aggregate species *Bacterium agile* Jensen, 1898, var. C.

The non-sporing rods are distinguished from var. A in that they do not hydrolyse starch and do not reduce nitrates.

From: Norwegian Sea, (st. **1752**), 0 m; (st. **1795**), 0 m; (st. **1798**), 50 m; (st. **1810**), 330 m;

Atlantic Ocean, (st. **346**), 0 m; (st. **364**), 4350 m; (st. **368**), 497 m; (st. **372**), 2500 m; (st. **374**), 1538 m; (st. **380**), 498 m; (st. **383**), 270, 358 m; (st. **389**), 3024 m;

Indian Ocean, (st. **259**), 1120 m; (st. **278**), 0 m; (st. **297**), 462, 3380 m; (st. **301**), 100, 565 m; (st. **305**), 552, 3820 m; (st. **307**), 25, 2350 m; (st. **309**), 25 m; (st. **322**), 775 m; (st. **327**), 25 m;

Pacific Ocean, (st. **3780**), 0, 46, 192 m; (st. **3791**), 979 m; (st. **3795**), 220, 422, 613, 3986 m; (st. **3801**), 340 m; (st. **3802**), 50 m; (st. **3805**), 2879 m; (st. **3814**), 605 m; (st. **3823**), 83, 2930 m; (st. **3825**), 490 m; (st. **3838**), 190 m; (st. **3842**), 382, 988 m; (st. **3843**), 48 m; (st. **3844**), 560 m; (st. **3845**), 482 m; (st. **3846**), 10, 297 m; (st. **3853**), 2124 m; (st. **3854**), 0 m; (st. **3855**), 310 m; (st. **3860**), 159, 1717 m; (st. **3861**), 148, 286, 496 m; (st. **3863**), 214 m; (st. **3866**), 150, 309 m; (st. **3869**), 26, 194, 600 m; (st. **3874**), 218 m; (st. **3875**), 153 m; (st. **3876**), 151, 252 m; (st. **3879**), 322, 594 m; (st. **3880**), 165 m; and also from mud (st. **3787**, **3827**, **3834**).

Assigned to the aggregate species *Bacterium agile* Jensen, 1898, var. D.

The non-sporing rods are distinguished from var. A in that they acidify peptone water containing glucose.

From: Greenland Sea, (st. **46**), 2000 m;

Atlantic Ocean, (st. **364**), 1007 m; (st. **367**), 0, 800, 4678 m; (st. **368**), 300, 800, 1494 m; (st. **369**), 780 m; (st. **370**), 91 m; (st. **376**), 213 m; (st. **378**), 483, 4400 m; (st. **380**), 78, 598, 5136 m; (st. **383**), 72, 450, 1745 m; (st. **387**), 139, 457, 546 m; (st. **389**), 82, 1260 m;

Indian Ocean, (st. **305**), 815 m;

Pacific Ocean, (st. **3834**), 1752 m; (st. **3837**), 248 m.

Assigned to aggregate species *Bacterium agile* Jensen, 1898, var. E.

The non-sporing rods are distinguished from var. A in that they acidify peptone water containing glucose and do not reduce nitrates.

From: Atlantic Ocean, (st. **364**), 31, 406, 607 m; (st. **366**), 0, 10 m; (st. **367**), 100, 150 m; (st. **376**), 154 m; (st. **378**), 966 m; (st. **380**), 0, 10 m; (st. **383**), 0 m;

Indian Ocean, (st. **267**), 25, 102, 1958 m; (st. **271**), 25 m; (st. **272**), 2007 m; (st. **276**), 100 m; (st. **282**), 0 m; (st. **297**), 230 m;

Pacific Ocean, (st. **3782**), 795, 994 m; (st. **3786**), 2013 m; (st. **3805**), 0 m; (st. **3812**), 5804 m; (st. **3834**), 180 m; (st. **3840**), 0, 48 m; (st. **3854**), 73 m; (st. **3855**), 205 m; (st. **3856**), 816 m; (st. **3864**), 394 m; (st. **3879**), 322 m; (st. **3880**), 0, 82 m.

Assigned to the aggregate species *Bacterium agile* **Jensen, 1898, var. F.**

The non-sporing rods are distinguished from var. A in that they acidify peptone water containing glucose, do not hydrolyse starch and do not reduce nitrates.

From: Indian Ocean, (st. **320**), 25 m.

Assigned to the aggregate species *Bacterium agile* **Jensen, 1898, var. G.**

The non-sporing rods are distinguished from var. A in that they acidify peptone water containing mannitol, glucose, sucrose or maltose, alkalinize lactose, do not hydrolyse starch and do not reduce nitrates.

From: Greenland Sea, (st. 7), 1450 m;

Atlantic Ocean, (st. **378**), 146, 291 m; (st. **387**), 0 m; (st. **389**), 488 m;

Indian Ocean, (st. **256**), 100 m; (st. **260**), 438 m; (st. **278**), 0 m; (st. **305**), 2450 m; (st. **328**), 40 m;

Pacific Ocean, (st. **3802**), 400 m; (st. **3808**), 372 m.

Assigned to the aggregate species *Bacterium agile* **Jensen, 1898, var. H.**

The non-sporing rods are distinguished from var. A in that they acidify peptone water containing mannitol, glucose, sucrose, maltose or lactose and do not hydrolyse starch.

From: Atlantic Ocean, (st. **378**), 98, 966, 1464, 3950 m; (st. **383**), 10, 90 m; (st. **387**), 368 m;

Indian Ocean, (st. **269**), 25 m; (st. **328**), 167 m.

Assigned to the aggregate species *Bacterium agile* **Jensen, 1898, var. I.**

The non-sporing rods are distinguished from var. A in that they acidify peptone water containing mannitol, glucose, sucrose, maltose or lactose and do not hydrolyse starch and do not reduce nitrates.

From: Atlantic Ocean, (st. **378**), 98 m;

Indian Ocean, (st. **293**), 100 m; (st. **295**), 25 m; (st. **297**), 2910 m; (st. **327**), 10, 50 m; (st. **329**), 39 m; and also from mud (st. **269**, **274**);

Pacific Ocean, (st. **3795**), 10 m; (st. **3855**), 0 m; and also from mud (st. **3865**).

Assigned to the aggregate species *Bacterium agile* Jensen, 1898, var. K.

The non-sporing rods are distinguished from var. A in that they slightly peptonize milk, acidify peptone water containing glucose, do not hydrolyse starch and do not reduce nitrates.

From: Indian Ocean, (st. **215**), 268 m.

Assigned to aggregate species *Bacterium agile* Jensen, 1898, var. L.

Non-sporing rods $1.2-7.7 \times 0.4-1.0\ \mu$, oval or oval-ovate, arranged singly, in pairs or in small clusters. Non-motile. Gram-negative.

On nutrient agar containing sea salt the streak is greyish-creamy in colour, slimy and runs down towards the bottom of the test tube.

On starch agar with asparagine the streak is white with a yellowish tinge and growth is slimy.

On potato slices, streak is pinkish-creamy and slimy or there is no growth.

On meat-peptone broth – turbidity, ring, sediment.

Gelatine not liquefied. Milk not peptonized. Peptone water containing mannitol, glucose, sucrose, maltose or lactose alkalinized or not altered. Starch hydrolysed. Mineral nitrogen assimilated. Nitrates reduced to nitrites.

From: Greenland Sea, (st. **6**), 750 m; (st. **23**), 1000 m; (st. **36**), 1000 m;

Atlantic Ocean, (st. **352**), 10 m; (st. **374**), 421 m; (st. **378**), 4440 m; (st. **380**), 2498 m;

Pacific Ocean, (st. **3786**), 1793 m; (st. **3791**), 10 m; (st. **3795**), 1540 m; (st. **3801**), 1783 m; (st. **3802**), 300, 499, 2024 m; (st. **3805**), 74, 773 m; (st. **3812**), 3883 m; (st. **3814**), 194, 500 m; (st. **3818**), 2900 m; (st. **3823**), 974, 3932, 7800 m; (st. **3825**), 10 m; (st. **3827**), 152 m; (st. **3831**), 183, 6950 m; (st. **3837**), 199, 1843 m; (st. **3838**), 10 m; (st. **3839**), 71 m; (st. **3840**), 48, 283, 375 m; (st. **3842**), 25, 189 m; (st. **3843**), 195, 1854 m; (st. **3844**), 185 m; (st. **3845**), 160, 373, 593 m; (st. **3846**), 247, 1427 m; (st. **3850**), 500, 962 m; (st. **3853**), 244, 478 m; (st. **3854**), 200 m; (st. **3856**), 200, 505 m; (st. **3857**), 415 m; (st. **3859**), 253 m; (st. **3860**), 10, 326 m; (st. **3866**), 75, 100 m; (st. **3868**), 2758 m; (st. **3873**), 155, 862 m; (st. **3874**), 648 m; (st. **3875**), 10, 255 m; (st. **3876**), 1287 m; (st. **3877**), 305, 501, 993, 1500 m; (st. **3879**), 390, 675, 923 m; (st. **3880**), 82, 328, 1582 m; (st. **3881**), 216, 262 m.

Assigned to aggregate species *Bacterium candicans* (G. et P. Frankland) Migula, 1900, var. A.

The non-sporing rods are distinguished from var. A in that they do not reduce nitrates.

From: Greenland Sea, (st. **7**), 1000 m; (st. **12**), 0 m; (st. **23**), 0 m; (st. **43**), 1000 m; (st. **55**), 400 m;

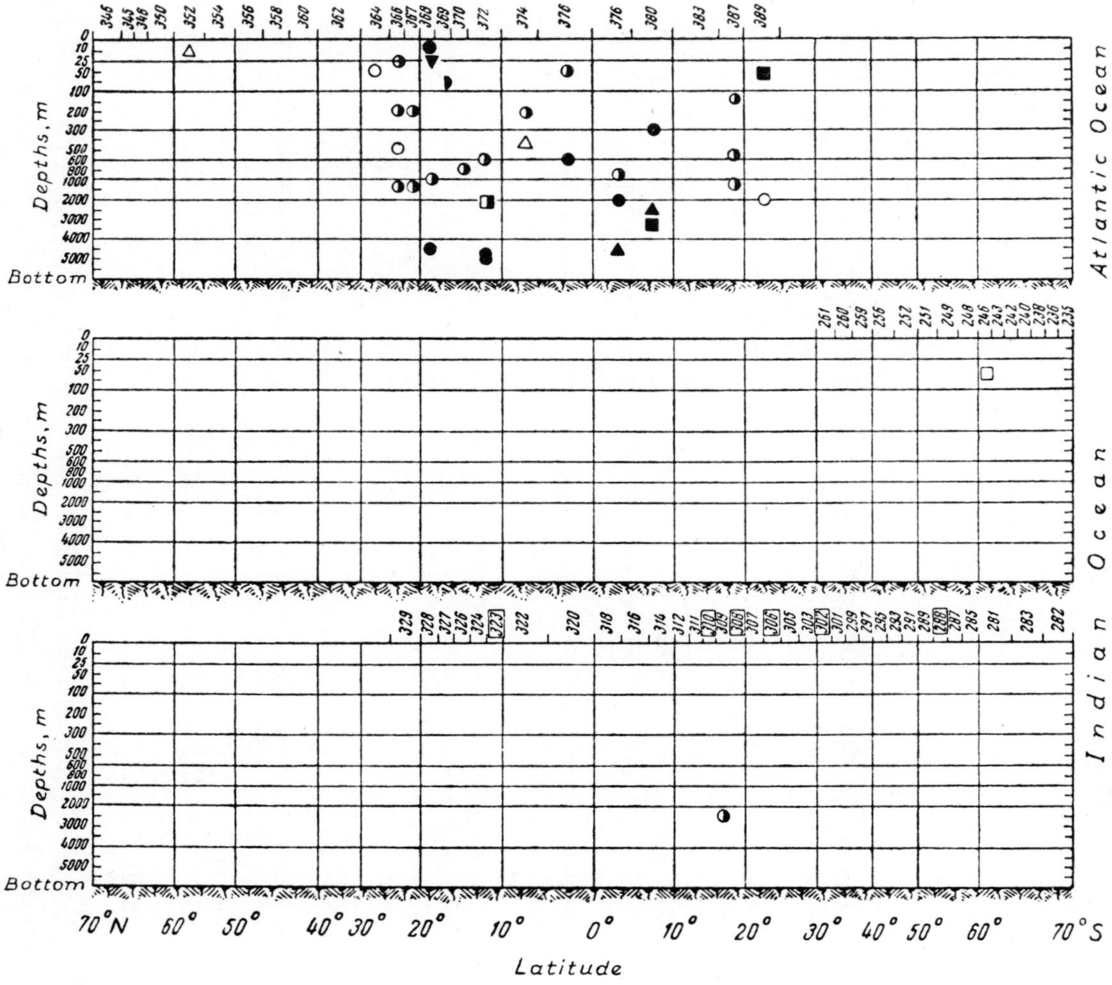

Atlantic Ocean
30°W
Ocean
20°E
Indian
90°-100°E
Depths, m
0
10
25
50
100
200
300
500
600
800
1000
2000
3000
4000
5000
Bottom
346 345 348 350 352 354 356 358 360 362 364 366 367 368 369 370 372 374 376 376 380 383 387 389
261 260 259 256 252 251 249 248 246 243 242 240 238 236 235
329 328 327 326 324 323 322 320 318 316 314 312 311 310 309 308 307 306 305 303 302 301 299 297 295 293 291 289 288 287 285 281 283 282
70°N 60° 50° 40° 30° 20° 10° 0° 10° 20° 30° 40° 50° 60° 70°S
Latitude

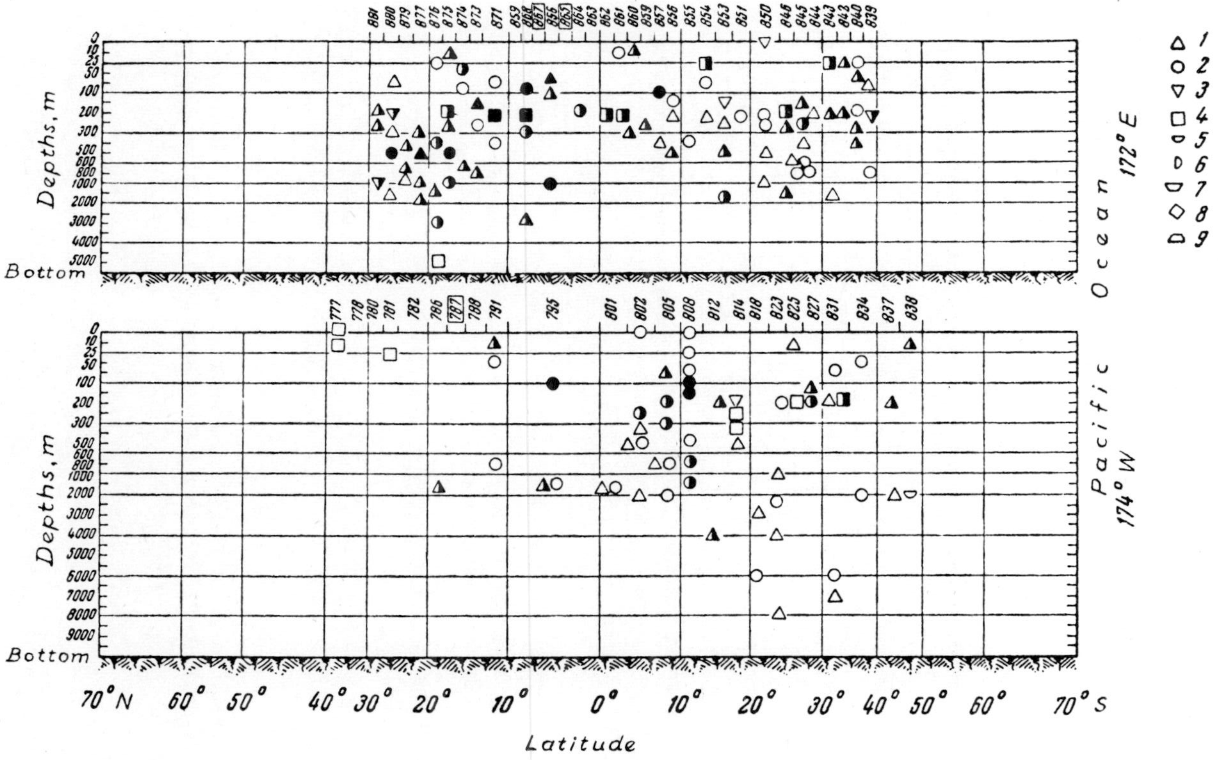

1 - *Bacterium candicans*, var. A; 2 - *Bact. candicans*, var. B; 3 - *Bact. candicans*, var. C; 4 - *Bact. candicans*, var. D; 5 - *Bact. candicans*, var. E; 6 - *Bact. candicans*, var. F; 7 - *Bact. candicans*, var. G; 8 - *Bact. candicans*, var. H; 9 - *Bact. candicans*, var. I

Fig. 3 Distribution of non-sporing bacteria in seas and oceans

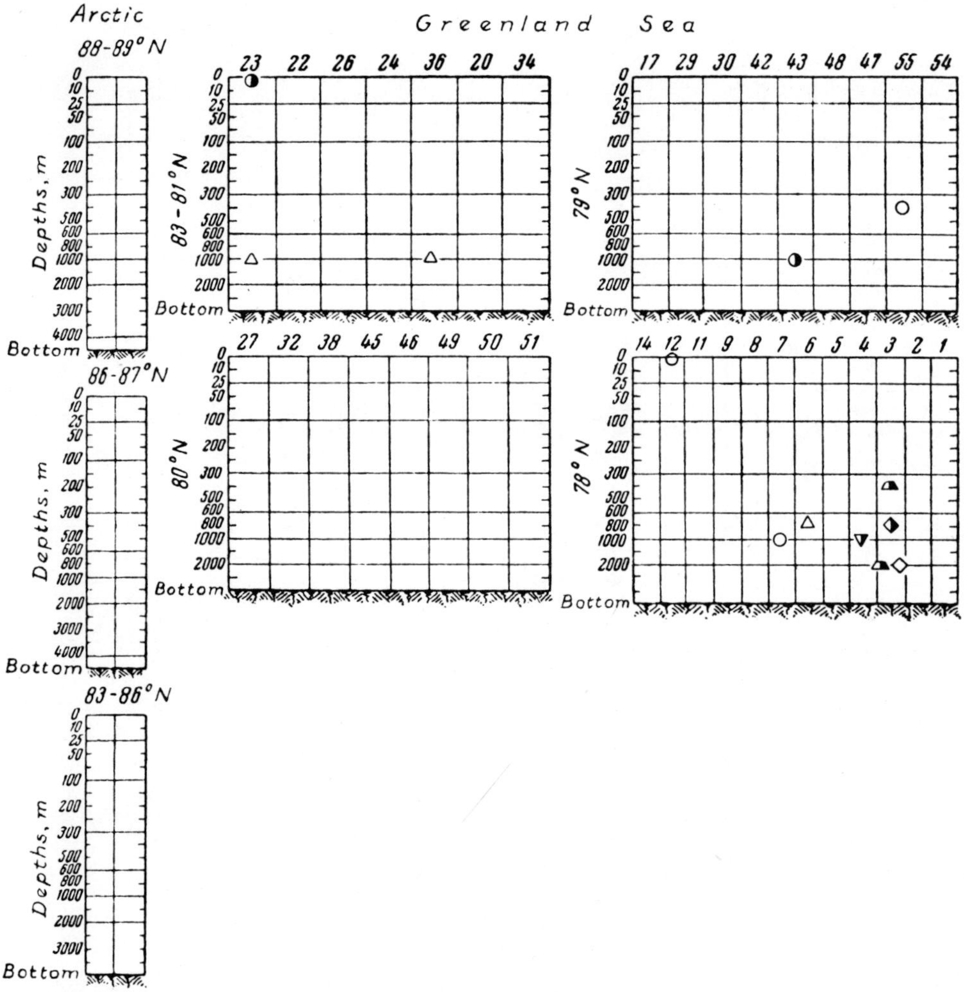

1 - *Bacterium candicans*, var. A; 2 - *Bact. candicans*, var. B; 3 - *Bact. candicans* var. C; 4 - *Bact. candicans*, var. D; 5 - *Bact. candicans*, var. E; 6 - *Bact. candicans*, var. F; 7 - *Bact. candicans*, var. G; 8 - *Bact. candicans*, var. H; 9 - *Bact. candicans*, var. I

Fig. 3a Distribution of non-sporing bacteria in seas and oceans

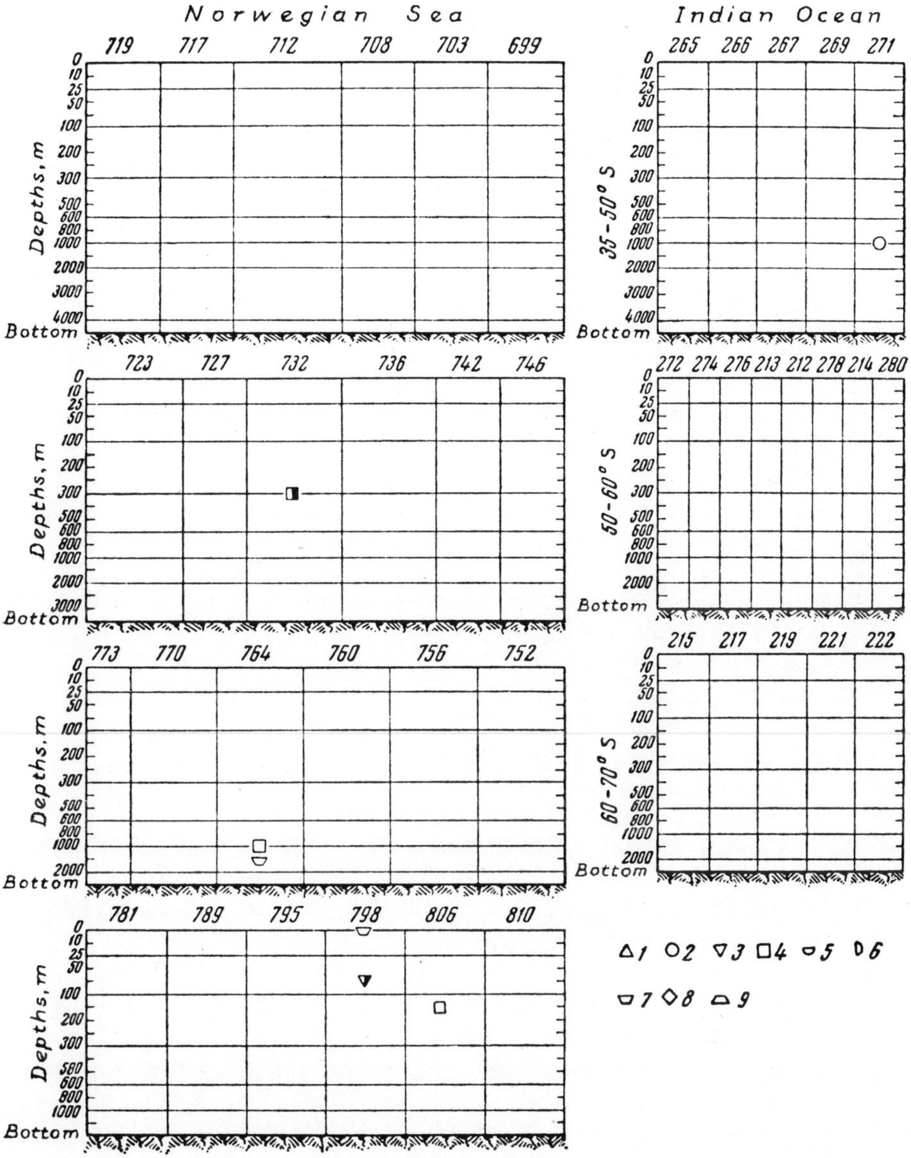
Norwegian Sea
Indian Ocean
719 717 712 708 703 699
265 266 267 269 271
723 727 732 736 742 746
272 274 276 213 212 278 214 280
773 770 764 760 756 752
215 217 219 221 222
781 789 795 798 806 810
Depths, m
0 10 25 50 100 200 300 500 600 800 1000 2000 3000 4000
Bottom
35-50° S
50-60° S
60-70° S
1 2 3 4 5 6 7 8 9

Atlantic Ocean, (st. **364**), 51 m; (st. **366**), 30, 200, 499, 1499 m; (st. **367**), 200, 1448 m; (st. **368**), 10, 990, 4555 m; (st. **370**), 716 m; (st. **372**), 592, 4927, 5137 m; (st. **374**), 198 m; (st. **376**), 44, 655 m; (st. **378**), 774, 2018 m; (st. **380**), 299 m; (st. **387**), 139, 546, 1380 m; (st. **389**), 1970 m;

Indian Ocean, (st. **271**), 1015 m; (st. **309**), 2440 m;

Pacific Ocean (st. **3791**), 54, 822 m; (st. **3795**), 91, 1540 m; (st. **3801**), 1783 m; (st. **3802**), 0, 248, 499 m; (st. **3805**), 189, 287, 773, 1950 m; (st. **3808**), 0, 25, 71, 95, 145, 455, 842, 1554 m; (st. **3818**), 5905 m; (st. **3823**), 2427 m; (st. **3825**), 188 m; (st. **3827**), 201 m; (st. **3831**), 69, 6033 m; (st. **3834**), 45, 2024 m; (st. **3839**), 790 m; (st. **3840**), 24, 188 m; (st. **3844**), 743 m; (st. **3845**), 247, 593, 780 m; (st. **3850**), 212, 263 m; (st. **3851**), 183 m; (st. **3853**), 1715 m; (st. **3854**), 73 m; (st. **3855**), 412 m; (st. **3856**), 150 m; (st. **3857**), 117 m; (st. **3861**), 10 m; (st. **3864**), 169 m; (st. **3866**), 1005 m; (st. **3868**), 81, 320 m; (st. **3871**); 75, 422 m; (st. **3873**), 245 m; (st. **3874**), 40, 82 m; (st. **3875**), 505, 1012 m; (st. **3876**), 25, 399, 2976 m; (st. **3880**), 538 m.

Assigned to aggregate species *Bacterium candicans* **(G. et P. Frankland) Migula, 1900, var. B.**

The non-sporing rods are distinguished from var. A in that they do not hydrolyse starch.

From: Greenland Sea, (st. **4**), 1000 m;

Norwegian Sea, (st. **1798**), 75 m;

Atlantic Ocean, (st. **368**), 29 m;

Pacific Ocean, (st. **3814**), 194 m; (st. **3839**), 192 m; (st. **3850**), 0 m; (st. **3853**), 146 m; (st. **3880**), 218 m; (st. **3881**), 940 m.

Assigned to aggregate species *Bacterium candicans* **(G. et P. Frankland) Migula, 1900, var. C.**

The non-sporing rods are distinguished from var. A in that they do not hydrolyse starch and do not reduce nitrates.

From: Norwegian Sea, (st. **1732**), 300 m; (st. **1764**), 1000 m; (st. **1806**), 130 m;

Atlantic Ocean, (st. **372**), 1990 m; (st. **380**), 2972 m; (st. **389**), 64 m;

Indian Ocean, (st. **246**), 48 m;

Pacific Ocean, (st. **3777**), 0, 11 m; (st. **3781**), 25 m; (st. **3814**), 245, 400 m; (st. **3825**), 188 m; (st. **3831**), 183 m; (st. **3843**), 25 m; (st. **3846**), 198 m; (st. **3854**), 25 m; (st. **3861**), 195 m; (st. **3862**), 186 m; (st. **3868**), 212 m; (st. **3871**), 200 m; (st. **3875**), 205 m; (st. **3876**), 4930 m.

Assigned to aggregate species *Bacterium candicans* **(G. et P. Frankland) Migula, 1900, var. D.**

The non-sporing rods are distinguished from var. A in that they acidify peptone water containing glucose.

From: Pacific Ocean, (st. 3838), 2171 m.

Assigned to aggregate species *Bacterium candicans* **(G. et P. Frankland) Migula, 1900, var. E.**

The non-sporing rods are distinguished from var. A in that they acidify peptone water containing glucose and do not reduce nitrates.

From: Atlantic Ocean, (st. 369), 82 m.

Assigned to aggregate species *Bacterium candicans* **(G. et P. Frankland) Migula, 1900, var. F.**

The non-sporing rods are distinguished from var. A in that they acidify peptone water containing glucose, do not hydrolyse starch and do not reduce nitrates.

From: Norwegian Sea, (st. 1764), 1500 m; (st. 1798), 0 m.

Assigned to aggregate species *Bacterium candicans* **(G. et P. Frankland) Migula, 1900, var. G.**

The non-sporing rods are distinguished from var. A in that they acidify peptone water containing mannitol, glucose, sucrose, maltose or lactose and do not hydrolyse starch.

From: Greenland Sea, (st. 3), 750, 2000 m.

Assigned to aggregate species *Bacterium candicans* **(G. et P. Frankland) Migula, 1900, var. H.**

The non-sporing rods are distinguished from var. A in that they acidify peptone water containing mannitol, glucose, sucrose or maltose, do not hydrolyse starch and do not reduce nitrates.

From: Greenland Sea, (st. 3), 400, 2000 m.

Assigned to aggregate species *Bacterium candicans* **(G. et P. Frankland) Migula, 1900, var. I.**

Non-sporing rods $1.5-4.0 \times 0.3-0.7\ \mu$, with rounded or acuminate ends. Non-motile. Gram-negative. Growth on nutrient media poor. Rapidly perish.

On nutrient media with sea salt, streak is greyish, semitransparent, slimy.

On meat-peptone broth, slight turbidity, sediment.

Gelatine not liquefied. Milk not peptonized. Peptone water containing mannitol, glucose, sucrose, maltose or lactose not changed. Starch not hydrolysed. Mineral nitrogen assimilated or slightly assimilated. Nitrates reduced to nitrites.

From: Pacific Ocean, (st. 3786), 195 m; (st. 3814), 194 m; (st. 3844), 1886 m; (st. 3866), 255 m.

Assigned to aggregate species *Bacterium parvulum* **Conn, 1922, var. A.**

The non-sporing rods are distinguished from var. A in that they do not reduce nitrates to nitrites.

From: Greenland Sea, (st. **3**), 400, 1000, 1500 m; (st. **5**), 400 m; (st. **6**), 1000 m; (st. **34**), 200 m;

Atlantic Ocean, (st. **372**), 71, 189, 1990 m; (st. **374**), 49, 526 m; (st. **376**), 869 m;

Indian Ocean, (st. **305**), 4420 m; and also from mud (st. **297**, **307**, **310**);

Pacific Ocean, (st. **3778**), 2150 m; (st. **3780**), 72 m; (st. **3782**), 1522 m; (st. **3786**), 24 m; (st. **3788**), 0, 70, 202 m; (st. **3791**), 227 m; (st. **3795**), 15 m; (st. **3808**), 455 m; (st. **3837**), 248 m; (st. **3840**), 963 m; (st. **3846**), 50, 2356 m; (st. **3850**), 594 m; (st. **3851**), 340 m; (st. **3862**), 209 m; (st. **3863**), 328 m; (st. **3869**), 194 m.

Assigned to aggregate species *Bacterium parvulum* **Conn, 1922, var. B.**

The non-sporing rods are distinguished from var. A in that they hydrolyse starch and do not reduce nitrates.

From: Greenland Sea, (st. **3**), 500 m; (st. **23**), 400 m;

Pacific Ocean, (st. **3778**), 618 m; (st. **3788**), 0 m; (st. **3802**), 2024 m; (st. **3864**), 253 m.

Assigned to aggregate species *Bacterium parvulum* **Conn, 1922, var. C.**

The non-sporing rods are distinguished from var. A in that they acidify peptone water containing glucose, sucrose, maltose and do not reduce nitrates.

From: Greenland Sea, (st. **34**), 1000 m;

Pacific Ocean, (st. **3814**), 50 m.

Assigned to aggregate species *Bacterium parvulum* **Conn, 1922, var. D.**

The non-sporing rods are distinguished from var. A in that they do not assimilate mineral nitrogen.

From: Indian Ocean mud, (st. **269**).

Pacific Ocean, (st. **3788**), 1010 m; (st. **3802**), 200 m; (st. **3842**), 988 m; (st. **3851**), 10 m; (st. **3855**), 50 m; (st. **3875**), 50 m.

Assigned to aggregate species *Bacterium parvulum* **Conn, 1922, var. E.**

The non-sporing rods are distinguished from var. A in that they hydrolyse starch and do not assimilate mineral nitrogen.

From: Pacific Ocean, (st. **3851**), 1373 m.

Assigned to aggregate species *Bacterium parvulum* **Conn, 1922, var. F.**

Non-sporing rods, 2.9 – 6.0 × 0.6 – 1.1 μ, straight, with blunt or rounded ends. Arranged singly, in pairs or in short chains. Filaments occur, Motile. Peritrichous. Gram-positive.

On nutrient agar with sea salt the streak is smooth, shiny, greyish-white, acquiring a yellowish tinge with age.

On meat-peptone broth – turbidity, sediment; some strains form hydrogen sulphide.

Gelatine very slightly liquefied or not at all. Milk not peptonized. Peptone water containing mannitol, glucose, sucrose, maltose or lactose alkalinized or not changed. Starch not hydrolysed. Mineral nitrogen poorly assimilated. Nitrates not reduced.

From: Indian Ocean, (st. **246**), 362 m; (st. **249**), 77, 1930 m; (st. **280**), 200 m; Pacific Ocean, (st. **3812**), 2456 m.

Assigned to aggregate species *Bacterium imperiale* **Steinhaus, 1941, var. A.**

The non-sporing rods are distinguished from var. A in that they reduce nitrates to nitrites.

From: Indian Ocean, (st. **318**), 2920 m.

Assigned to aggregate species *Bacterium imperiale* **Steinhaus, 1941, var. B.**

Non-sporing rods 2.6 – 6.4 × 0.7 – 1.5 μ, with blunt ends, singly or in pairs. Motile. Peritrichous. Gram-positive.

On nutrient agar with sea salt the streak is creamy-white, smooth, shiny, with slightly undulate edge.

On meat-peptone broth – turbidity.

Gelatine not liquefied. Milk not peptonized. Peptone water containing mannitol, glucose, sucrose, maltose or lactose not changed. Starch not hydrolysed. Mineral nitrogen assimilated. Nitrates reduced to nitrites.

From: Greenland Sea, (st. 34), 750 m.

Assigned to aggregate species *Bacterium zopfii* **Kurth, 1883.**

Non-sporing rods, 2.3 – 5.3 × 0.5 – 0.9 μ, with rounded ends, arranged singly or in pairs; filaments occur. Motile. Peritrichous. Gram-positive.

On nutrient agar with sea salt the streak is creamy-grey, smooth, with scalloped edge.

On meat-peptone broth – turbidity, ring, sediment.

Gelatine not liquefied. Milk slightly peptonized. Peptone water containing mannitol, glucose, sucrose, maltose or lactose acidified. Starch not hydrolysed. Mineral nitrogen assimilated. Nitrates not reduced.

From: Indian Ocean, (st. **215**), 268 m.

Assigned to aggregate species *Bacterium stearophilum* **Weinzirl.**

Non-sporing rods, 1.7 – 4.1 × 0.3 – 0.7 μ, with rounded or acuminate ends,

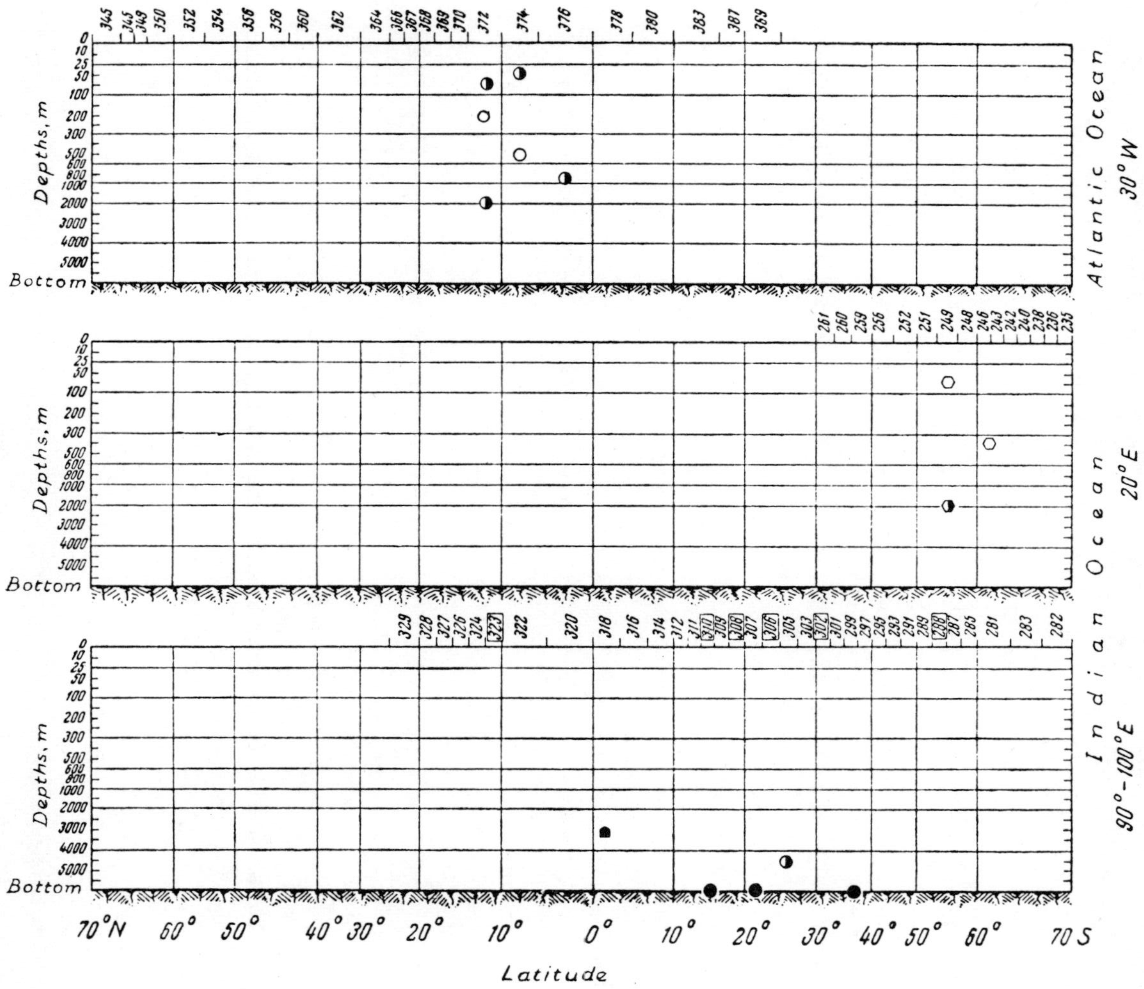

Atlantic Ocean
30° W
Ocean
20° E
Indian
90°–100° E
Depths, m
0
10
25
50
100
200
300
500
600
800
1000
2000
3000
4000
5000
Bottom
70° N
60°
50°
40°
30°
20°
10°
0°
10°
20°
30°
40°
50°
60°
70 S
Latitude

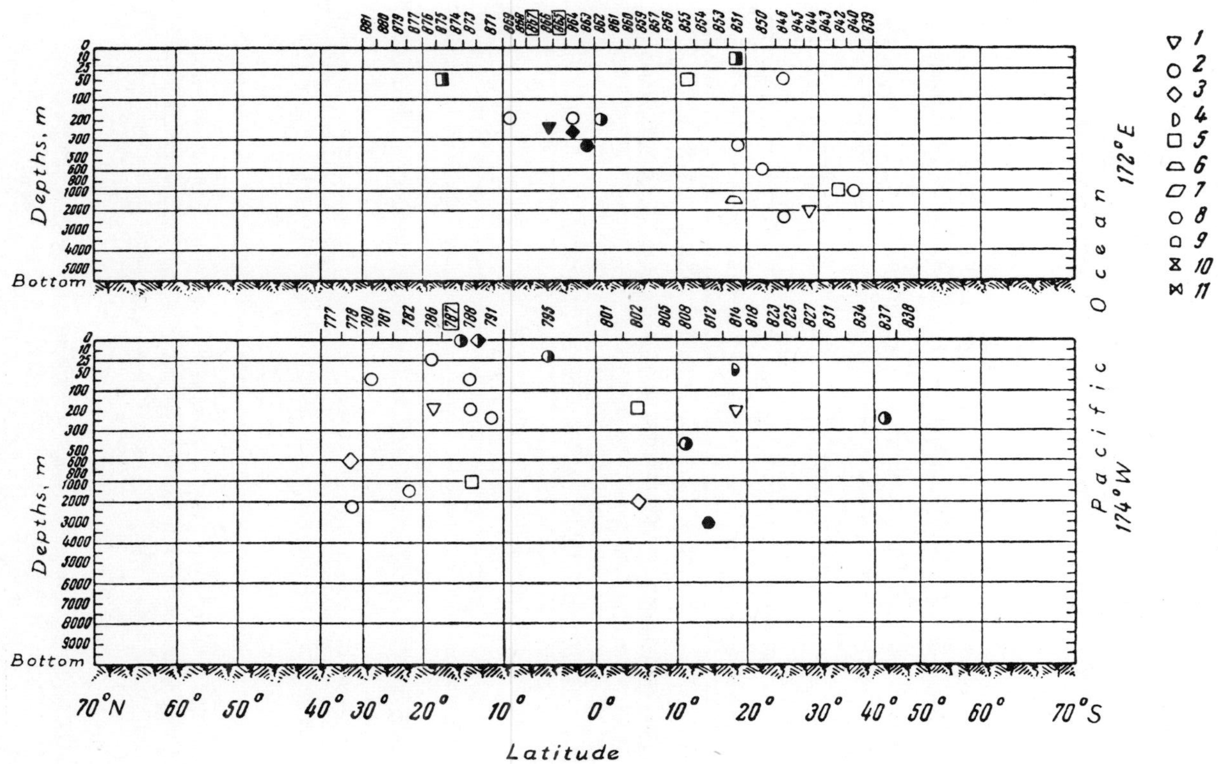

1 - *Bacterium parvulum*, var. A; 2 - *Bact. parvulum*, var. B; 3 - *Bact. parvulum*, var. C; 4 - *Bact. parvulum*, var. D 5 - *Bact. parvulum*, var. E; 6 - *Bact. parvulum*, var. F; 7 - *Vibrio nigricans*; 8 - *Bact. imperiale*, var. A; 9 - *Bact. imperiale*, var. B; 10 - *Bact. zopfii*; 11 - *Bact. stearophilum*

Fig. 4 Distribution of non-sporing bacteria in seas and oceans

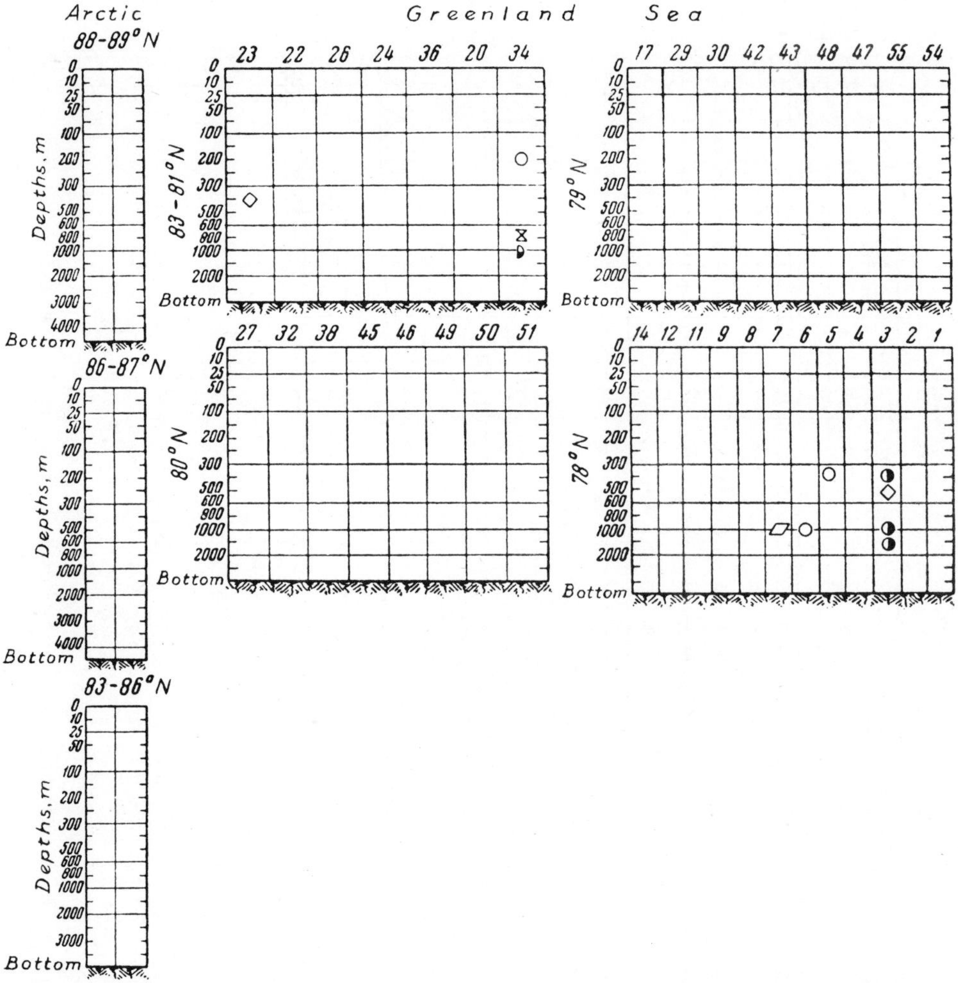

1 - *Bacterium parvulum*, var. A; 2 - *Bact. parvulum*, var. B; 3 - *Bact. parvulum*, var. C; 4 - *Bact. parvulum*, var. D; 5 - *Bact. parvulum*, var. E; 6 - *Bact. parvulum*, var. F; 7 - *Vibrio nigricans*; 8 - *Bact. imperiale*, var. A; 9 - *Bact. imperiale*, var. B; 10 - *Bact. zopfii*; 11 - *Bact. stearophilum*

Fig. 4a Distribution of non-sporing bacteria in seas and oceans

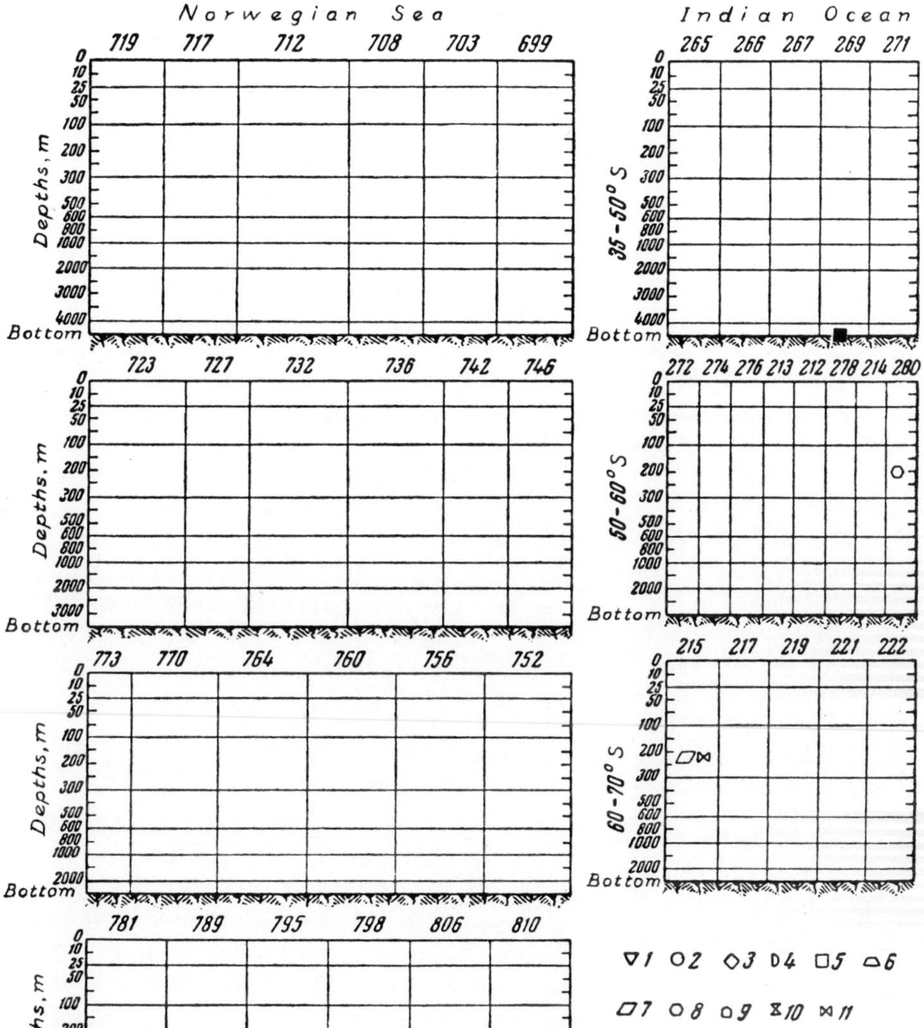

Norwegian Sea
719 717 712 708 703 699
723 727 732 736 742 746
773 770 764 760 756 752
781 789 795 798 806 810
Depths, m
0 10 25 50 100 200 300 500 600 800 1000 2000 3000 4000
Bottom
Indian Ocean
35-50° S
265 266 267 269 271
50-60° S
272 274 276 213 212 278 214 280
60-70° S
215 217 219 221 222
1 2 3 4 5 6
7 8 9 10 11

often curved. In old cultures cells swollen. Motile. Monotrichous. Gram-negative.

Growth on nutrient media poor. Rods rapidly perish.

On nutrient agar with sea salt, streak at first pinkish-white, semitransparent, slimy, becoming greyish-white, with disintegrating transparent margin.

On meat-peptone broth, slight turbidity and sediment; some strains do not grow.

Gelatine not liquefied. Milk not peptonized. Peptone water containing mannitol, glucose, sucrose, maltose and lactose not changed or alkalinized. Starch not hydrolysed. Mineral nitrogen poorly assimilated. Nitrates not reduced.

From: Atlantic Ocean, (st. **360**), 10 m; (st. **364**), 0 m; (st. **368**), 0 m; (st. **372**), 984 m; (st. **383**), 536 m;

Greenland Sea, (st. 4), 1500 m; (st. **49**), 75 m; (st. **50**), 10 m; (st. **55**), 300 m;

Indian Ocean, (st. **212**), 10, 50, 75, 100 m; (st. **213**), 197 m; (st. **214**), 54, 158, 475 m; (st. **215**), 54, 1029, 1600, 2172 m; (st. **217**), 221, 274, 838 m; (st. **219**), 226, 715 m; (st. **221**), 144, 487, 1082 m; (st. **235**), 400, 520 m; (st. **238**), 779 m; (st. **240**), 104, 319, 3632 m; (st. **242**), 79 m; (st. **243**), 10, 2360, 3330 m; (st. **249**), 77 m; (st. **259**), 2300 m; (st. **260**), 78 m; (st. **271**), 1986 m; (st. **272**), 51 m; (st. **274**), 266, 2416 m; (st. **291**), 430 m; (st. **305**), 10, 3320 m; (st. **320**), 748 m; (st. **322**), 1471 m; (st. **326**), 25 m; and also from mud (st. **297, 310, 323**);

Pacific Ocean, (st. **3782**), 61, 1979 m; (st. **3786**), 70, 144 m; (st. **3788**), 70 m; (st. **3795**), 1540 m; (st. **3805**), 189, 481 m; (st. **3818**), 51m; (st. **3825**), 239, 390 m; (st. **3837**), 248 m; (st. **3839**), 492 m; (st. **3842**), 807 m; (st. **3843**), 744 m; (st. **3850**), 159, 777, 962 m; (st. **3851**), 183 m; (st. **3853**), 386 m; (st. **3857**), 790 m; (st. **3862**), 10, 79 m; (st. **3863**), 826 m; (st. **3868**), 265m; (st. **3869**), 237, 291 m; (st. **3873**), 40 m; (st. **3874**), 286 m; (st. **3875**), 25, 50, 1012 m; (st. **3876**), 50 m; (st. **3877**), 255 m; (st. **3880**), 1051 m; (st. **3881**), 408 m.

Assigned to aggregate species *Pseudomonas sinuosa* Wright, var. A.

The non-sporing rods are distinguished from var. A in that they reduce nitrates to nitrites.

From: Greenland Sea, (st. **34**), 300 m; (st. **54**), 600 m;

Indian Ocean, (st. **214**), 273 m; (st. **221**), 192 m; (st. **236**), 408, 517 m; (st. **246**), 413 m; (st. **251**), 1135, 2312 m; (st. **252**), 1426 m; (st. **256**), 49, 74 m; (st. **259**), 2092 m; (st. **260**), 856, 1311 m; (st. **271**), 74, 1530 m; (st. **272**), 76 m; (st. **312**), 220 m; and also from mud (st. **306**);

Pacific Ocean, (st. **3778**), 25 m; (st. **3781**), 72 m; (st. **3786**), 70, 195 m; (st. **3788**), 803 m; (st. **3802**), 2586 m; (st. **3814**), 500 m; (st. **3823**), 775 m; (st. **3825**), 0 m; (st. **3837**), 298 m; (st. **3838**), 239 m; (st. **3845**), 247, 2776 m; (st. **3851**), 230 m; (st. **3873**), 192, 345 m; (st. **3877**), 406 m; (st. **3879**), 214, 675 m.

Assigned to aggregate species *Pseudomonas sinuosa* Wright, var. B.

The non-sporing rods are distinguished from var. A in that they hydrolyse starch.

From: Atlantic Ocean, (st. **369**), 0 m; (st. **372**), 0 m; (st. **376**), 69 m; Greenland Sea, (st. **23**), 75 m;

Indian Ocean, (st. **214**), 54, 212 m; (st. **251**), 301 m; (st. **271**), 3390 m; (st. **276**), 75 m; (st. **278**), 0 m; (st. **280**), 200 m; (st. **287**), 461 m; (st. **295**), 200 m; (st. **301**), 10, 225 m;

Pacific Ocean, (st. **3778**), 618 m; (st. **3795**), 170, 2496 m; (st. **3805**), 582 m; (st. **3808**), 95 m; (st. **3855**), 2518 m; (st. **3860**), 438 m; (st. **3861**), 75 m; (st. **3863**), 80 m; (st. **3869**), 73, 291 m; (st. **3871**), 10 m; (st. **3873**), 10 m.

Assigned to aggregate species *Pseudomonas sinuosa* Wright, var. C.

The non-sporing rods are distinguished from var. A in that they hydrolyse starch and reduce nitrates to nitrites.

From: Indian Ocean, (st. **214**), 653 m; (st. **240**), 10 m;

Pacific Ocean, (st. **3839**), 1669 m; (st. **3850**), 962 m; (st. **3871**), 10, 422, 2782 m; (st. **3874**), 182, 218 m; (st. **3875**), 75 m.

Assigned to aggregate species *Pseudomonas sinuosa* Wright, var. D.

The non-sporing rods are distinguished from var. A in that they form gas in or acidify peptone water containing mannitol, glucose or maltose and hydrolyse starch.

From: Greenland Sea, (st. **8**), 345 m; (st. **34**), 75, 200 m;

Indian Ocean, (st. **214**), 28 m; (st. **215**), 166 m; (st. **221**), 27 m; (st. **243**), 51 m; (st. **246**), 0 m; (st. **248**), 1040 m; (st. **252**), 258 m; (st. **278**), 425 m; (st. **295**), 3000 m;

Pacific Ocean, (st. **3778**), 618 m; (st. **3786**), 555 m; (st. **3814**), 500 m.

Assigned to aggregate species *Pseudomonas sinuosa* Wright, var. E.

The non-sporing rods are distinguished from var. A in that they do not assimilate mineral nitrogen.

From: Atlantic Ocean, (st. **346**), 0 m;

Indian Ocean, (st. **299**), 1563 m;

Pacific Ocean, (st. **3791**), 227 m; (st. **3823**), 83 m; (st. **3827**), 1508 m; (st. **3834**), 225 m; (st. **3839**), 1471 m; (st. **3850**), 263 m; (st. **3853**), 146 m; (st. **3868**), 161 m; (st. **3873**), 862 m; (st. **3875**), 406 m.

Assigned to aggregate species *Pseudomonas sinuosa* Wright, var. F.

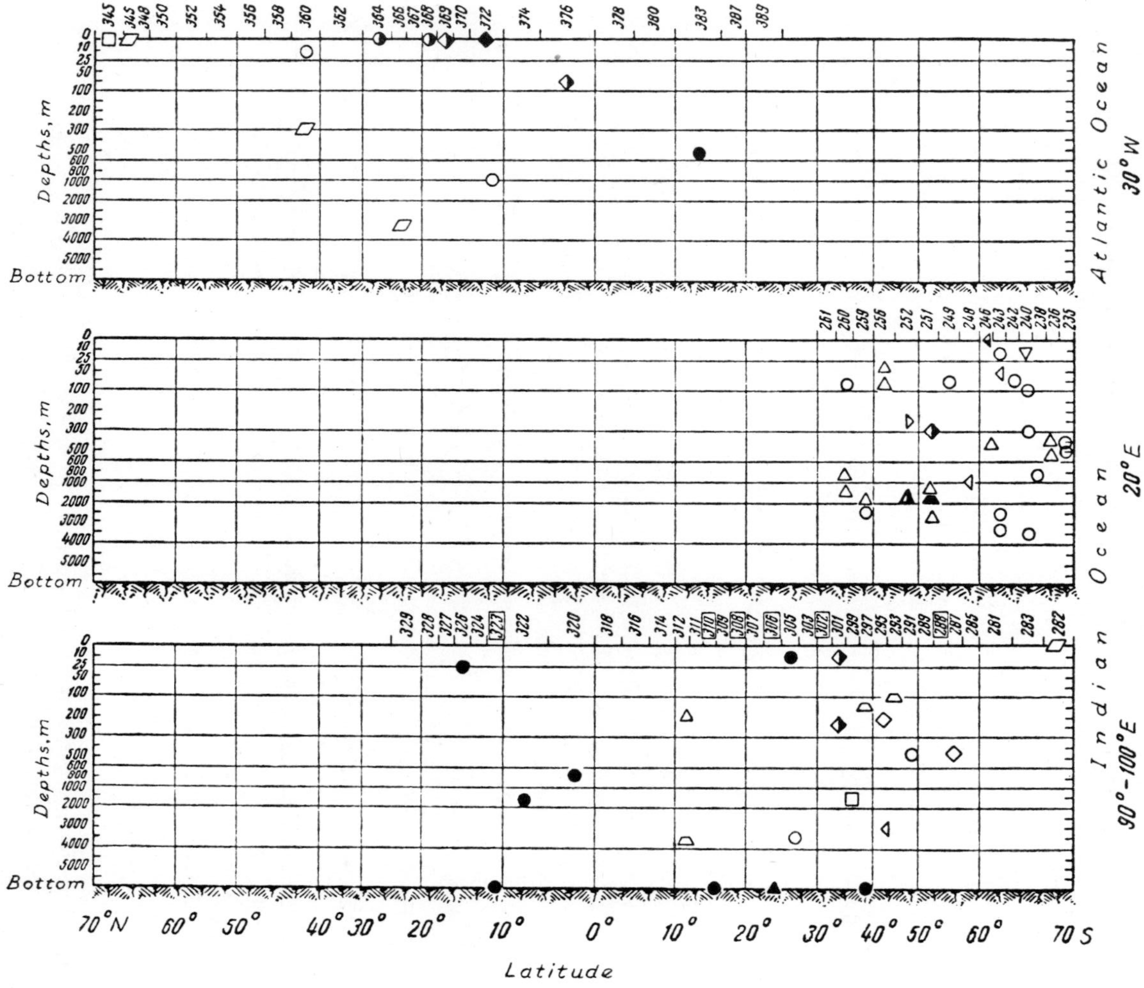
Atlantic Ocean
30°W
Ocean
20°E
Indian
90°-100°E
Depths, m
Bottom
70°N 60° 50° 40° 30° 20° 10° 0° 10° 20° 30° 40° 50° 60° 70 S
Latitude

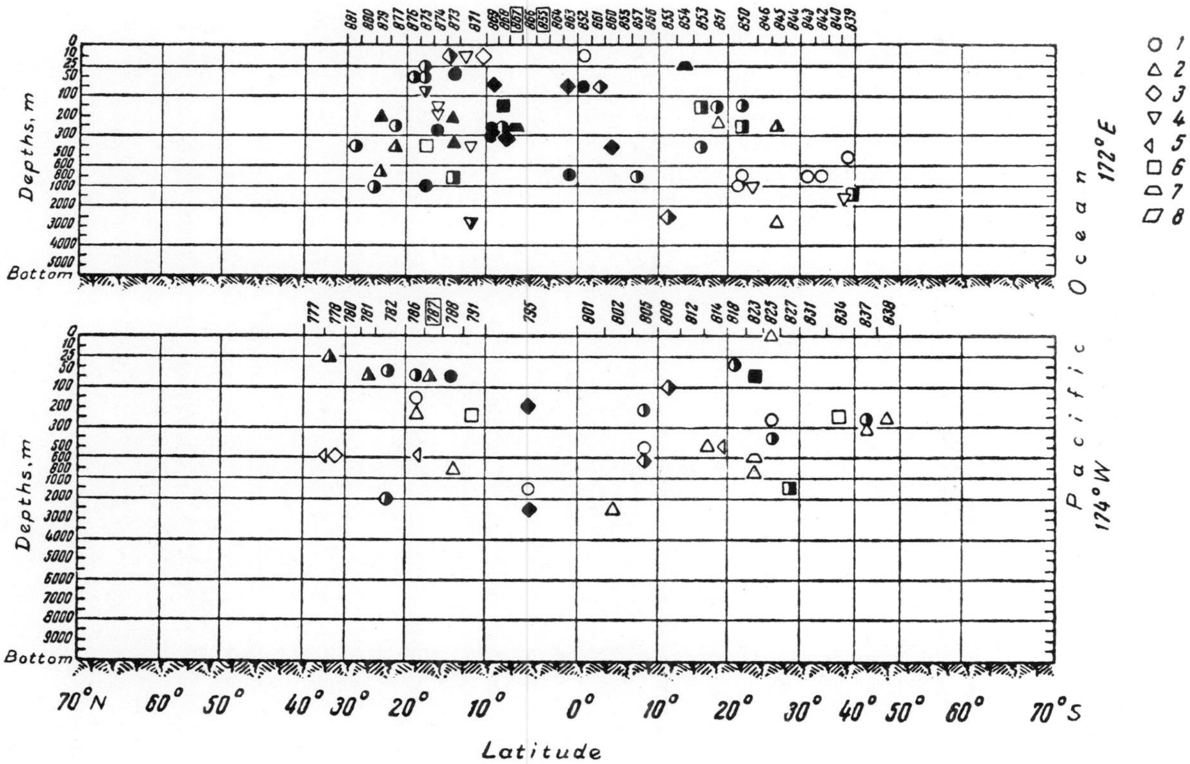

1 - *Pseudomonas sinuosa*, var. A; 2 - *Ps. sinuosa*, var. B; 3 - *Ps. sinuosa*, var. C; 4 - *Ps. sinuosa*, var. D; 5 - *Ps. sinuosa*, var. E; 6 - *Ps. sinuosa*, var. F; 7 - *Ps. sinuosa*, var. G; 8 - *Pseudomonas liquida*, var. A

Fig. 5 Distribution of non-sporing bacteria in seas and oceans

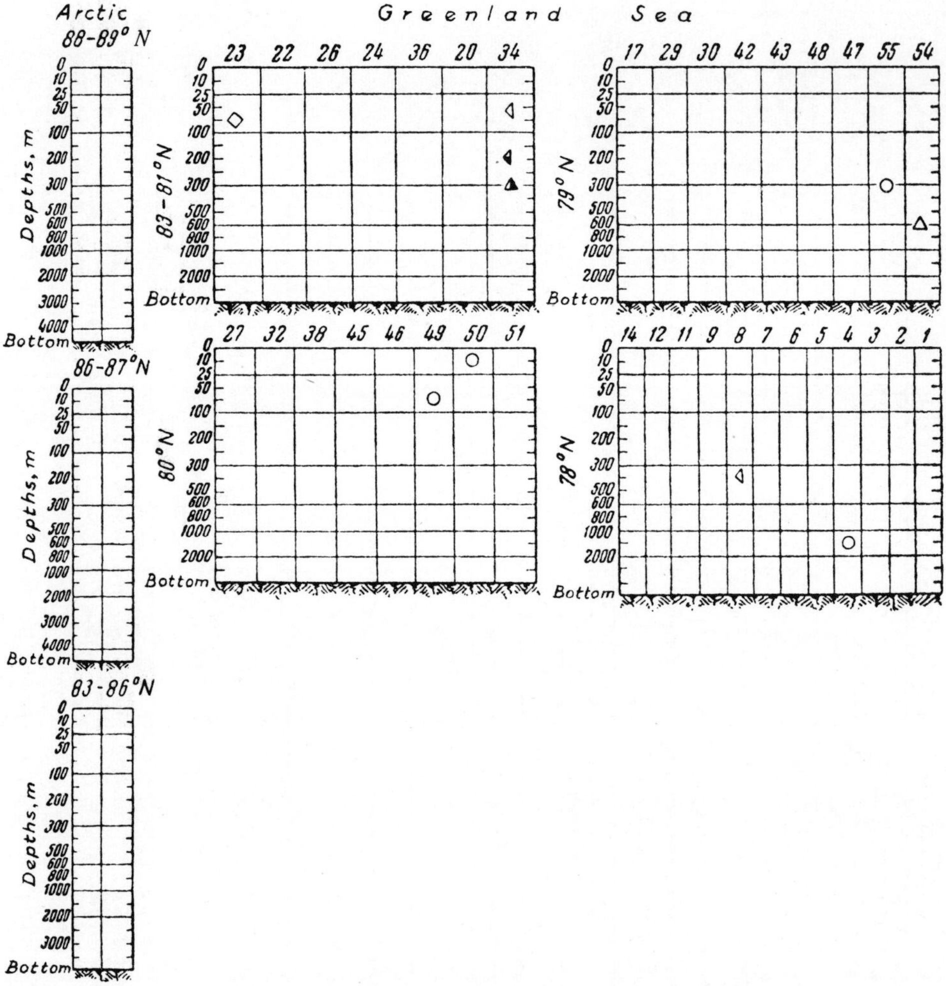

1 - *Pseudomonas sinuosa*, var. A; 2 - *Ps. sinuosa*, var. B; 3 - *Ps. sinuosa*, var. C; 4 - *Ps. sinuosa*, var. D; 5 - *Ps. sinuosa*, var. E; 6 - *Ps. sinuosa*, var. F 7 - *Ps. sinuosa*, var. G

Fig. 5a Distribution of non-sporing bacteria in seas and oceans

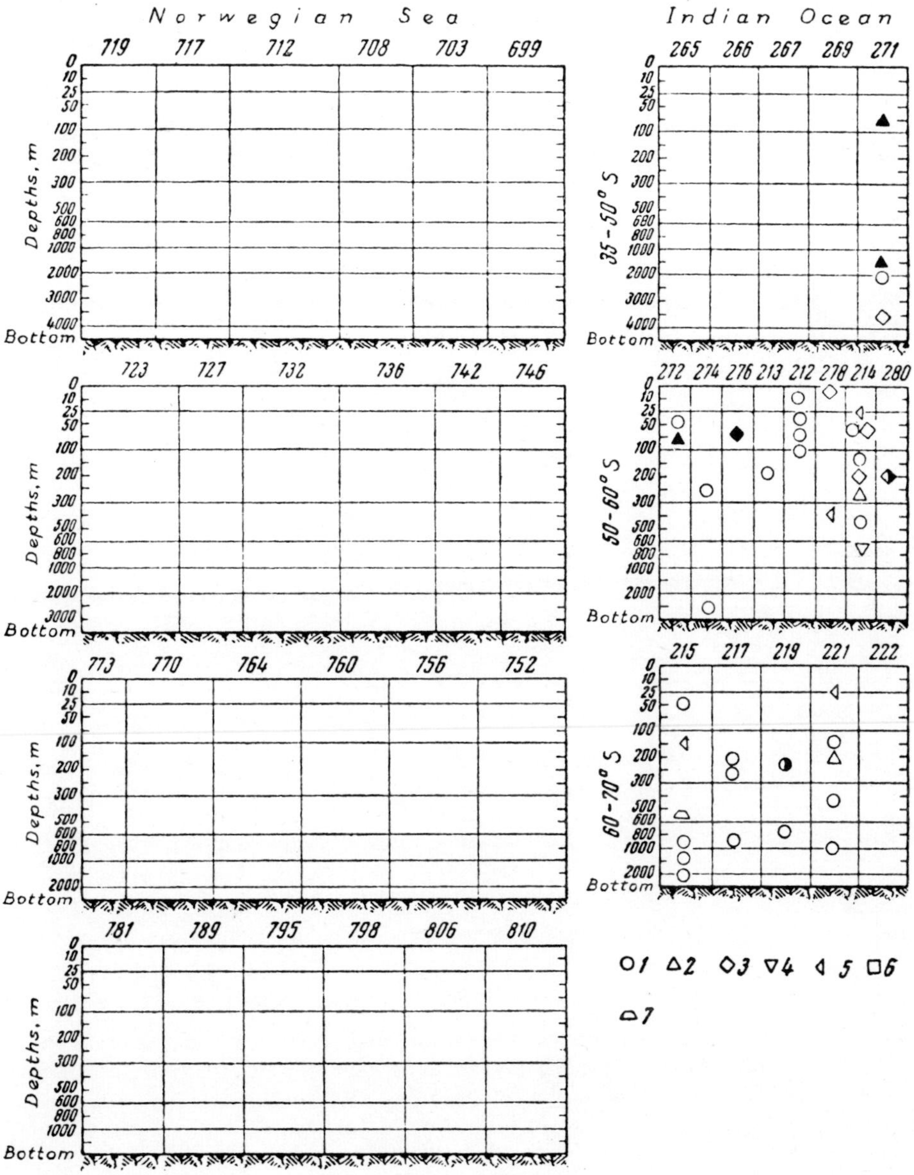
Norwegian Sea
719 717 712 708 703 699
723 727 732 736 742 746
773 770 764 760 756 752
781 789 795 798 806 810
Depths, m
0 10 25 50 100 200 300 500 600 800 1000 2000 3000 4000
Bottom
Indian Ocean
265 266 267 269 271
35-50° S
272 274 276 213 212 278 214 280
50-60° S
215 217 219 221 222
60-70° S
1 2 3 4 5 6
7

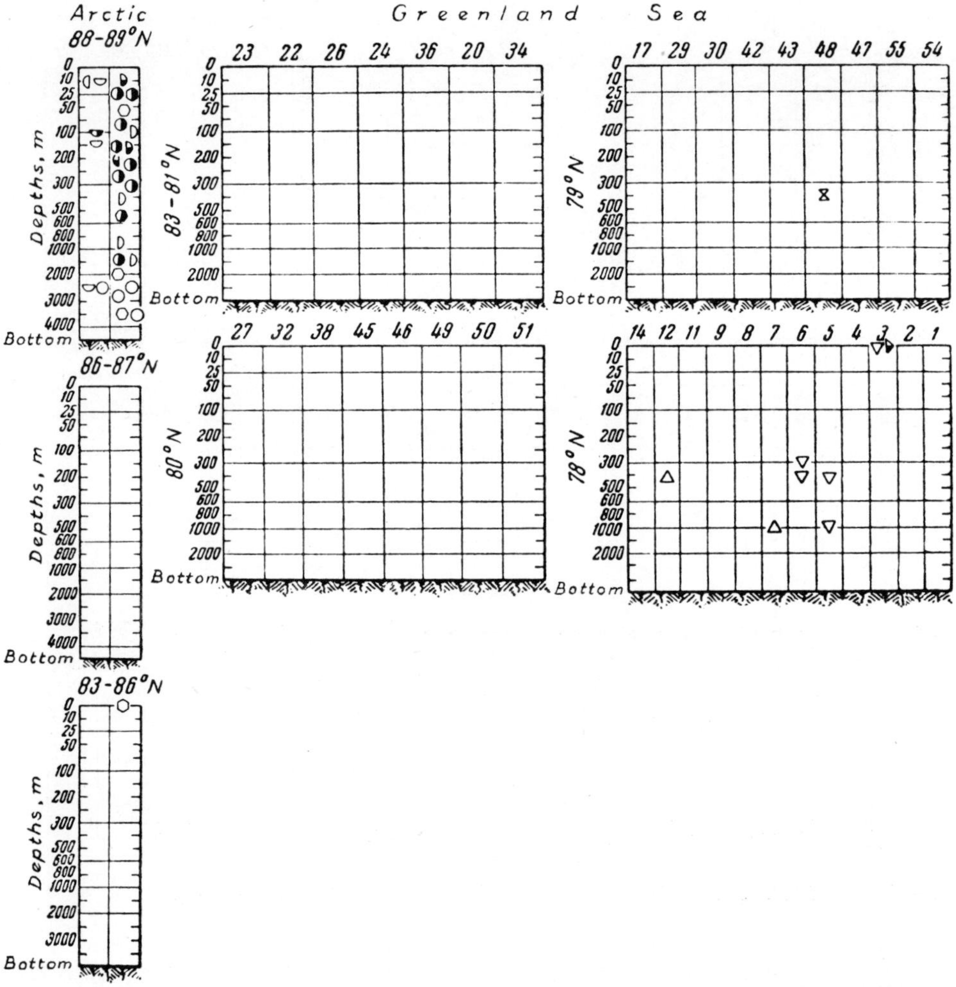

1 - *Pseudomonas caudatus*, var. A; 2 - *Ps. caudatus*, var. B; 3 - *Ps. caudatus*, var. C; 4 - *Ps. caudatus*, var. D; 5 - *Ps. fluorescens*, var. A; 6 - *Ps. fluorescens*, var. B; 7 - *Ps. fluorescens*, var. C; 8 - *Ps. fluorescens*, var. D; 9 - *Ps. liquida*, var. A; 10 - *Ps. liquida*, var. B

Fig. 6 Distribution of non-sporing bacteria in seas and oceans

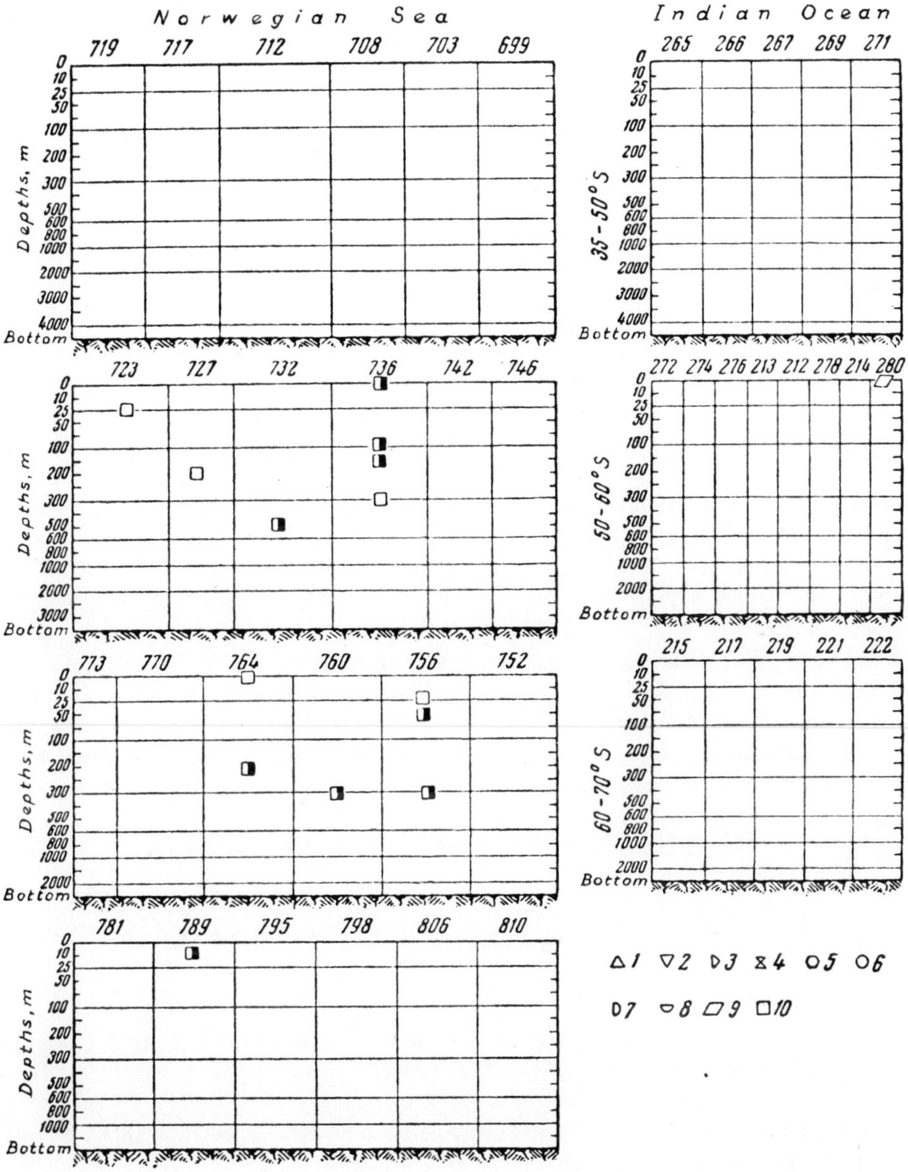
Norwegian Sea
Indian Ocean
719 717 712 708 703 699
265 266 267 269 271
723 727 732 736 742 746
272 274 276 213 212 278 214 280
773 770 764 760 756 752
215 217 219 221 222
781 789 795 798 806 810
Depths, m
0 10 25 50 100 200 300 500 600 800 1000 2000 3000 4000
Bottom
35-50° S
50-60° S
60-70° S
1 2 3 4 5 6
7 8 9 10

The non-sporing rods are distinguished from var. A in that they hydrolyse starch and do not assimilate mineral nitrogen.

From: Indian Ocean, (st. **215**), 535 m; (st. **251**), 1403 m; (st. **293**), 110 m; (st. **297**), 137 m; (st. **312**), 3760 m;

Pacific Ocean, (st. **3823**), 578 m; (st. **3854**), 25 m; (st. **3868**), 265 m.

Assigned to aggregate species *Pseudomonas sinuosa* Wright, var. G.

Non-sporing rods, $1.7-3.1 \times 0.5-0.9\ \mu$, with rounded or acuminate ends, arranged singly or in pairs. In old cultures (ten days) many greatly swollen cells with homogeneous plasma together with very small cells in conglomerates. In young cultures the rods are motile. Monotrichous. Gram-negative.

On nutrient agar with sea salt the streak is yellowish-creamy, with smooth surface, finely scalloped edge and pasty consistency.

On starch agar with asparagine the streak is yellow, in some of the strains the tinge varies from light yellow and bright yellow to dirty yellow or orange.

On meat-peptone broth – ring, turbidity, sediment.

Gelatine not liquefied. Milk not peptonized. Acid in peptone water containing glucose but not in peptone water containing mannitol, sucrose, maltose, or lactose. Starch hydrolysed. Mineral nitrogen assimilated. Nitrates reduced to nitrites.

From: Greenland Sea, (st. 7), 1000 m; (st. 12), 400 m.

Assigned to aggregate species *Pseudomonas caudatus* (Wright) Conn, 1919, var. A.

The non-sporing rods are distinguished from var. A in that they do not reduce nitrates.

From: Greenland Sea, (st. **3**), 0 m; (st. **5**), 400, 1000 m; (st. **6**), 300, 400 m.

Assigned to aggregate species *Pseudomonas caudatus* (Wright) Conn, 1919, var. B.

The non-sporing rods are distinguished from var. A in that they do not hydrolyse starch and do not reduce nitrates.

From: Greenland Sea, (st. 3), 0 m.

Assigned to aggregate species *Pseudomonas caudatus* (Wright) Conn, 1919, var. C.

The non-sporing rods are distinguished from var. A in that the streak is wrinkled on nutrient media, milk peptonized, nitrates not reduced.

From: Greenland Sea, (st. **48**), 400 m.

Assigned to aggregate species *Pseudomonas caudatus* (Wright) Conn, 1919, var. D.

Non-sporing rods, 2.1 – 9.0 × 0.5 – 1.1 μ, with rounded ends, curved. Motile. Monotrichous. Gram-negative.

On nutrient agar with sea salt the streak is creamy or greyish-creamy, smooth, shiny, with even edges. Some strains secrete a yellowish-green pigment into the media.

On potato – greyish-creamy slime or pinkish-creamy slime.

On meat-peptone broth – turbidity, ring, sediment.

Gelatine liquefied. Milk peptonized. Acid in peptone water containing glucose but not in peptone water containing mannitol, sucrose, lactose or maltose. Starch not hydrolysed. Mineral nitrogen assimilated. Nitrates reduced to nitrites.

From: Arctic Ocean, (st. 89°29′ N, 65°43′ W), 25, 50, 150, 500, 2000, 3500 m; (st. 85°53′ N, 27°30′ W), 0 m.

Assigned to aggregate species ***Pseudomonas fluorescens*** **Migula, 1895, var. A.**

The non-sporing rods are distinguished from var. A in that they do not reduce nitrates.

From: Arctic Ocean, (st. 88°04′ N, 151°16′ W), 2500 m; (st. 89°29′ N, 65°43′ W), 25, 75, 200, 250, 300, 1500, 2500, 3000, 3700 m.

Assigned to aggregate species ***Pseudomonas fluorescens*** **Migula, 1895, var. B.**

The non-sporing rods are distinguished from var. A in that they do not liquefy gelatine nor peptonize milk.

From: Arctic Ocean, (st. 88°04′ N, 151°16′ W), 10 m; (st. 89°29′ N, 65°43′ W), 10, 100, 150, 200, 400, 1000, 1500 m.

Assigned to aggregate species ***Pseudomonas fluorescens*** **Migula, 1895, var. C.**

The non-sporing rods are distinguished from var. A in that they do not liquefy gelatine, do not peptonize milk, do not reduce nitrates.

From: Arctic Ocean, (st. 88°04′ N, 151°16′ W), 10, 100, 150, 2500 m.

Assigned to aggregate species ***Pseudomonas fluorescens*** **Migula, 1895, var. D.**

Non-sporing rods, 1.7 – 6.6 × 0.4 – 1.1 μ, with rounded and acuminate edges, polymorphous. In old cultures swollen cells and filaments occur. Monotrichous. Motile. Gram-negative.

On nutrient agar with sea salt growth at first poor. From fifth to tenth day the streak is creamy, shiny, semitransparent, slimy, with even edges. In old cultures orange coating occurrs on the surface of the streak. Some strains secrete a brownish pigment into the medium.

On meat-peptone broth – turbidity, ring, sediment, hydrogen sulphide is formed.

Gelatine liquefied. Milk not peptonized. No acid in peptone water containing mannitol, glucose, sucrose, maltose or lactose. Starch not hydrolysed. Mineral nitrogen not assimilated or very slightly assimilated. Nitrates not reduced.

From: Atlantic Ocean, (st. **345**), 0 m; (st. **360**), 292 m; (st. **366**), 3002 m; Indian Ocean, (st. **280**), 0 m; (st. **282**), 0 m.

Assigned to aggregate species *Pseudomonas liquida* Frankl. et Frankl., n. comb., var. A.

The non-sporing rods are distinguished from var. A in that they peptonize milk.

From: Norwegian Sea, (st. **1723**), 30 m; (st. **1727**), 200 m; (st. **1732**), 500 m; (st. **1736**), 0, 100, 150, 300 m; (st. **1756**), 30, 50 m; (st. **1760**), 300 m; (st. **1764**), 0, 200 m; (st. **1789**), 10 m.

Assigned to aggregate species *Pseudomonas liquida* Frankl. et Frankl., n. comb., var. B.

Non-sporing, curved rods, $1.4-3.3 \times 0.4-0.9\ \mu$, with acuminate ends. Motile. Gram-negative.

On nutrient agar with sea salt the streak is smooth, creamy, acquiring a brownish pigment with age.

On meat-peptone broth – ring, turbidity, reddish-brown sediment; medium acquires brownish stain. Rods form hydrogen sulphide and ammonia.

Gelatine not liquefied. Milk not peptonized. No acid in peptone water containing mannitol, glucose, sucrose, maltose or lactose. Starch not hydrolysed. Mineral nitrogen not assimilated. Nitrates not reduced.

From: Greenland Sea, (st. 7), 1000 m.

Assigned to aggregate species *Vibrio nigricans* Weibel, var. A.

The non-sporing rods are distinguished from var. A in that they hydrolyse starch and slightly assimilate mineral nitrogen.

From: Indian Ocean, (st. **215**), 220 m.

Assigned to aggregate species *Vibrio nigricans* Weibel, var. B.

Non-sporing rods, $1.3-2.3 \times 0.6-1.0\ \mu$, oval or oval-ovate, arranged singly, in pairs or in small clusters. Non-motile. Gram-positive.

On nutrient agar containing sea salt growth noticeable only on fourth and fifth days. At first the streak is a dirty pink, light, shiny, with smooth surface and even edges, darkening to crimson with age (on fifteenth day).

On meat-peptone broth – turbidity, sediment brownish or reddish in colour.

Gelatine not liquefied. Milk not peptonized. No acid in peptone water containing mannitol, glucose, sucrose, maltose or lactose. Starch not hydrolysed. Mineral nitrogen assimilated. Nitrates reduced to nitrites.

From: Greenland Sea, (st. **36**), 2500 m; also from mud (st. **3** and **23**);

Indian Ocean, (st. **249**), 380 m.

Assigned to aggregate species *Pseudobacterium rosea-album* (Sack.) **Krass., var. A.**

The non-sporing rods are distinguished from var. A in that they do not reduce nitrates.

From: Greenland Sea, (st. **36**), 2500 m; also from mud (st. **23**);
Indian Ocean, (st. **246**), 362 m.

Assigned to aggregate species *Pseudobacterium rosea-album* (Sack.) **Krass.,** var. **B.**

Non-sporing rods, 2.0 – 6.0 × 0.5 – 1.0 μ, with blunt ends, straight or slightly curved, single or paired, often at an angle to one another or joined laterally, forming clusters.

In old cultures one end sometimes slightly swollen. Non-motile. Gram-positive.

Growth on organic media abundant, on mineral media poor.

On nutrient agar containing sea salt the streak is yellowish-white, with smooth surface and even margin. Pasty consistency. Rods sometimes secrete a brown pigment into medium.

On meat-peptone broth – ring, strong turbidity, sediment or no turbidity formed. Many strains form hydrogen sulphide.

Gelatine liquefied. Milk peptonized. No acid in peptone water containing mannitol, glucose, sucrose, maltose or lactose. Starch not hydrolysed. Mineral nitrogen assimilated. Nitrates not reduced.

From: Indian Ocean, (st. **213**), 197 m; (st. **236**), 150 m; (st. **249**), 0, 210 m; (st. **251**), 0, 2788 m; (st. **259**), 218 m; (st. **271**), 200 m; (st. **287**), 2020 m; (st. **293**), 20 m; (st. **295**), 3170 m; (st. **297**), 275, 942, 3380 m; (st. **305**), 4420 m; (st. **307**), 100, 205, 250 m; (st. **311**), 0, 25 m; also from mud (st. **251**);
Pacific Ocean, (st. **3825**), 2120 m.

Assigned to aggregate species *Pseudobacterium biforme* **Eggerth.**

Non-sporing rods, 0.6 – 1.9 × 0.4 – 0.9 μ, oval, with rounded ends, single or in pairs, rarely conglomerates. Non-motile. Gram-positive.

On nutrient agar with sea salt the streak is yellowish-white, with smooth surface and even edges.

On meat-peptone broth – ring, turbidity, sediment.

Gelatine not liquefied. Milk not peptonized. No acid in peptone water containing mannitol, glucose, sucrose, maltose or lactose. Starch not hydrolysed. Mineral nitrogen assimilated. Nitrates not reduced.

From: Arctic Ocean, (st. 82°55′ N, 151°32′ E), 0 m;
Indian Ocean, (st. **248**), 1040 m;
Norwegian Sea, (st. **1717**), 50 m;
Pacific Ocean, (st. **3851**), 45, 68 m; (st. **3859**), 10 m.

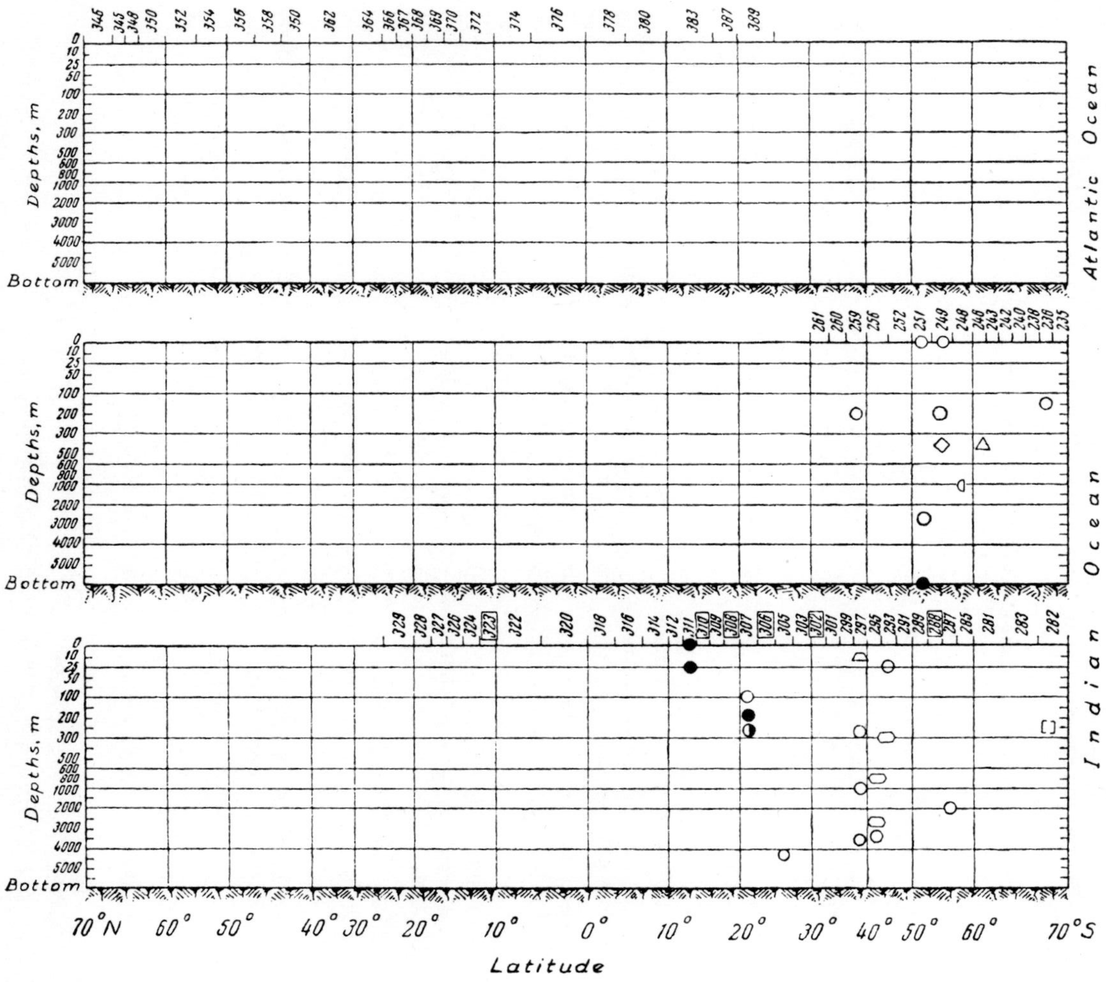
Atlantic Ocean
30°W
20°E
Ocean
Indian
90°-100°E
Depths, m
0
10
25
50
100
200
300
500
600
800
1000
2000
3000
4000
5000
Bottom
70°N
60°
50°
40°
30°
20°
10°
0°
10°
20°
30°
40°
50°
60°
70°S
Latitude

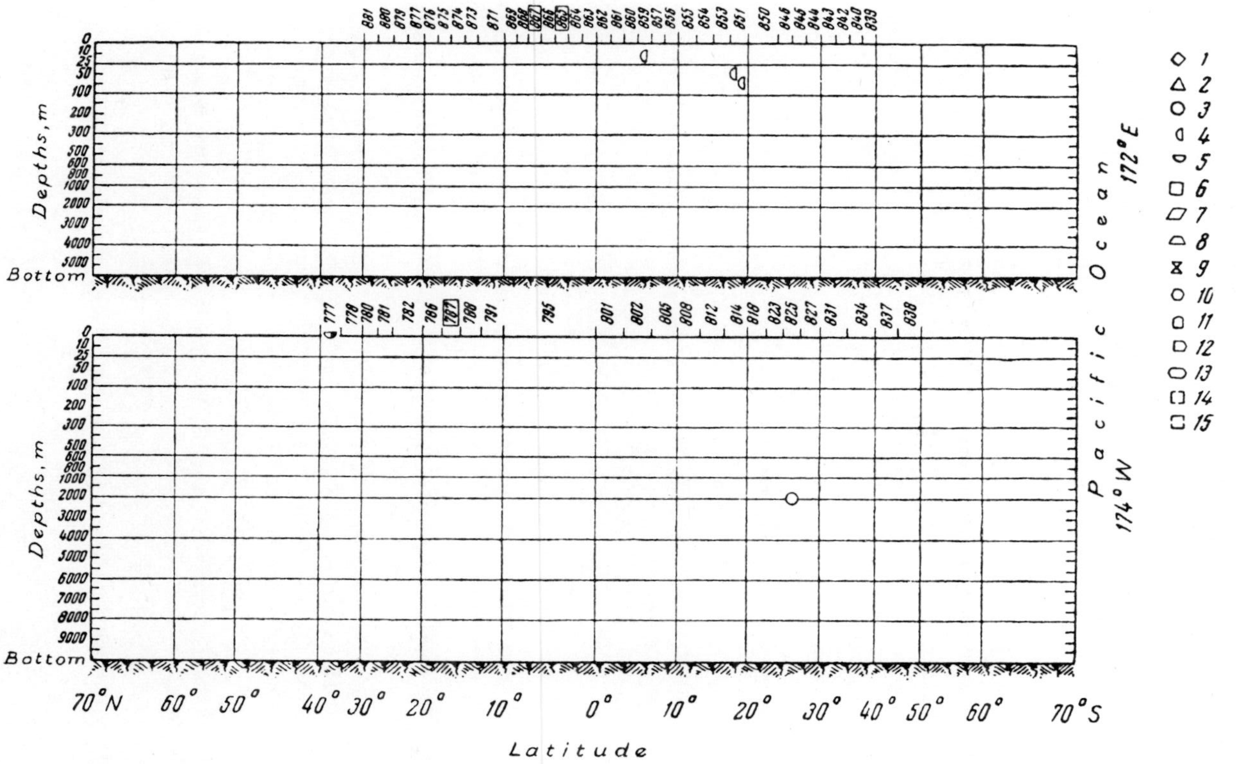

1 - *Pseudobacterium rosea-album*, var. A; 2 - *Pseudob. rosea-album*, var. B; 3 - *Pseudob. biforme*; 4 - *Pseudob. cocciformis*, var. A; 5 - *Pseudob. cocciformis*, var. B; 6 - *Pseudob. opacum*, var. A; 7 - *Pseudob. opacum*, var. B 8 - *Pseudob. marinopiscosum*; 9 - *Pseudob. vulgatum*; 10 - *Pseudob. variabilis*, var. A; 11 - *Pseudob. variabilis*, var. B; 12 - *Pseudob. variabilis*, var. C; 13 - *Pseudob. variabilis*, var. D; 14 - *Pseudob. variabilis*, var. E; 15 - *Pseudob. variabilis*, var. F

Fig. 7 Distribution of non-sporing bacteria in seas and oceans

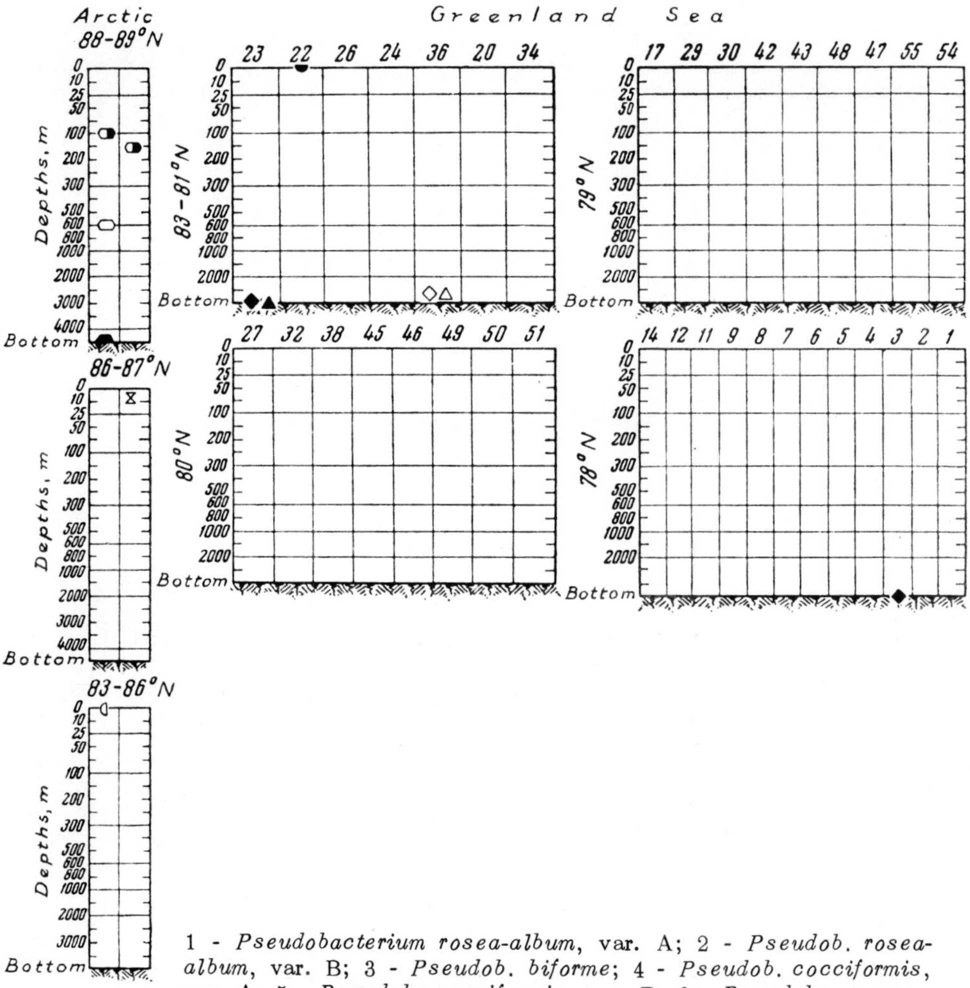

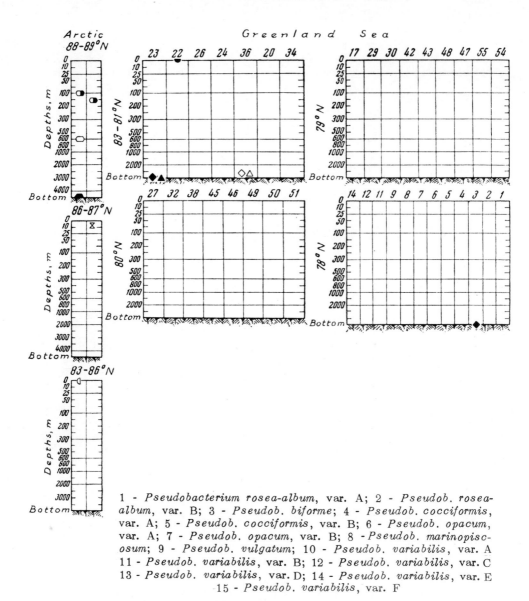

1 - *Pseudobacterium rosea-album*, var. A; 2 - *Pseudob. rosea-album*, var. B; 3 - *Pseudob. biforme*; 4 - *Pseudob. cocciformis*, var. A; 5 - *Pseudob. cocciformis*, var. B; 6 - *Pseudob. opacum*, var. A; 7 - *Pseudob. opacum*, var. B; 8 - *Pseudob. marinopiscosum*; 9 - *Pseudob. vulgatum*; 10 - *Pseudob. variabilis*, var. A 11 - *Pseudob. variabilis*, var. B; 12 - *Pseudob. variabilis*, var. C 13 - *Pseudob. variabilis*, var. D; 14 - *Pseudob. variabilis*, var. E 15 - *Pseudob. variabilis*, var. F

Fig. 7a Distribution of non-sporing bacteria in seas and oceans

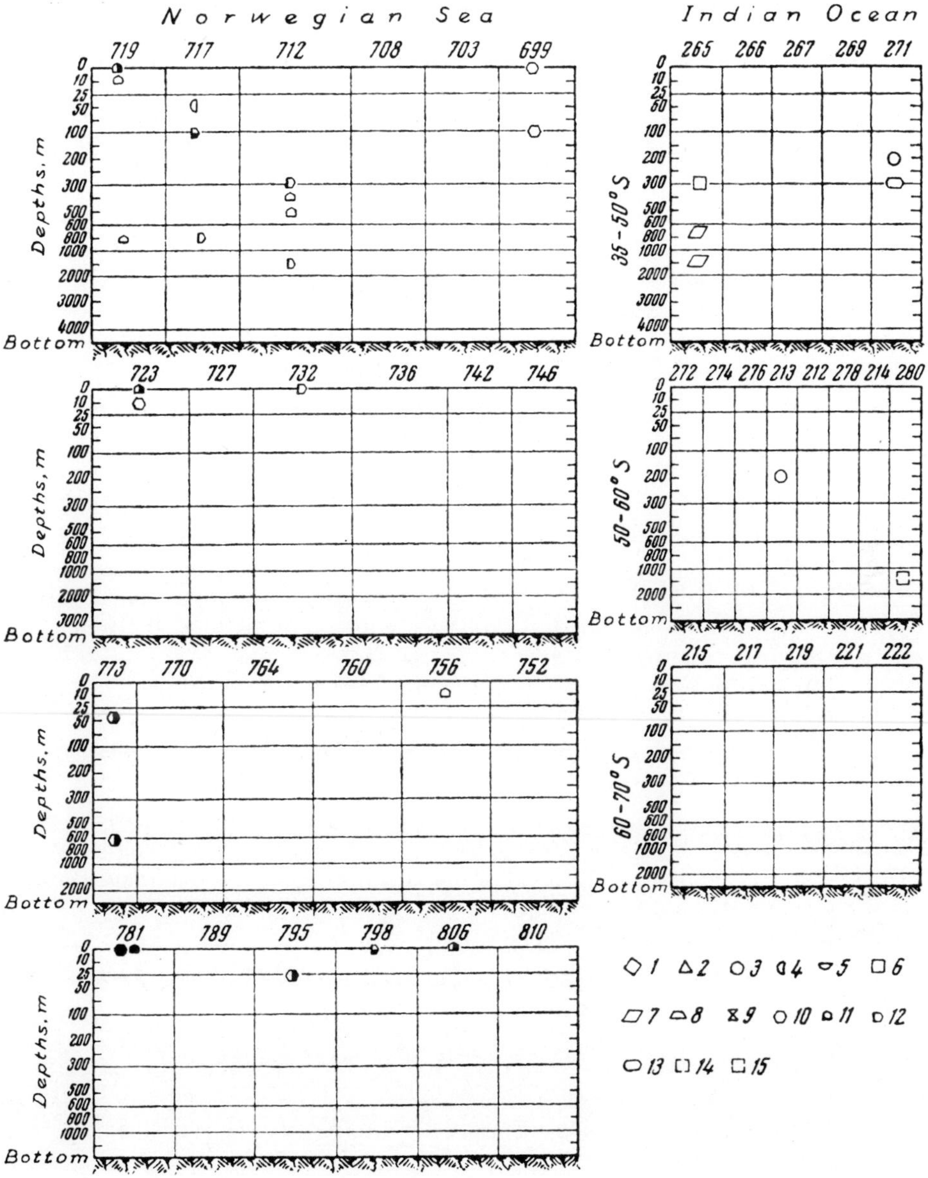

Norwegian Sea
Indian Ocean
719 717 712 708 703 699
723 727 732 736 742 746
773 770 764 760 756 752
781 789 795 798 806 810
265 266 267 269 271
272 274 276 213 212 278 214 280
215 217 219 221 222
Depths, m
0 10 25 50 100 200 300 500 600 800 1000 2000 3000 4000
Bottom
35-50° S
50-60° S
60-70° S
1 2 3 4 5 6
7 8 9 10 11 12
13 14 15

Assigned to aggregate species ***Pseudobacterium cocciformis*** **Severin, var. A.**

The non-sporing rods are distinguished from var. A in that they reduce nitrates to nitrites.

From: Greenland Sea, (st. 22), 0 m;
Pacific Ocean, (st. 3777), 0 m.

Assigned to aggregate species ***Pseudobacterium cocciformis*** **Severin, var. B.**

Non-sporing rods, $2.8-5.3 \times 0.9-1.6$ μ, with truncated ends of varying length, from coccoidal to long filaments. Arranged singly or in chains. Non-motile. Gram-positive (staining not distinct).

On nutrient agar containing sea salt, growth at first poor, semitransparent, with orange tinge at bottom of the slant, later becoming pinkish-grey with smooth surface and shiny edges.

On meat-peptone broth – turbidity, reddish-brown sediment.

Gelatine liquefied. Milk not peptonized or slightly peptonized. Peptone water containing mannitol, glucose, sucrose or maltose acidified. No acid in peptone water containing lactose. Starch not hydrolysed. Mineral nitrogen assimilated. Nitrates reduced to nitrites.

From: Indian Ocean, (st. 265), 294 m.

Assigned to aggregate species ***Pseudobacterium opacum*** **Sack, var. A.**

Non-sporing rods distinguished from var. A in that they do not produce acid in peptone water containing mannitol, glucose, sucrose, maltose or lactose and do not reduce nitrates.

From: Indian Ocean, (st. 265), 716, 1430 m.

Assigned to aggregate species ***Pseudobacterium opacum*** **Sack, var. B.**

Non-sporing rods, $4.4-9.8 \times 0.7-1.4$ μ, forming long filaments. Non-motile. Gram-positive.

On nutrient agar containing sea salt the streak is creamy, semitransparent, slimy, secreting a brown pigment into the medium with age.

On meat-peptone broth – ring, turbidity, sediment.

Gelatine liquefied. Milk peptonized. Peptone water containing mannitol, glucose, sucrose, maltose or lactose acidified. Starch not hydrolysed. Mineral nitrogen assimilated. Nitrates not reduced.

From: Indian Ocean, (st. 297), 10 m.

Assigned to aggregate species ***Pseudobacterium marinopiscosum*** **ZoBell et Upham.**

Non-sporing rods, with rounded ends and sharply granulated plasma. Forming long filaments. Non-motile. Gram-negative.

On nutrient agar containing sea salt whitish, flat colonies with smooth surface and even edges.

On meat-peptone broth – slimy ring and film, turbidity, slimy sediment; rods form hydrogen sulphide and ammonia.

Gelatine liquefied. Milk slightly peptonized. Acid in peptone water containing mannitol, glucose or sucrose but not in peptone water with maltose and lactose. Starch not hydrolysed. Mineral nitrogen assimilated. Nitrates reduced to nitrites.

From: Arctic Ocean, (st. 87°28′N, 177°12′ W), 5 m.

Assigned to aggregate species ***Pseudobacterium vulgatum*** **Egg. et Gagn, n. comb.**

Non-sporing rods, 1.4 – 4.3 × 0.5 – 1.5 μ, coccoidal and irregularly rounded, single or paired, small chains occur. Granulated plasma. Non-motile. Gram-negative (Gram-staining not distinct).

On nutrient agar containing sea salt the streak is yellowish-cream, smooth, with even edges.

On meat-peptone broth – turbidity.

Gelatine not liquefied. Milk slightly peptonized. No acid in peptone water containing mannitol, glucose, sucrose, maltose or lactose. Starch not hydrolysed. Mineral nitrogen assimilated. Nitrates not reduced.

From: Norwegian Sea, (st. **1699**), 0, 100 m; (st. **1723**), 10 m; (st. **1773**), 50, 600 m; (st. **1781**), 0 m; (st. **1795**), 30 m.

Assigned to aggregate species ***Pseudobacterium variabilis*** **Distaso, n. comb., var. A.**

The non-sporing rods are distinguished from var. A in that they reduce nitrates to nitrites.

From: Norwegian Sea, (st. **1712**), 400, 500 m; (st. **1719**), 0, 10, 800 m; (st. **1723**), 0 m; (st. **1756**), 10 m; (st. **1781**), 0 m; (st. **1798**), 200 m; (st. **1806**), 0 m.

Assigned to aggregate species ***Pseudobacterium variabilis*** **Distaso, n. comb., var. B.**

The non-sporing rods are distinguished from var. A in that they produce acid in peptone water with glucose.

From: Norwegian Sea, (st. **1712**), 300, 1500 m; (st. **1717**), 100, 800 m; (st. **1732**), 0 m; (st. **1798**), 0 m.

Assigned to aggregate species ***Pseudobacterium variabilis*** **Distaso, n. comb., var. C.**

The non-sporing rods are distinguished from var. A in that they form filaments in young cultures and do not peptonize milk.

From: Arctic Ocean, (st. 88°04′N, 151°16′ W), 100, 600 m; (st. 89°29′N,

65°43′ W), 150 m;

Indian Ocean, (st. 271), 300 m; (st. 293), 300 m; (st. 295), 790, 3000 m.

Assigned to aggregate species *Pseudobacterium variabilis* Distaso, n. comb., var. D.

The non-sporing rods are distinguished from var. A in that they liquefy gelatine, do not peptonize milk and reduce nitrates to nitrites.

From: Indian Ocean, (st. 282), 265 m.

Assigned to aggregate species *Pseudobacterium variabilis* Distaso, n. comb., var. E.

The non-sporing rods are distinguished from var. A in that they liquefy gelatine, do not peptonize milk, and produce acid in peptone water containing mannitol, glucose, sucrose, maltose or lactose.

From: Indian Ocean, (st. 280), 1500 m.

Assigned to aggregate species *Pseudobacterium variabilis* Distaso, n. comb., var. F.

7

Spore-forming bacteria

Spore-forming rods $0.5-0.7 \times 3-9\ \mu$, motile, forming chainlets. The spores are oval-cylindrical and not strictly localized. Gram-positive.

On nutrient agar with sea salt they give a finely wrinkled, dry streak with mat surface.

On meat-peptone agar plus wort agar, colonies with a mat, folded surface are produced. The cultures often dissociate into two types of colonies, some more transparent and difficult to remove from the agar, with an even margin, others more dense, with villi on the margin.

On meat-peptone agar with 1% glucose, growth occurs only on the surface of the agar column in the form of a finely gophered, wrinkled, whitish film. The agar turns brown.

On potato a mucous, light cinnamon-coloured, shiny film with even margin is formed. The slight wrinkling of the streak increases in the downward direction. In time the liquid at the bottom of the test tube acquires a greenish colour.

On meat-peptone broth a thin, dry film is produced and the liquid is transparent. The majority of the cultures vigorously form ammonia.

Milk peptonized. Gelatine liquefied. Peptone water with mannitol, glucose or sucrose acidified, but not water with maltose or lactose. Starch unchanged. Mineral nitrogen assimilated. Nitrates reduced.

From: Indian Ocean, (st. **215**), 81 m; (st. **235**), 400 m; (st. **314**), 3270, 4235 m.

Assigned to aggregate species *Bacillus catenula* Migula, 1900, var. A.

Spore-forming rods distinguished from var. A by inability to peptonize milk or reduce nitrates. Starch slightly hydrolysed.

From: Indian Ocean, (st. **309**), 5180 m.

Assigned to aggregate species *B. catenula* Migula, 1900, var. B.

Spore-forming rods distinguished from var. A by inability to reduce nitrates.

From: Greenland Sea, (st. **12**), 0 m;
Indian Ocean, mud (st. **285**).

Assigned to aggregate species *B. catenula* **Migula, 1900, var. C.**

Spore-forming rods distinguished from var. A by the character of the growth on nutrient agar with sea salt, where the streak does not show dry folding and the surface of the streak is shiny. Nitrates not reduced.

From: Arctic Ocean, (st. 88°04′ N, 151°16′ W), 500 m;
Indian Ocean, (st. **215**), 27 m; (st. **236**), 924 m; (st. **249**), 0 m; (st. **260**), 262 m; (st. **266**), 512 m; (st. **267**), 415 m; (st. **278**), 570 m; (st. **299**), 294 m; (st. **324**), 2375 m;
Pacific Ocean, (st. **3801**), 340 m.

Assigned to aggregate species *B. catenula* **Migula, 1900, var. D.**

Spore-forming rods distinguished from var. A by the character of growth on nutrient agar with sea salt, where the streak resembles var. D growth. Peptone water with maltose acidified. Nitrates not reduced.

From: Greenland Sea, (st. **2**), 10 m;
Indian Ocean (st. **260**), 262, 650 m; (st. **276**), 264 m.

Assigned to aggregate species *B. catenula* **Migula, 1900, var. E.**

Spore-forming rods distinguished from var. A by character of growth on nutrient agar with sea salt, where streak resembles var. D growth. Peptone water with mannitol not acidified. Nitrates not reduced.

From: Indian Ocean, (st. **267**), 1034, 2416 m; (st. **271**), 1015 m; (st. **293**), 70 m; from mud (st. **326**).

Assigned to aggregate species *B. catenula* **Migula, 1900, var. F.**

Spore-forming rods distinguished from var. A by character of growth on nutrient agar with sea salt where streak resembles var. D growth. Peptone water with maltose acidified. Nitrates not reduced.

From: Indian Ocean, (st. **267**), 207, 778 m.

Assigned to aggregate species *B. catenula* **Migula, 1900, var. G.**

Spore-forming rods distinguished from var. A by formation of pinkish cinnamon-coloured, folded colonies on meat-peptone agar with wort agar, concrescent with the agar, secreting a fluorescent pigment on meat-peptone agar with 1% glucose. Nitrates not reduced.

From: Arctic Ocean, (st. 87°28′ N, 177°12′ W), 5 m;
Greenland Sea, (st. **30**), 150 m;
Indian Ocean, mud (st. **271**);
Norwegian Sea, (st. **1727**), 150 m.

Assigned to aggregate species *B. catenula* **Migula, 1900, var. H.**

Spore-forming rods distinguished from var. A by character of growth on nutrient agar with sea salt, where the streak does not display folding and the surface of the streak is shiny.

On meat-peptone agar with wort agar, colonies yellowish with smooth or folded surface. Peptone water with maltose acidified

From: Arctic Ocean, (st. 82°55′ N, 151°32′ E), 150 m; (st. 87°28′ N, 177°12′ W), 5 m; (st. 89°29′ N, 65°43′ W), 2000 m; from mud (st. 88°04′ N), 151°16′ W and st. 89°29′ N, 65°43′ W);

Indian Ocean, (st. **256**), 4389 m; (st. **261**), 75 m.

Assigned to aggregate species *B. catenula* **Migula, 1900, var. I.**

Spore-forming rods $0.6-1.0 \times 2.4-8\ \mu$, motile, joined into long chainlets. Spore lies at centre or near one end. Gram-positive.

On nutrient agar with sea salt a light cinnamon-coloured, shiny streak occurs.

On meat-peptone agar with wort agar, flat, disintegrating colonies with a white, dry film on the surface. Margin fibrous. On ageing the middle of a colony becomes transparent and the edges acquire fine plication.

On potato, a dry, finely folded film with a mat surface appears. Margin thickened to form a ridge. Film sometimes has swellings and becomes slimy on ageing. Potato turns black.

On meat-peptone broth a thin, folded film and turbidity occurs. Ammonia formed.

Milk peptonized. Gelatine liquefied. Peptone water with mannitol, glucose sucrose, maltose or lactose not acidified. Starch hydrolysed. Mineral nitrogen assimilated. Nitrates not reduced.

From: Arctic Ocean, (st. 88°04′ N, 151°16′ W), 300, 2000 m; (st. 89°29′ N, 65°43′ W), 0, 50, 1500, 2000, 2500 m; from mud (st. 87°28′ N, 177°12′ W);

Greenland Sea, (st. **5**), 10 m; (st. **17**), 10 m; (st. **32**), 50 m; (st. **43**), 10 m; (st. **45**), 0 m;

Indian Ocean, (st. **256**), 4389 m.

Assigned to aggregate species *Bacillus idosus* **Burchard, 1897, var. A.**

Spore-forming rods distinguished from var. A by capacity to acidify peptone water with glucose or sucrose.

From: Greenland Sea, (st. **1**), 50 m.

Assigned to aggregate species *B. idosus* **Burchard, 1897, var. B.**

Spore-forming rods distinguished from var. A by capacity to acidify peptone water with mannitol, glucose or maltose.

From: Greenland Sea, (st. **43**), 25 m;

Indian Ocean, (st. **243**), 1420 m.

Assigned to aggregate species *B. idosus* **Burchard, 1897, var. C.**

Spore-forming rods distinguished from var. A by capacity to reduce nitrates.

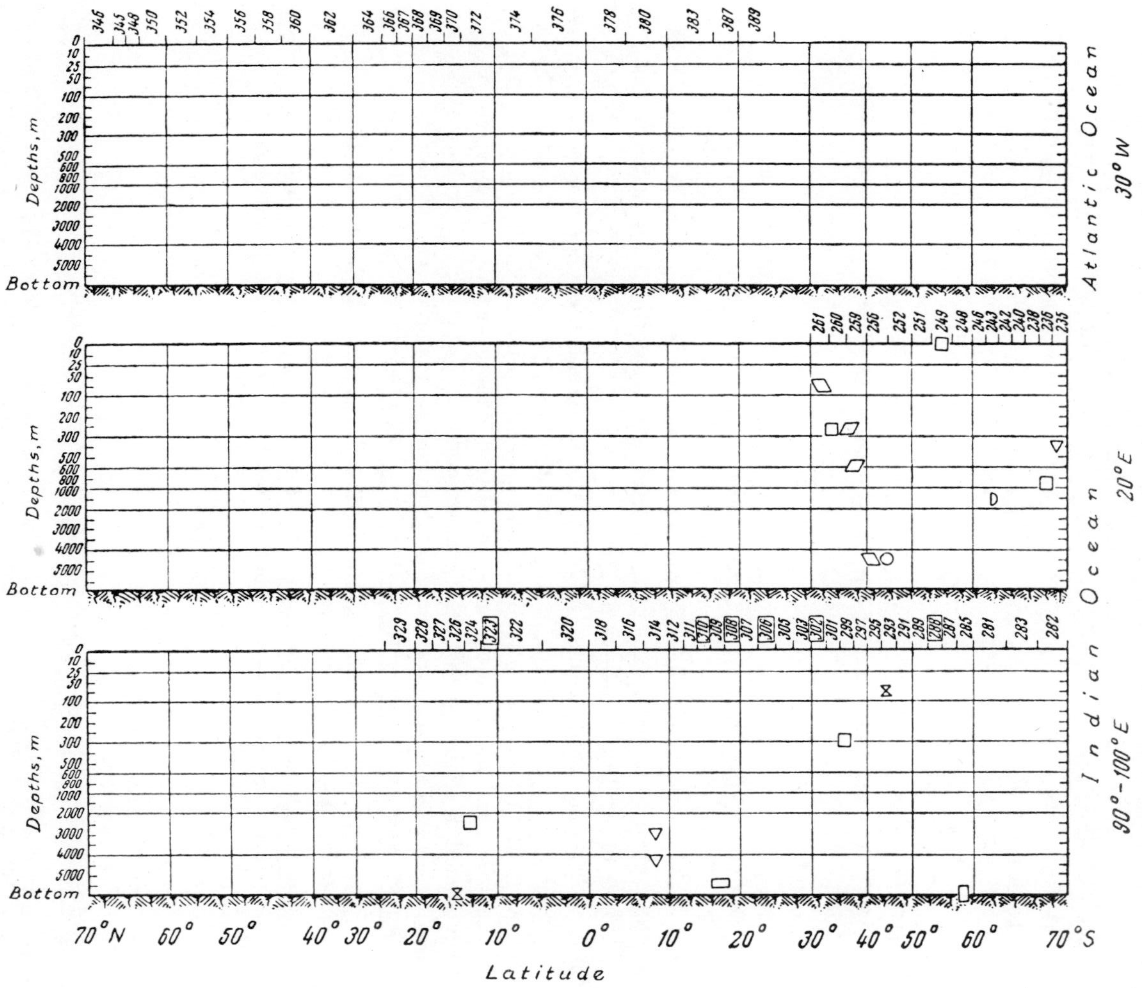

Atlantic Ocean
30° W
Indian Ocean
20° E
90°-100° E
Depths, m
Bottom
Latitude
70° N
60°
50°
40°
30°
20°
10°
0°
70° S

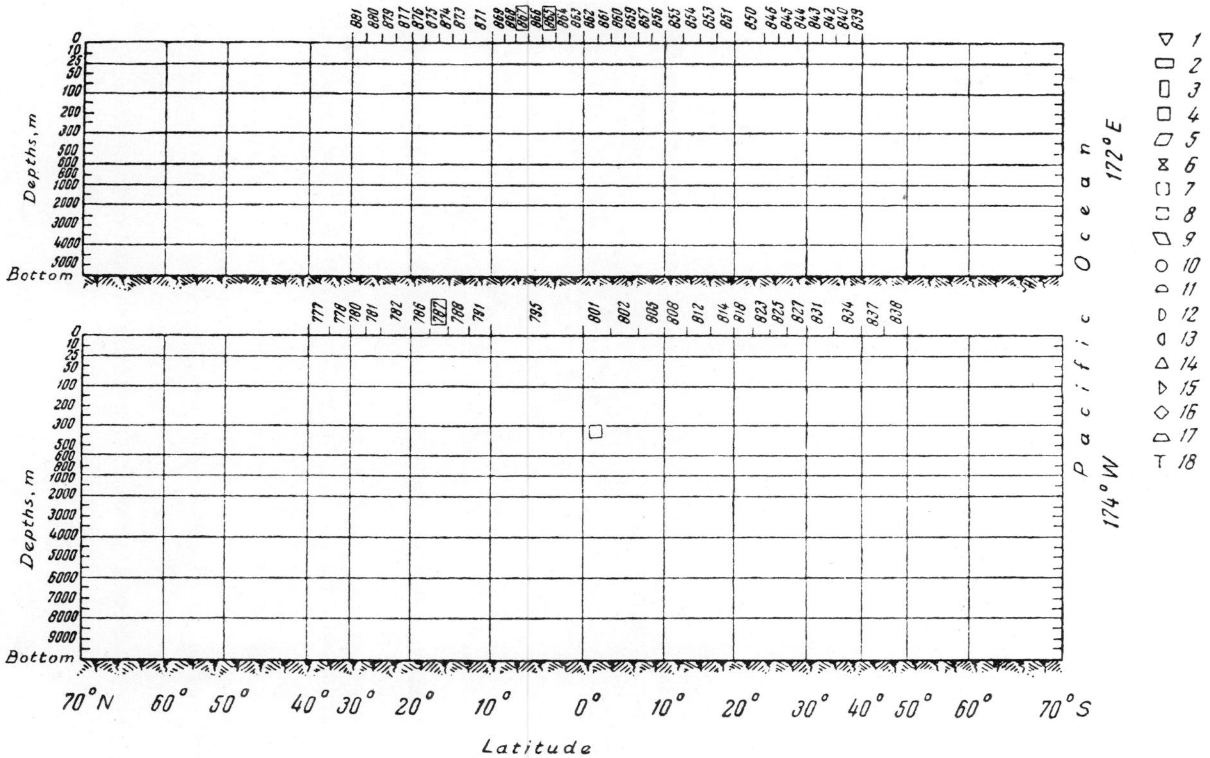

1 - *Bac. catenula*, var. A; 2 - *Bac. catenula*, var. B; 3 - *Bac. catenula*, var. C; 4 - *Bac. catenula*, var. D; 5 - *Bac. catenula*, var. E; 6 - *Bac. catenula*, var. F; 7 - *Bac. catenula*, var. G; 8 - *Bac. catenula*, var. H; 9 - *Bac. catenula*, var. I; 10 - *Bac. idosus*, var. A; 11 - *Bac. idosus*, var. B; 12 - *Bac. idosus*, var. C; 13 - *Bac. idosus*, var. D 14 - *Bac. idosus*, var. E; 15 - *Bac. idosus*, var. F; 16 - *Bac. glutinosus*, var. A; 17 - *Bac. glutinosus*, var. B 18 - *Bac. glutinosus*, var. C

Fig. 8 Distribution of spore-forming bacteria in seas and oceans

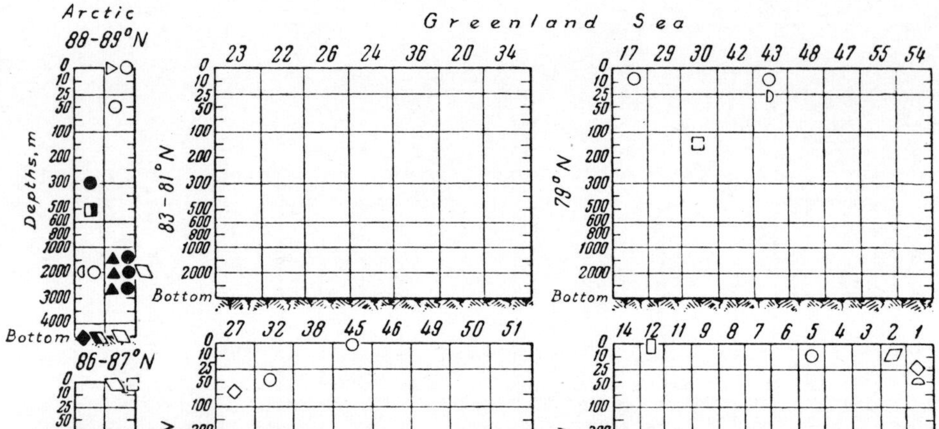

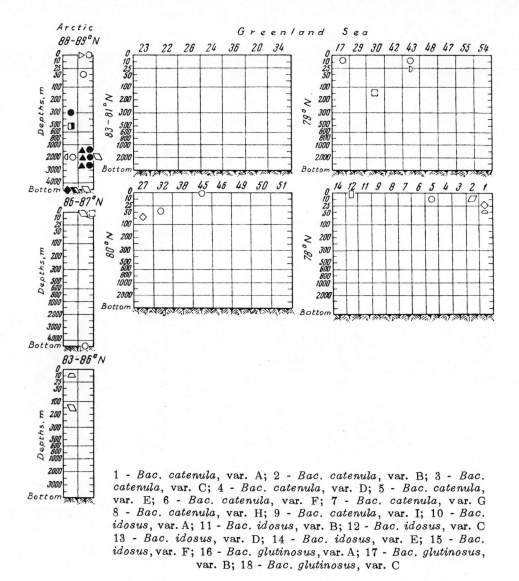

1 - *Bac. catenula*, var. A; 2 - *Bac. catenula*, var. B; 3 - *Bac. catenula*, var. C; 4 - *Bac. catenula*, var. D; 5 - *Bac. catenula*, var. E; 6 - *Bac. catenula*, var. F; 7 - *Bac. catenula*, var. G 8 - *Bac. catenula*, var. H; 9 - *Bac. catenula*, var. I; 10 - *Bac. idosus*, var. A; 11 - *Bac. idosus*, var. B; 12 - *Bac. idosus*, var. C 13 - *Bac. idosus*, var. D; 14 - *Bac. idosus*, var. E; 15 - *Bac. idosus*, var. F; 16 - *Bac. glutinosus*, var. A; 17 - *Bac. glutinosus*, var. B; 18 - *Bac. glutinosus*, var. C

Fig. 8a Distribution of spore-forming bacteria in seas and oceans

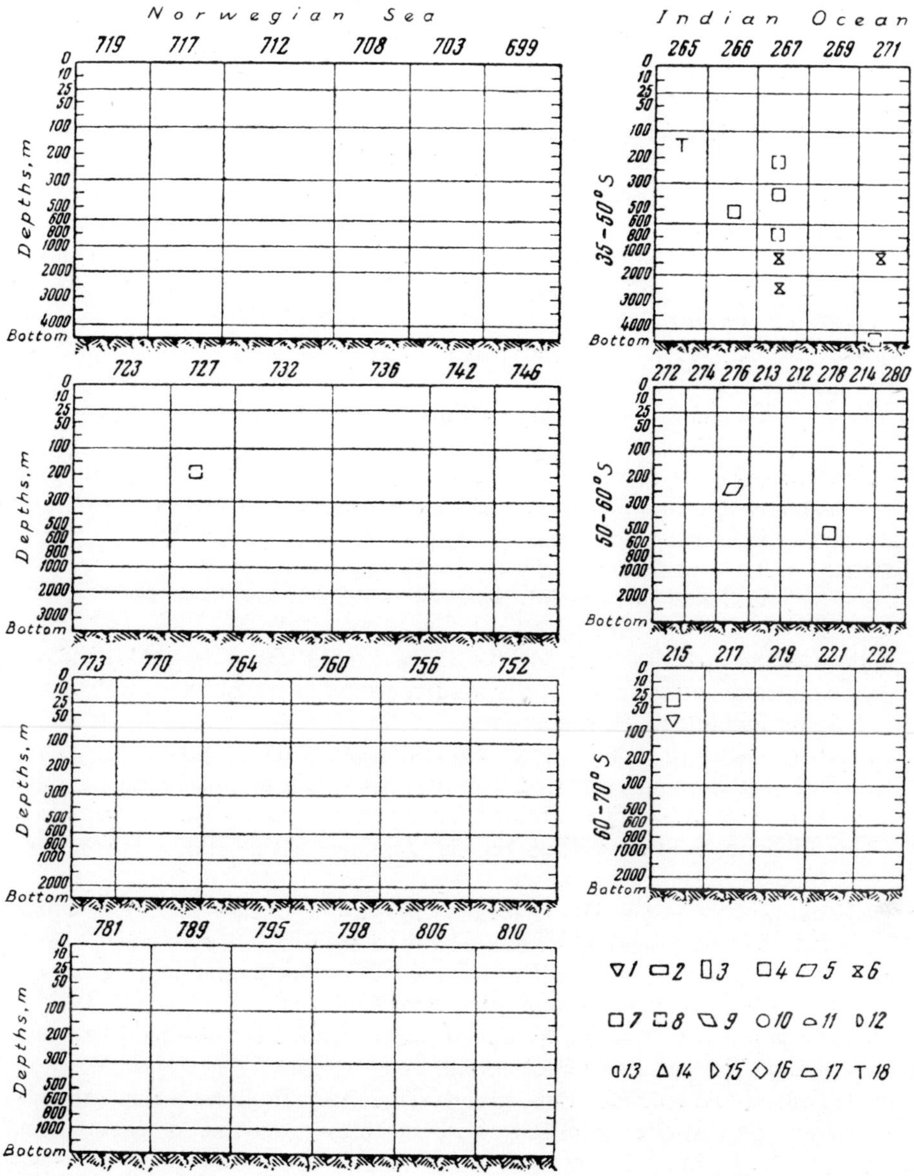
Norwegian Sea
719 717 712 708 703 699
723 727 732 736 742 746
773 770 764 760 756 752
781 789 795 798 806 810
Depths, m
0 10 25 50 100 200 300 500 600 800 1000 2000 3000 4000
Bottom
Indian Ocean
35–50° S
265 266 267 269 271
50–60° S
272 274 276 213 212 278 214 280
60–70° S
215 217 219 221 222
▽1 ▭2 ▯3 □4 ▱5 ⧖6
□7 □8 ◺9 ○10 ⌓11 ◗12
◖13 △14 ▷15 ◇16 ⏢17 T18

From: Arctic Ocean, (st. 88°04′N, 151°16′W), 2000 m;
Greenland Sea, (st. 34), 200 m.

Assigned to aggregate species *B. idosus* Burchard, 1897, var. D.

Spore-forming rods slightly distinguished from var. A by character of growth on media: on meat-peptone agar with wort agar, colonies form folds round centre, resembling a mesentery; on potato and meat-peptone agar with 1% glucose, a red pigment forms. Peptone water with mannitol, glucose, sucrose or maltose acidified.

From: Arctic Ocean water and mud (st. 89°29′N, 65°43′W), 1500, 2000, 2500 m.

Assigned to aggregate species *B. idosus* Burchard, 1897, var. E.

Spore-forming rods distinguished from var. A by yellow pigmentation of colonies on potato and on meat-peptone agar with wort agar. Peptone water with mannitol, glucose, sucrose or maltose acidified.

From: Arctic Ocean, (st. 89°29′N, 65°43′W), 0 m.

Assigned to aggregate species *B. idosus* Burchard, 1897, var. F.

Spore-forming rods $0.6-0.8 \times 2.0-3.0$ μ, joined into long chains. Spores oval, more often than not situated centrally; cells do not swell during spore formation. Gram-positive.

On nutrient agar whitish cinnamon-coloured, shiny streak forms.

On meat-peptone agar, slimy, convex colonies with a shiny surface, which in time becomes dry and folded, are produced. Margins of colonies have a filiform structure. When the cultures are plated out a dissociation effect is observed.

On meat-peptone agar with 1% glucose, growth occurs along the whole line of inoculation and a yellowish leathery film forms on top.

On potato a whitish, slimy film is produced, acquiring dry folding on ageing. The base of the potato slice turns blue or red.

On meat-peptone broth a shiny, folded film is formed and the broth is transparent. The cultures form ammonia.

Milk not peptonized. Gelatine slightly liquefied. Peptone water with glucose or maltose acidified, with mannitol, sucrose or lactose not acidified. Starch hydrolysed. Mineral nitrogen assimilated. Nitrates slightly reduced.

From: Arctic Ocean, (st. 82°55′N, 151°32′E), 0 m.

Assigned to aggregate species *Bacillus filaris* Migula, 1900, var. A.

Spore-forming rods $0.6-1 \times 3$ μ, with oval ends, joined into chainlets, motile. Spores oval-cylindrical, lying near one end of the cell. Gram-positive.

On nutrient agar with sea salt a cinnamon-coloured streak with slight radial striation at the surface is formed. Margin serrated.

On meat-peptone agar with 1% glucose – punctate growth on the agar surface.

On meat-peptone agar with wort agar – whitish, convex colonies.

On pieces of potato immersed in water – growth in the form of a white coating.

On meat-peptone broth – a slimy ring and film, uniform turbidity; ammonia and hydrogen sulphide formed.

Milk not changed. Gelatine not liquefied. Peptone water with mannitol, glucose, sucrose or maltose acidified, but not peptone water with lactose. Starch not hydrolysed. Mineral nitrogen assimilated. Nitrates reduced.

From: Arctic,Ocean, (st. 88°04′ N, 151°16′ W), 250 m;
Greenland Sea, (st. **32**), 25 m; (st. **45**), 75 m;
Indian Ocean, (st. **265**), 485 m.

Assigned to aggregate species *B. filaris* **Migula, 1900, var. B.**

Spore-forming rods distinguished from var. A by acidifying peptone water with mannitol and not liquefying gelatine.

From: Arctic Ocean, (st. 82°55′ N, 151°32′ E), 0 m.

Assigned to aggregate species *B. filaris* **Migula, 1900, var. C.**

Spore-forming rods distinguished from var. A by acidifying peptone water with mannitol.

On meat-peptone agar with 1% glucose, the underside of the colony is pink.

From: Arctic Ocean, (st. 85°53′ N, 27°30′ W), 0 m.

Assigned to aggregate species *B. filaris* **Migula, 1900, var. D.**

Spore-forming rods distinguished from var. A by character of growth on meat-peptone agar with wort agar, where colonies have a pinkish tint.

On meat-peptone broth cultures form a dry, folded film.

Gelatine not liquefied. Peptone water with sucrose acidified.

From: Greenland Sea, (st. **22**), 750 m;
Indian Ocean mud, (st. **326**).

Assigned to aggregate species *B. filaris* **Migula, 1900, var. E.**

Spore-forming rods distinguished from var. A by not liquefying gelatine, by peptonizing milk and acidifying peptone water with sucrose.

From: Greenland Sea, (st. **23**), 75 m; from mud (st. **3**).

Assigned to aggregate species *B. filaris* **Migula, 1900, var. F.**

Spore-forming rods distinguished from var. A by acid formation in peptone water with mannitol and inability to reduce nitrates.

From: Greenland Sea, (st. **22**), 2000 m.

Assigned to aggregate species *B. filaris* **Migula, 1900, var. G.**

Spore-forming rods distinguished from var. A by inability to liquefy gelatine or reduce nitrates and capacity to peptonize milk and acidify peptone water with mannitol or sucrose.

From: Indian Ocean mud, (st. 323),

Assigned to aggregate species *B. filaris* **Migula, 1900, var. H.**

Spore-forming rods distinguished from var. B by inability to reduce nitrates.

From: Greenland Sea, (st. 45), 100 m;
Indian Ocean (st. 256), 1018 m;
Pacific Ocean, (st. 3788), 2034 m; (st. 3795), 0, 518 m.

Assigned to aggregate species *B. filaris* **Migula, 1900, var. I.**

Spore-forming rods distinguished from var. B by inability to reduce nitrates. or acidify peptone water with sucrose and maltose.

From: Greenland Sea, (st. 43), 25 m.

Assigned to aggregate species *B. filaris* **Migula, 1900, var. J.**

Spore-forming rods $0.4-0.8 \times 2.7-5.2\ \mu$, motile, forming long chainlets. Spore lies nearer end of cell. Gram-positive.

On nutrient agar with sea salt – slimy, whitish cinnamon-coloured, shiny streak.

On meat-peptone agar with wort agar – mat colonies, finely verrucose; characteristic structures – bundles of filaments run in various directions from margin of colony.

On meat-peptone agar plus 1% glucose – shiny, folded growth; agar turns brown.

On meat-peptone broth – turbidity, sediment, ammonia formation.

Milk not changed. Gelatine liquefied. Peptone water with mannitol, glucose, sucrose, maltose or lactose not acidified. Starch not hydrolysed. Mineral nitrogen not assimilated. Nitrates not reduced.

From: Pacific Ocean, (st. 3834), 0 m.

Assigned to aggregate species *Bacillus mycoides* **Flügge, 1886.**

Spore-forming rods $0.4-1.2 \times 3.1-6.5\ \mu$, forming long threads. Spores oval, situated nearer one end. Gram-positive.

On nutrient agar with sea salt forms a mat, cinnamon-coloured, finely verrucose streak.

On meat-peptone agar with wort agar – convex, whitish colonies with mat surface, finely verrucose, with villous margin.

On potato – whitish cinnamon-coloured growth with mat surface.

On meat-peptone broth – film, turbidity, sediment.

Milk peptonized. Gelatine not liquefied. Peptone water with mannitol, glucose, sucrose or maltose acidified; with lactose not acidified.

Starch hydrolysed. Mineral nitrogen assimilated. Nitrates not reduced.

From: Indian Ocean, (st. 236), 1526 m.

Assigned to aggregate species *Bacillus cereus* Frankland, 1887, n. comb.

Spore-forming rods 0.5 – 0.9 × 2 – 6 μ, with rounded ends, motile. Spore oval, situated nearer one end; cells not swollen. Long chainlets, which decay into blunt-ended rods, form in the broth. Gram-positive.

On nutrient agar with sea salt – cinnamon-coloured, flat streak, with rough surface and slight transverse striation; streak not easily removed from the agar.

On meat-peptone agar with wort agar – white or yellowish colonies, leathery, with gophered surface, can be entirely removed from agar. Margin undulate, sharply outlined.

On meat-peptone agar with 1% glucose – growth in depth along the line of inoculation.

On potato – no visible growth.

On meat-peptone broth – turbidity, slimy sediment. Ammonia and hydrogen sulphide not formed.

Milk unchanged. Gelatine liquefied. Peptone water with mannitol, glucose, sucrose, maltose or lactose not acidified. Starch not hydrolysed. Mineral nitrogen poorly assimilated. Nitrates not reduced.

From: Indian Ocean, (st. 249), 10 m.

Assigned to aggregate species *Bacillus virgulus* Duclaux, 1887.

Spore-forming rods 1.2 – 1.5 × 4 – 6.6 μ. Non-motile, forming short chainlets. In some cultures characteristic grains are observed inside the cell and near its membrane, sometimes pushing it apart, making the cell verrucose. Spores oval, small cells not swollen, forming nearer one end. Gram-positive.

On nutrient agar with sea salt – a greasy, cream-coloured streak, with even margin.

On meat-peptone agar with wort agar – shiny, rounded colonies, slimy, with even margin. On ageing, the surface of the colonies becomes coarsely folded.

On potato – flat colonies, light cinnamon-coloured, with pinkish tint, ridge-shaped margin.

On meat-peptone broth – liquid transparent, loose sediment; ammonia formed.

Milk peptonized. Gelatine liquefied. Peptone water with mannitol, glucose, sucrose or maltose acidified, with lactose not altered. Starch hydrolysed. Mineral nitrogen assimilated. Nitrates not reduced.

From: Arctic Ocean mud, (st. 88°04′ N, 151°16′ W);
Greenland Sea, (st. 1), 25 m; (st. 27), 75 m.

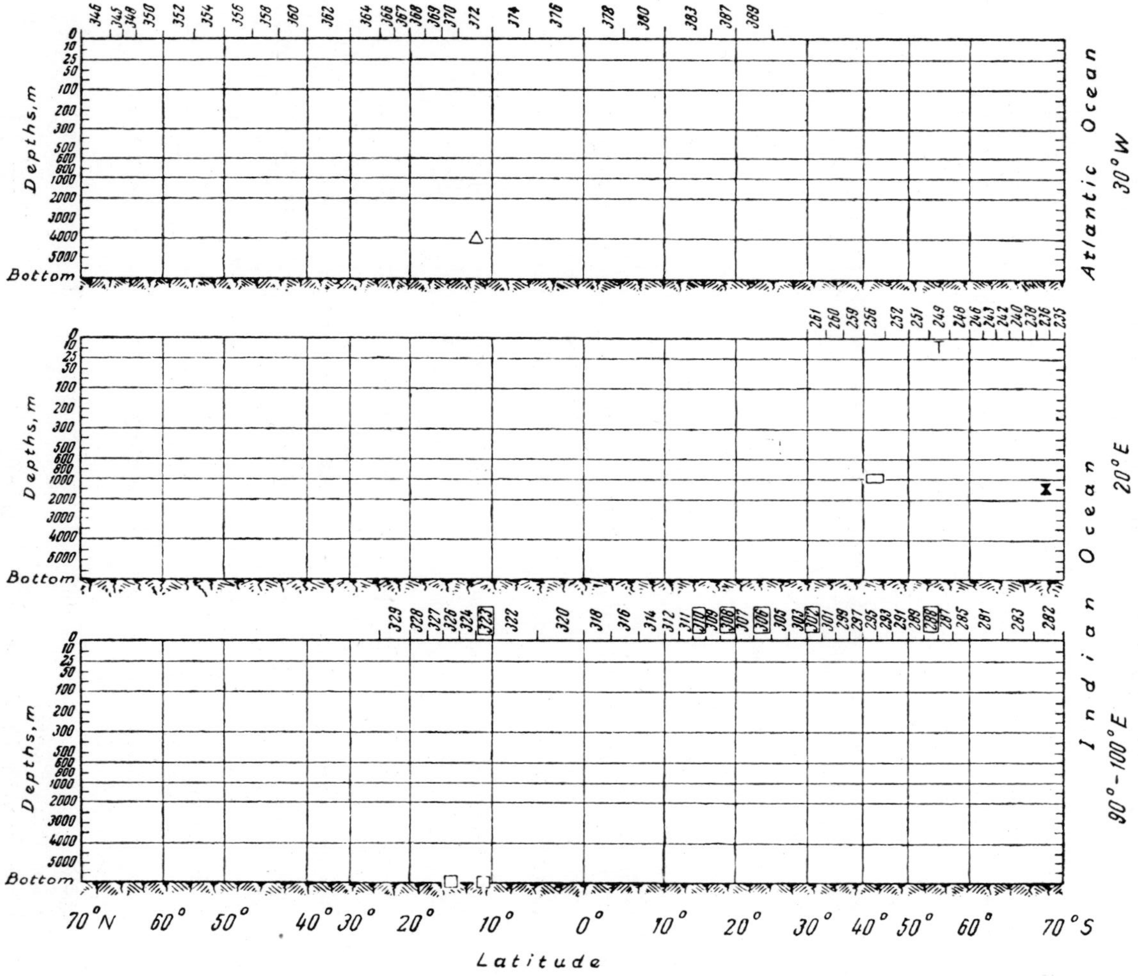
Atlantic Ocean
30°W
Indian Ocean
20°E
90°-100°E
Depths, m
Bottom
Latitude
70°N
70°S

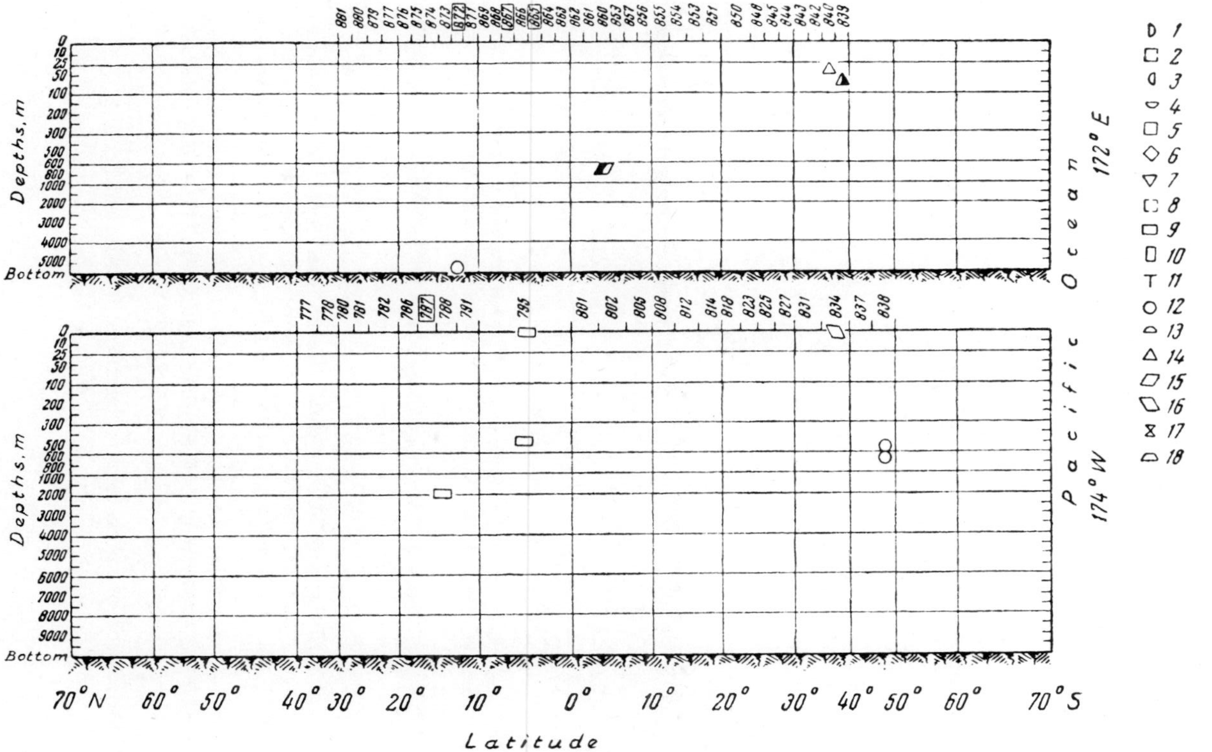

1 - *Bac. filaris*, var. A; 2 - *Bac. filaris*, var. B; 3 - *Bac. filaris*, var. C; 4 - *Bac. filaris*, var. D; 5 - *Bac. filaris*, var. E; 6 - *Bac. filaris*, var. F; 7 - *Bac. filaris*, var. G; 8 - *Bac. filaris*, var. H; 9 - *Bac. filaris*, var. I; 10 - *Bac. filaris*, var. J; 11 - *Bac. virgulus*; 12 - *Bac. brevis*; 13 - *Bac. circulans*; 14 - *Bac. lubinskii*; 15 - *Bac. sphaericus*; 16 - *Bac. mycoides*; 17 - *Bac. cereus*; 18 - *Bac. solidus*

Fig. 9 Distribution of spore-forming bacteria in seas and oceans

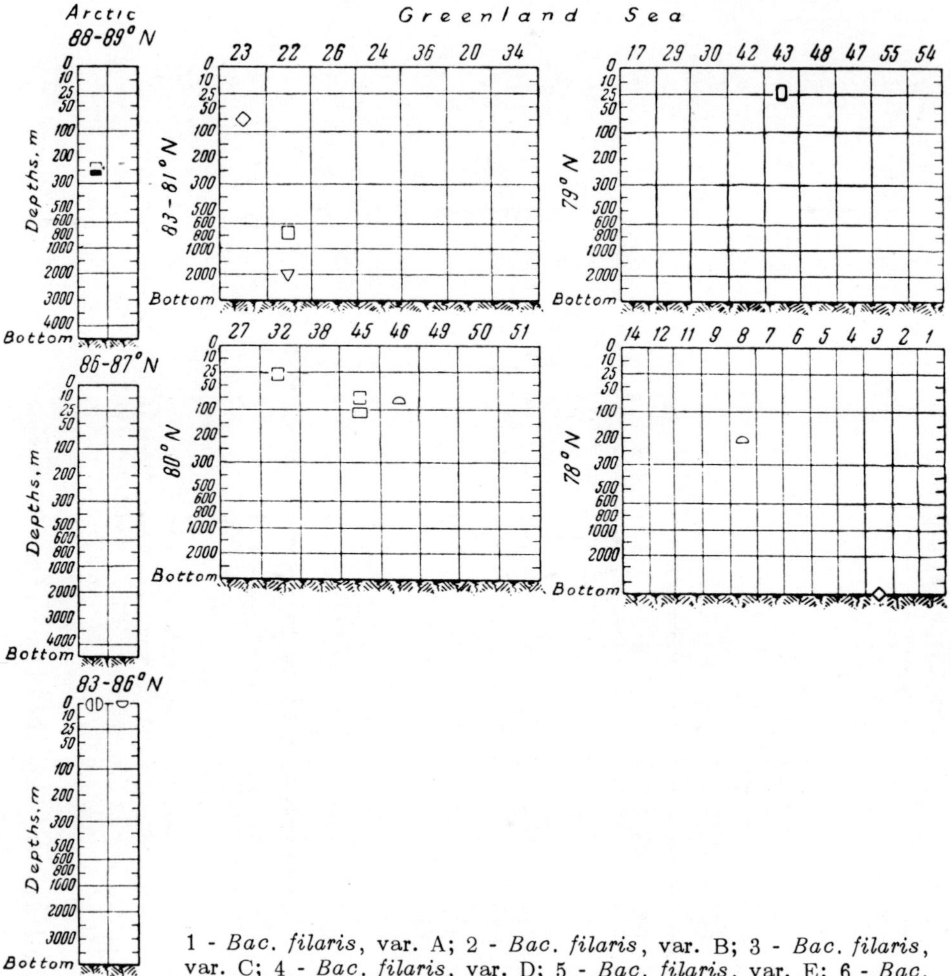

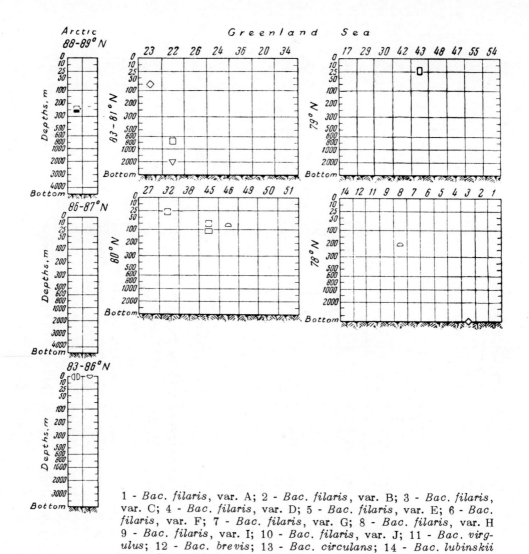

1 - *Bac. filaris*, var. A; 2 - *Bac. filaris*, var. B; 3 - *Bac. filaris*, var. C; 4 - *Bac. filaris*, var. D; 5 - *Bac. filaris*, var. E; 6 - *Bac. filaris*, var. F; 7 - *Bac. filaris*, var. G; 8 - *Bac. filaris*, var. H 9 - *Bac. filaris*, var. I; 10 - *Bac. filaris*, var. J; 11 - *Bac. virgulus*; 12 - *Bac. brevis*; 13 - *Bac. circulans*; 14 - *Bac. lubinskii* 15 - *Bac. sphaericus*; 16 - *Bac. mycoides*; 17 - *Bac. cereus* 18 - *Bac. solidus*

Fig. 9a Distribution of spore-forming bacteria in seas and oceans

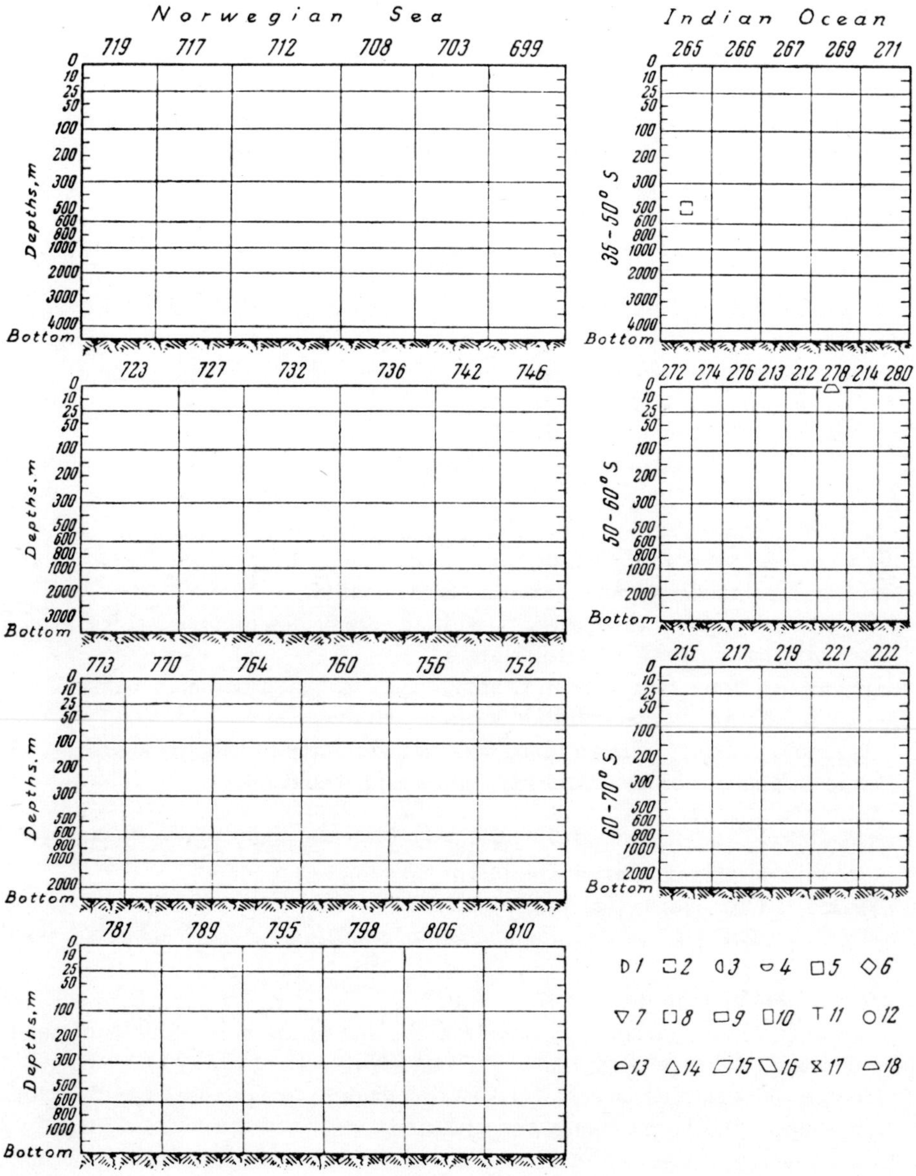
Norwegian Sea
719 717 712 708 703 699
723 727 732 736 742 746
773 770 764 760 756 752
781 789 795 798 806 810
Depths, m
0 10 25 50 100 200 300 500 600 800 1000 2000 3000 4000
Bottom
Indian Ocean
265 266 267 269 271
35-50° S
272 274 276 213 212 278 214 280
50-60° S
215 217 219 221 222
60-70° S
1 2 3 4 5 6
7 8 9 10 11 12
13 14 15 16 17 18

Assigned to aggregate species ***Bacillus glutinosus*** **Kern, 1896, var. A.**

Spore-forming rods distinguished from var. A by inability to acidify peptone water with mannitol.

From: Arctic Ocean, (st. 82°55′ N, 151°32′ E), 10 m.

Assigned to aggregate species ***Bac. glutinosus*** **Kern, 1896, var. B.**

Spore-forming rods distinguished from var. A by character of growth on meat-peptone agar with wort agar, where the colonies are convex, of pasty consistency, with humpy, mat surface. Peptone water with mannitol not acidified.

From: Indian Ocean, (st. 265), 148 m.

Assigned to aggregate species ***Bac. glutinosus*** **Kern, 1896, var. C.**

Spore-forming rods $0.4-0.9 \times 2.1-6.4$ μ, motile, single and in short chains. The large spore lies nearer one end. In spore formation the cell becomes slightly swollen. Gram-positive.

On nutrient agar with sea salt – whitish cinnamon-coloured, shiny streak with transparent, serrated margin.

On meat-peptone agar with wort agar – small, whitish colonies with convex centre, mat, slightly folded surface and even margin.

On potato – dense, whitish cinnamon-coloured streak, smooth, shiny.

On meat-peptone broth – turbidity, slimy ring, sediment.

Milk not changed. Gelatine not liquefied. Peptone water with mannitol, glucose, sucrose, maltose or lactose not changed. Starch hydrolysed. Mineral nitrogen not assimilated. Nitrates not reduced.

From: Indian Ocean, (st. 278), 0 m.

Assigned to aggregate species ***Bacillus solidus*** **Lüderitz, 1889.**

Spore-forming rods 0.6×1.6 μ, motile, single and in short chains. Spore oval, lies at one end or away from the end of the cell, slightly distending it. Gram-positive.

On nutrient agar with sea salt a semitransparent, humpy streak, with villous margin and slight transverse striation.

On meat-peptone agar – semitransparent, humpy streak, pinkish cinnamon-coloured. Margin flounced.

On meat-peptone agar with wort agar – greyish colonies, round, with shiny surface.

On potato – slimy, transparent streak.

On meat-peptone broth – thin film, uniform turbidity, ring. Some cultures form ammonia and hydrogen sulphide.

Milk not peptonized. Gelatine liquefied. Peptone water with mannitol, glucose, sucrose, maltose or lactose unchanged. Starch not hydrolysed. Mineral nitrogen assimilated. Nitrates reduced.

From: Pacific Ocean (st. 3838), 560, 744 m; from mud (st. 3872).

Assigned to aggregate species *Bacillus brevis* Migula, 1900.

Spore-forming rods 0.6 – 0.9 × 4 – 8 μ, motile forming long chains. Spore oval, situated at end of cell, slightly distending it. Gram-positive.

On nutrient agar with sea salt – light creamy, shiny streak with even margin.

On meat-peptone agar with wort agar – transparent, irridescent colonies with uneven, serrated margin.

On potato – transparent streak.

On meat-peptone broth – ring, turbidity, slimy sediment, ammonia and hydrogen sulphide formed.

Milk unchanged. Gelatine slightly liquefied. Peptone water with glucose, sucrose or maltose acidified, with mannitol or lactose not acidified. Starch not hydrolysed. Mineral nitrogen assimilated. Nitrates not reduced.

From: Greenland Sea, (st. 8), 200 m; (st. 46), 75 m.

Assigned to aggregate species *Bacillus circulans* Jordan, 1890.

Spore-forming rods 0.5 – 0.7 × 3 – 9 μ, motile, forming short, coiled chainlets. Spore lies at end or slightly away from it, slightly distending the cell. Gram-positive.

On nutrient agar with sea salt, semitransparent, rough streak, with slight transverse striation, cinnamon-yellowish in colour.

On meat-peptone agar – streak semitransparent, cinnamon-coloured, with pinkish-yellow tint.

On meat-peptone agar with wort agar – transparent, yellowish colonies.

On meat-peptone agar with 1% glucose – slight, transparent growth on surface of column.

On potato – transparent, slimy growth, flocculent sediment and evolution of gas bubbles.

On meat-peptone broth – ring, film, turbidity; ammonia formed.

Milk unchanged. No growth on gelatine. Peptone water with mannitol, glucose, sucrose, maltose or lactose not acidified. Starch not hydrolysed. Mineral nitrogen not assimilated. Nitrates not reduced.

From: Atlantic Ocean, (st. 372), 3946 m;
Pacific Ocean, (st. 3839), 71 m; (st. 3840), 48 m.

Assigned to aggregate species *Bacillus lubinskii* Migula, 1900.

Spore-forming rods 0.6 – 1.1 × 3.0 – 6.3 μ, motile. Spores round, form at end of cells. Gram-positive.

On nutrient agar with sea salt, semitransparent, flat streak. On ageing the cultures form a white coating on the surface of the streak.

On meat-peptone agar with wort agar – small, convex, greyish, shiny colonies.

On potato – no growth.
On meat-peptone broth – turbidity, sediment.
Milk not peptonized. Gelatine unchanged. Peptone water with mannitol, glucose, sucrose, maltose or lactose acidified. Starch hydrolysed. Mineral nitrogen assimilated. Nitrates reduced.
From: Pacific Ocean, (st. **3860**), 677 m.

Assigned to aggregate species *Bacillus sphaericus* Neide, 1904.

8

Species of cocci

Cocci 0.8 – 1.4 μ, single, paired and in short chains. Gram-positive.

On nutrient agar with sea salt – streak greyish-white, with rough surface and undulate margin, which has branched processes here and there.

On nutrient agar without sea salt and on meat-peptone agar with 1% glucose – film with mat surface.

On potato – streak white, shiny.

On wort agar – no growth.

On meat-peptone broth – turbidity, film.

Milk not peptonized. Gelatine liquefied. Peptone water with mannitol, glucose, sucrose, maltose or lactose acidified. Starch not hydrolysed. Mineral nitrogen assimilated. Nitrates reduced.

From: Greenland Sea, (st. **29**), 50 m;
Norwegian Sea, (st. **1789**), 150, 210 m;
Pacific Ocean, (st. **3788**), 10 m.

Assigned to aggregate species *Micrococcus radiatus* Flügge, 1886, var. A.

Cocci 0.4 – 1.5 μ, single and in small, loose clusters. Gram-positive.

On nutrient agar with sea salt – white, semitransparent streak with shiny, slightly humpy surface and even, transparent margin.

On nutrient agar without sea salt – white, convex streak with shiny surface, pasty consistency

On meat-peptone agar with 1% glucose – greyish-white, convex, shiny streak with even margin.

On potato – flat, shiny streak, dirty-white colour.

On wort agar – modest growth in the form of individual greyish-white, small colonies or a slight, semitransparent greyish-white streak.

On meat-peptone broth – uniform turbidity, sediment; ammonia formation observed in the majority of cultures.

Milk not peptonized. Gelatine liquefied. Peptone water with mannitol, glucose, sucrose, maltose or lactose acidified. Starch not hydrolysed.

Mineral nitrogen assimilated. Nitrates not reduced.

From: Atlantic Ocean, (st. **354**), 43, 565 m; (st. **358**), 376, 946, 2817 m; Greenland Sea, (st. **24**), 1000 m; (st. **55**), 200 m;
Indian Ocean, (st. **238**), 77 m; (st. **240**), 76 m; (st. **267**), 518 m; (st. **291**), 10 m; (st. **303**), 51, 101, 2864 m;
Pacific Ocean, (st. **3802**), 3077 m.

Assigned to aggregate species *M. radiatus* Flügge, 1886, var. B.

Cocci 0.8–1.1 μ, single, paired and in short chains. Gram-positive.
On nutrient agar with sea salt—beige streak with shiny, humpy surface. Margin ribbed.
On nutrient agar without sea salt—whitish cinnamon-coloured, shiny streak, pasty consistency.
On meat-peptone agar with 1% glucose—abundant, slimy, whitish-grey growth.
On potato and wort agar—no growth.
On meat-peptone broth—turbidity.
Milk not peptonized. Gelatine liquefied. Peptone water with mannitol, glucose, sucrose, maltose or lactose not acidified. Starch not hydrolysed. Mineral nitrogen assimilated. Nitrates not reduced.

From: Greenland Sea, (st. **48**), 250 m; (st. **49**), 750 m; (st. **50**), 400 m.

Assigned to aggregate species *M. radiatus* Flügge, 1886, var. C.

Cocci distinguished from var. A by cinnamon-coloured tone of streak on nutrient agar without sea salt, meat-peptone agar with 1% glucose and potato and by incapacity to reduce nitrates.

From: Indian Ocean, (st. **280**), 730, 1050 m; (st. **281**), 87 m; (st. **293**), 300 m; (st. **303**), 2864 m.

Assigned to aggregate species *M. radiatus* Flügge, 1886, var. D.

Cocci distinguished from var. B by character of growth on potato, namely, beige streak, convex, with mat, shiny surface.

From: Indian Ocean, (st. **240**), 157 m; (st. **267**), 518 m.

Assigned to aggregate species *M. radiatus* Flügge, 1886, var. E.

Cocci distinguished from var. B by absence of growth on potato.

From: Pacific Ocean, (st. **3823**), 7800 m; (st. **3831**), 69 m; (st. **3853**), 50 m.

Assigned to aggregate species *M. radiatus* Flügge, 1886, var. F.

Cocci distinguished from var. B by inability to form acid in peptone water with mannitol.

From: Atlantic Ocean, (st. **354**), 27 m; (st. **356**), 0 m;
Norwegian Sea, (st. **1717**), 10 m.

Assigned to aggregate species *M. radiatus* Flügge, 1886, var. G.

Cocci distinguished from var. B by absence of growth on potato and inability to form acid in peptone water with mannitol.

From: Arctic Ocean, (st. 88°04′ N, 151°16′ W), 400 m;
Greenland Sea, (st. **45**), 400 m;
Indian Ocean, (st. **318**), 2290 m;
Pacific Ocean, (st. **3843**), 48 m; (st. **3844**), 467 m; (st. **3854**), 73 m; (st. **3856**), 400 m; from mud (st. **3802**).

Assigned to aggregate species *M. radiatus* Flügge, 1886, var. H.

Cocci distinguished from var. B by absence of acid formation on peptone water with lactose.

From: Atlantic Ocean, (st. **358**), 278 m;
Norwegian Sea, (st. **1746**), 100 m.

Assigned to aggregate species *M. radiatus* Flügge, 1886, var. I.

Cocci distinguished from var. B by slight growth on potato in the form of a transparent streak and capacity to hydrolyse starch and reduce nitrates.

From: Atlantic Ocean, (st. **350**), 400 m.

Assigned to aggregate species *M. radiatus* Flügge, 1886, var. J.

Cocci distinguished from var. B by absence of growth on potato and by capacity to reduce nitrates.

From: Greenland Sea, (st. **3**), 100 m; (st. **45**), 10 m;
Indian Ocean, (st. **305**), 2450 m;
Norwegian Sea, (st. **1719**), 800 m;
Pacific Ocean, (st. **3845**), 32 m.

Assigned to aggregate species *M. radiatus* Flügge, 1886, var. K.

Cocci distinguished from var. B by character of growth on series of media.

On nutrient agar without sea salt – flat, grey, dense streak with pinkish-cinnamon tinge.

On meat-peptone agar with 1% glucose – streak slimy, convex, white with straw-coloured tint.

On potato – growth poor, in the form of a transparent streak. The potato turns black. Nitrates reduced.

From: Greenland Sea, (st. **24**), 750 m;
Pacific Ocean, (st. **3831**), 1334 m; (st. **3839**), 48 m; (st. **3845**), 482 m; (st. **3853**), 25, 50 m; (st. **3860**), 26 m.

Assigned to aggregate species *M. radiatus* Flügge, 1886, var. L.

Cocci 0.8 – 1.4 μ, single or in short chains and clusters. Gram-positive.

On nutrient agar with sea salt – white, semitransparent streak with smooth, shiny surface and finely ribbed margin.

On nutrient agar without sea salt and on meat-peptone agar with 1% glucose – greyish-white, convex, shiny streak with even margin.

On potato – white, semitransparent, slimy streak.
On wort agar – growth poor, in the form of a semitransparent, greyish streak.
On meat-peptone broth – uniform turbidity, sediment, ammonia formation.
Milk not peptonized. Gelatine liquefied. Peptone water with mannitol, glucose, sucrose, maltose or lactose acidified. Starch not hydrolysed. Mineral nitrogen not assimilated. Nitrates not reduced.
From: Atlantic Ocean, (st. **350**), 1000 m; (st. **354**), 10 m;
Indian Ocean, (st. **287**), 2020 m.

Assigned to aggregate species *Micrococcus albus* Buchanan, 1911, var. A.

Cocci distinguished from var. A by character of growth on potato, where the streak is very inconspicuous but the potato darkens.
From: Pacific Ocean, (st. **3845**), 15 m.

Assigned to aggregate species *M. albus* Buchanan, 1911, var. B.

Cocci distinguished from var. A by character of growth on potato, where streak resembles var. B, and by inability to acidify peptone water with mannitol.
From: Indian Ocean, (st. **309**), 10 m.

Assigned to aggregate species *M. albus* Buchanan, 1911, var. C.

Cocci distinguished from var. A by absence of growth on potato and inability to acidify peptone water with mannitol.
From: Pacific Ocean, (st. **3791**), 1846 m; (st. **3845**), 997 m; (st. **3850**), 500 m; (st. **3853**), 244, 386 m.

Assigned to aggregate species *M. albus* Buchanan, 1911, var. D.

Cocci distinguished from var. A by absence of growth on potato and inabil- to acidify peptone water with lactose.
From: Pacific Ocean, (st. **3802**), 499 m.

Assigned to aggregate species *M. albus* Buchanan, 1911, var. E.

Cocci distinguished from var. A by inability to acidify peptone water with lactose.
From: Pacific Ocean, (st. **3837**), 982 m.

Assigned to aggregate species *M. albus* Buchanan, 1911, var. F.

Cocci 0.6 – 1.1 μ, single or in short chains. Gram-positive.
On nutrient agar with sea salt – whitish with creamy tint, humpy streak with slightly undulate margin.
On nutrient agar without sea salt and on meat-peptone agar with 1% glucose – individual, small, whitish colonies.
On potato and wort agar – no growth.

On meat-peptone broth – slight turbidity and sediment.

Milk not peptonized. Gelatine not liquefied. Peptone water with glucose, sucrose, maltose or lactose acidified; peptone water with mannitol unchanged. Starch not hydrolysed. Mineral nitrogen not assimilated. Nitrates not reduced.

From: Greenland Sea, (st. 12), 75 m; (st. 32), 25 m;
Pacific Ocean, (st. 3851), 635 m.

Assigned to aggregate species *Micrococcus viticulosus* Flügge, 1886, var. A.

Cocci distinguished from var. A by inability to acidify peptone water with lactose.

From: Greenland Sea mud, (st. 23);
Pacific Ocean, (st. 3795), 0 m.

Assigned to aggregate species *M. viticulosus* Flügge, 1886, var. B.

Cocci 0.4 – 1.5 μ; in young cultures the cells vary greatly in size, some are ovate-oblong in shape. On ageing the cells become more uniform and rounded-oval; singly, paired and in clusters. Gram-positive.

On nutrient agar with or without sea salt and also on meat-peptone agar with 1% glucose – growth poor, in the form of a whitish, semitransparent coating.

On potato, wort agar, meat-peptone broth – no growth.

Milk not peptonized. Gelatine not liquefied. Peptone water with glucose, sucrose or maltose acidified, with mannitol or lactose not acidified. Starch not hydrolysed. Mineral nitrogen not assimilated. Nitrates not reduced.

From: Pacific Ocean, (st. 3825), 490 m.

Assigned to aggregate species *M. viticulosus* Flügge, 1886, var. C.

Cocci distinguished from var. C by ability to acidify peptone water with mannitol.

From: Greenland Sea, (st. 4), 2500 m.

Assigned to aggregate species *M. viticulosus* Flügge, 1886, var. D.

Cocci distinguished from var. C by ability to acidify peptone water with lactose.

From: Greenland Sea (st. 4), 400 m;
Indian Ocean, (st. 278), 380 m.

Assigned to aggregate species *M. viticulosus* Flügge, 1886, var. E.

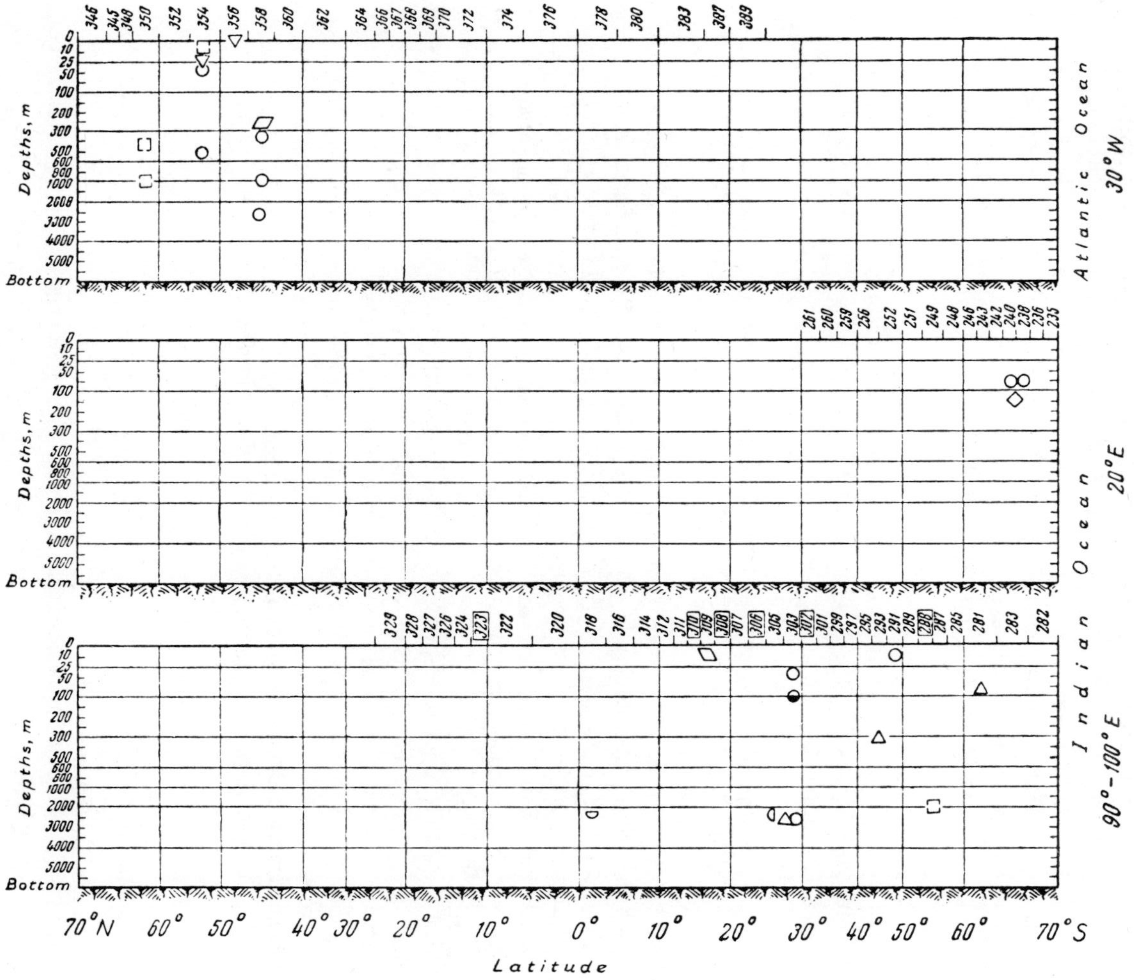
Atlantic Ocean
30°W
Ocean
20°E
Indian
90°-100°E
Depths, m
Bottom
Latitude
70°N
60°
50°
40°
30°
20°
10°
0°
10°
20°
30°
40°
50°
60°
70°S

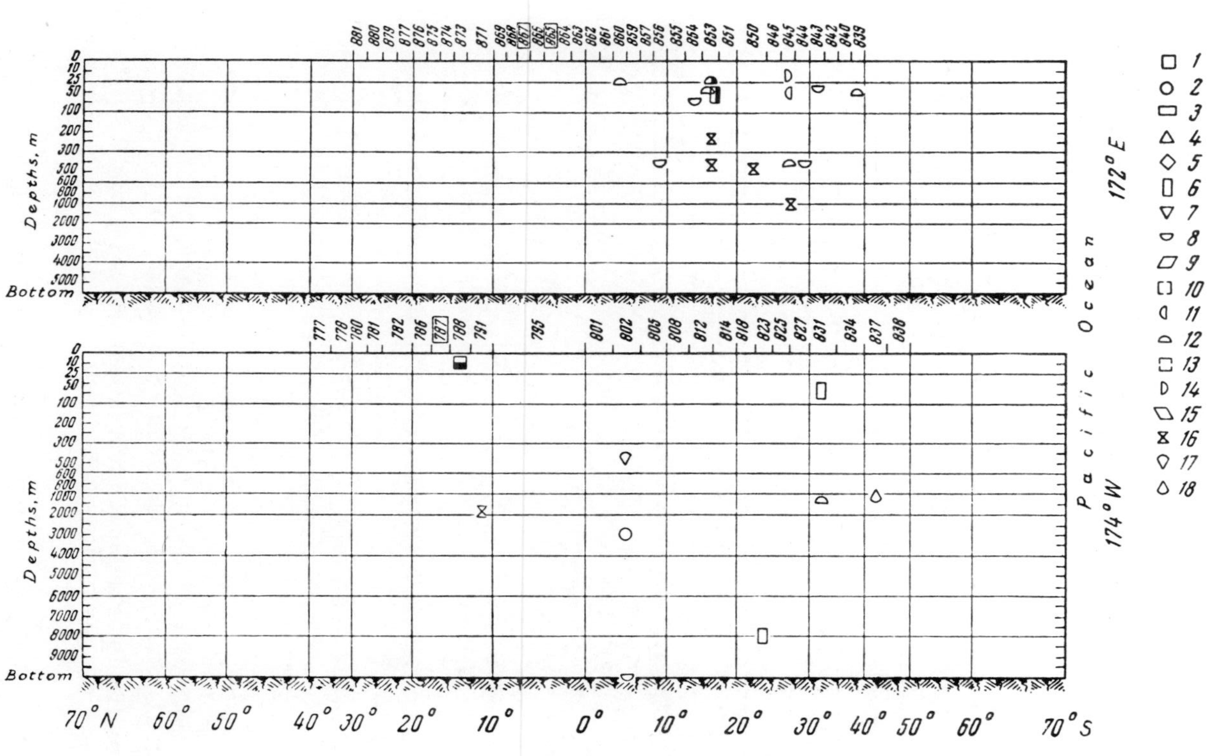

1 - *Micrococcus radiatus*, var. A; 2 - *M. radiatus*, var. B; 3 - *M. radiatus*, var. C; 4 - *M. radiatus*, var. D; 5 - *M. radiatus*, var. E; 6 - *M. radiatus*, var. F; 7 - *M. radiatus*, var. G; 8 - *M. radiatus*, var. H; 9 - *M. radiatus*, var. I 10 - *M. radiatus*, var. J; 11 - *M. radiatus*, var. K; 12 - *M. radiatus*, var. L; 13 - *M. albus*, var. A; 14 - *M. albus*, var. B; 15 - *M. albus*, var. C; 16 - *M. albus*, var. D; 17 - *M. albus*, var. E; 18 - *M. albus*, var. F

Fig. 10 Distribution of cocci in seas and oceans

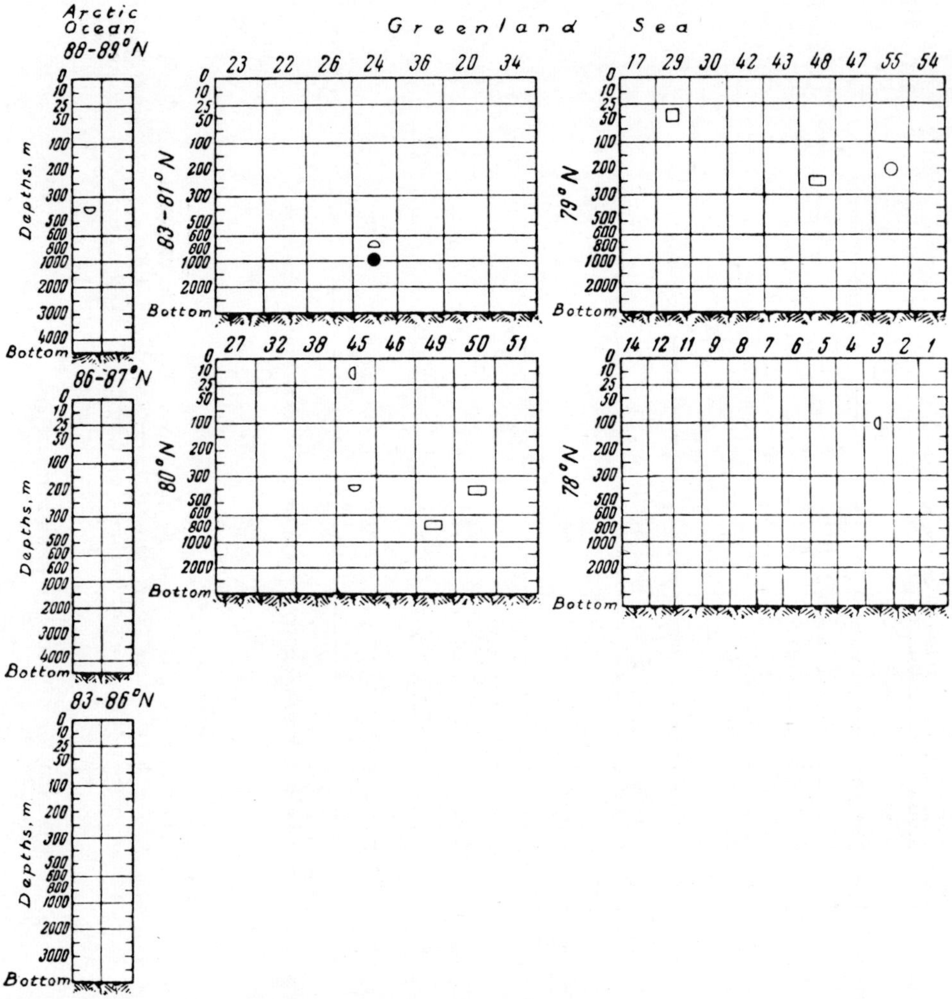

1 - *Micrococcus radiatus*, var. A; 2 - *M. radiatus*, var. B; 3 - *M. radiatus*, var. C 4 - *M. radiatus*, var. D; 5 - *M. radiatus*, var. E; 6 - *M. radiatus*, var. F; 7 - *M. radiatus*, var. G; 8 - *M. radiatus*, var. H; 9 - *M. radiatus*, var. I; 10 - *M. radiatus*, var. J; 11 - *M. radiatus*, var. K; 12 - *M. radiatus*, var. L

Fig. 10a Distribution of cocci in seas and oceans

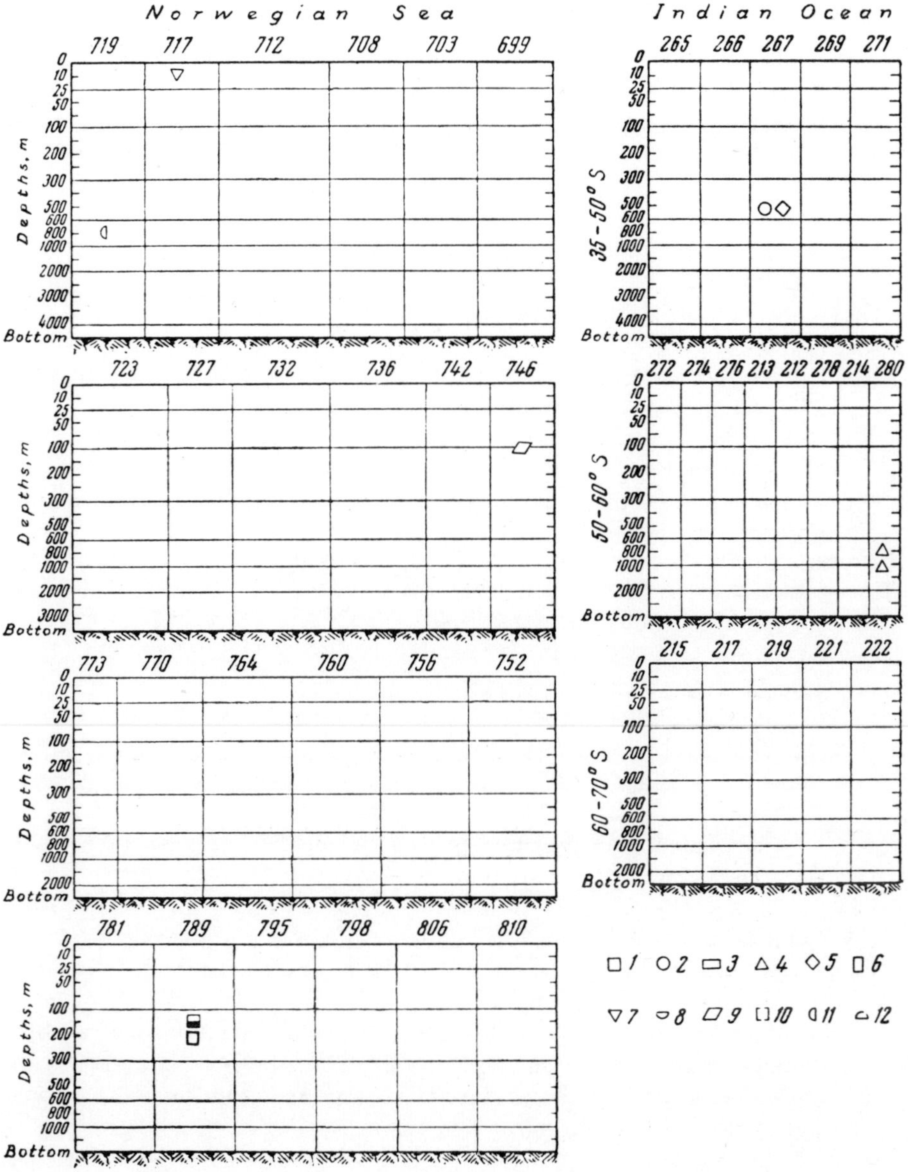

Norwegian Sea
Indian Ocean
719 717 712 708 703 699
265 266 267 269 271
723 727 732 736 742 746
272 274 276 213 212 278 214 280
773 770 764 760 756 752
215 217 219 221 222
781 789 795 798 806 810
Depths, m
35-50° S
50-60° S
60-70° S
0 10 25 50 100 200 300 500 600 800 1000 2000 3000 4000
Bottom
1 2 3 4 5 6
7 8 9 10 11 12

Cocci 0.9 – 1.7 μ, single or forming short chainlets and small clusters. Gram-positive.

On nutrient agar with sea salt – whitish-grey, semitransparent streak with undulate margin and shiny surface.

On nutrient agar without sea salt – streak white, shiny, with slight ivory tint.

On meat-peptone agar with 1% glucose – greyish-white, shiny streak with even margin.

On potato – white, slightly convex or flat streak.

On wort agar – no growth.

On meat-peptone broth – turbidity, ring, sediment, sometimes film; in some cultures ammonia formation observed.

Milk not peptonized. Gelatine not liquefied. Peptone water with mannitol, glucose, sucrose or maltose acidified; with lactose – not acidified. Starch not hydrolysed. Mineral nitrogen assimilated. Nitrates not reduced.

From: Atlantic Ocean, (st. **348**), 78 m; (st. **350**), 94 m; (st. **356**), 28 m; (st. **358**), 136, 578 m;

Greenland Sea, (st. **2**), 200 m; (st. **4**), 500 m; (st. **6**), 150 m; (st. **26**), 0 m; (st. **36**), 1500 m; (st. **38**), 0, 25, 50, 75, 100, 1000 m; (st. **43**), 25, 1000, 2600 m; (st. **51**), 100 m;

Indian Ocean and Antarctic seas, (st. **213**), 10 m; (st. **238**), 121 m; (st. **246**), 362 m; (st. **251**), 2312 m; (st. **265**), 76 m; (st. **266**), 409 m; (st. **267**), 207 m; (st. **271**), 250 m; (st. **295**), 250 m; (st. **303**), 2864 m;

Norwegian Sea, (st. **723**), 600 m; (st. **746**), 150 m.

Assigned to aggregate species *Micrococcus albicans* Trevisan, 1889, var. A.

Cocci 0.5 – 1.4 μ, single, in short chains or clusters. Gram-positive.

On nutrient agar with sea salt – whitish-grey, semitransparent streak with even margin and shiny surface.

On nutrient agar without sea salt – growth modest, in the form of a transparent streak.

On meat-peptone agar with 1% glucose, potato and wort agar – no growth.

On meat-peptone broth – turbidity.

Milk not peptonized. Gelatine not liquefied. Peptone water with mannitol, glucose, sucrose, maltose or lactose acidified. Starch hydrolysed. Mineral nitrogen assimilated. Nitrates reduced.

From: Greenland Sea, (st. **26**), 100 m;

Indian Ocean, (st. **311**), 10 m.

Assigned to aggregate species *M. albicans* Trevisan, 1889, var. B.

Cocci distinguished from var. A by absence of growth on potato.

From: Indian Ocean and Antarctic seas (st. **221**), 192 m; (st. **265**), 76 m; (st. **318**), 2290 m;

Pacific Ocean (st. **3856**), 606 m.

Assigned to aggregate species *M. albicans* **Trevisan, 1889, var. C.**

Cocci distinguished from var. A by acidifying peptone water with lactose.

From: Arctic Ocean mud (st. 89°29′ N, 65°43′ W);
Greenland Sea (st. **55**), 500, 1000 m;
Indian Ocean, (st. **219**), 131 m; (st. **246**), 362 m; (st. **289**), 1500 m; (st. **297**), 2440 m;
Norwegian Sea, (st. **708**), 500 m.

Assigned to aggregate species *M. albicans* **Trevisan, 1889, var. D.**

Cocci distinguished from var. A by acidifying peptone water with lactose and not altering peptone water with mannitol.

From: Greenland Sea, (st. **4**), 1000 m; (st. **38**), 1500 m; (st. **48**), 10 m;
Pacific Ocean, (st. **3791**), 1429 m; (st. **3850**), 777 m.

Assigned to aggregate species *M. albicans* **Trevisan, 1889, var. E.**

Cocci distinguished from var. A by not altering peptone water with mannitol.

From: Arctic Ocean mud (st. 89°29′ N, 65°43′ W);
Greenland Sea, (st. **14**), 45 m; (st. **30**), 10 m;
Pacific Ocean, (st. **3814**), 300 m.

Assigned to aggregate species *M. albicans* **Trevisan, 1889, var. F.**

Cocci distinguished from var. A by producing slimy, semitransparent growth with yellowish-green tint on potato. Peptone water with lactose acidified, peptone water with mannitol unchanged.

From: Greenland Sea, (st. **12**), 50 m.

Assigned to aggregate species *M. albicans* **Trevisan, 1889, var. G.**

Cocci distinguished from var. A by producing transparent, whitish streak with greenish tinge on potato, also transparent streak on nutrient agar without sea salt, and acidifying peptone water with lactose.

From: Greenland Sea, (st. **26**), 10 m.

Assigned to aggregate species *M. albicans* **Trevisan, 1889, var. H.**

Cocci 0.8 – 1.7 μ, single and paired, sometimes forming tetrads. Gram-positive.

On nutrient agar with sea salt – streak consists of individual, small, whitish, semitransparent colonies with even margin.

On nutrient agar without sea salt – growth in the form of small, whitish-beige, convex colonies.

On meat-peptone agar with 1% glucose – greyish-white, semitransparent streak.

On potato and wort agar – no growth or modest growth.

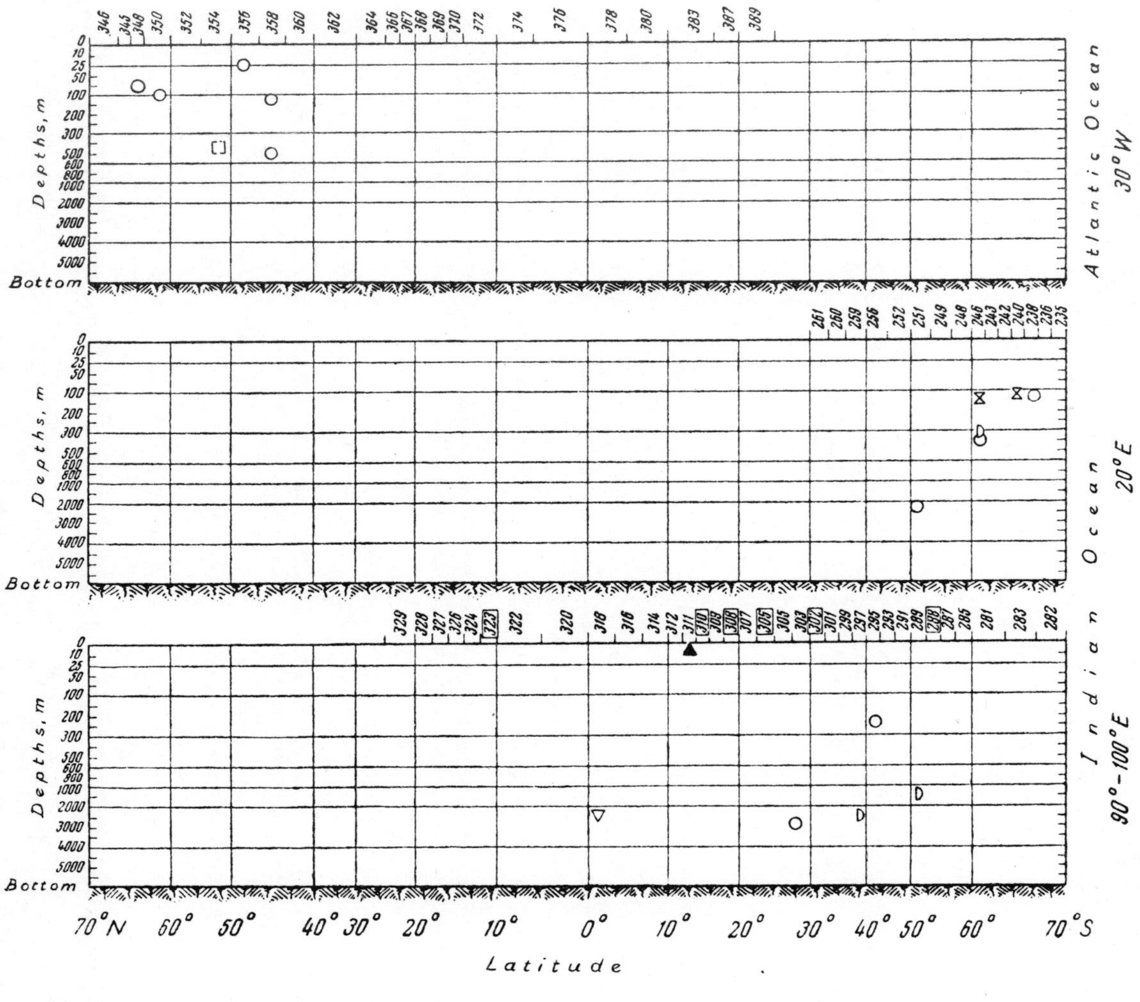

Atlantic Ocean
30°W
Ocean
20°E
Indian
90°-100°E
Depths,m
Bottom
Latitude
70°N
70°S

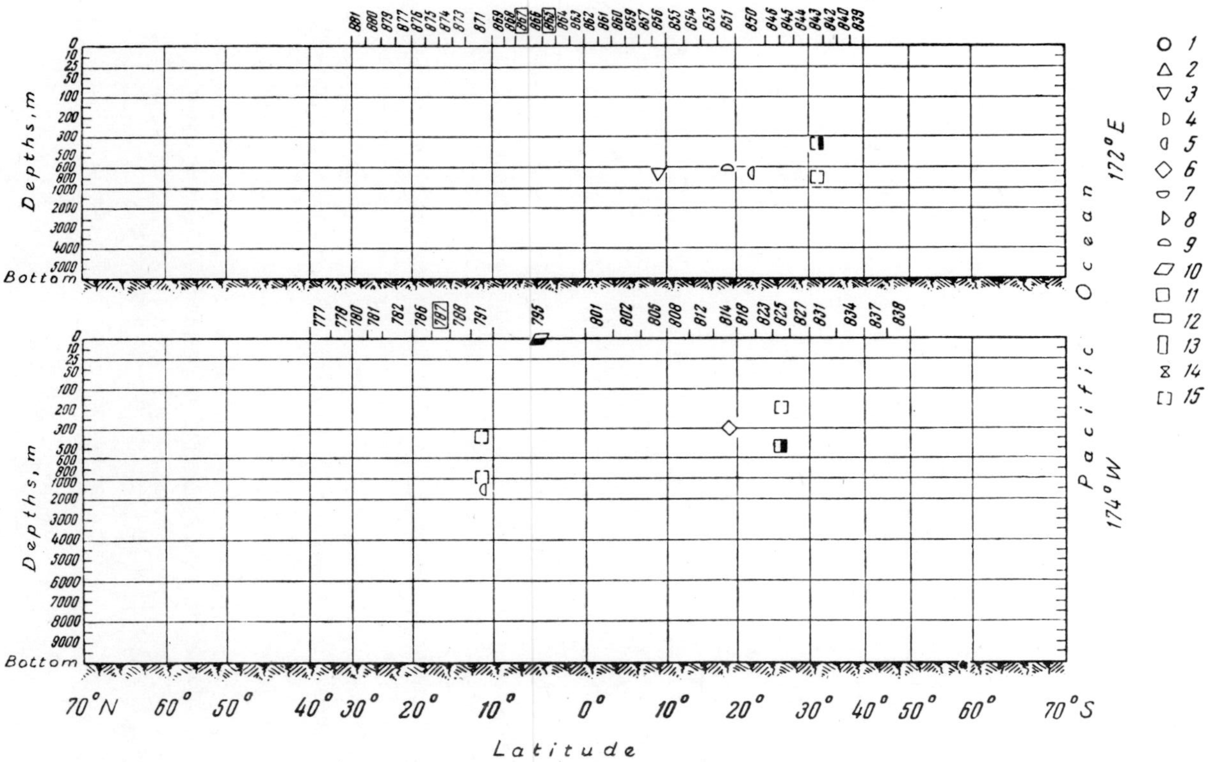

1 - *Micrococcus albicans*, var. A; 2 - *M. albicans*, var. B; 3 - *M. albicans*, var. C; 4 - *M. albicans*, var. D; 5 - *M. albicans*, var. E; 6 - *M. albicans*, var. F; 7 - *M. albicans*, var. G; 8 - *M. albicans*, var. H; 9 - *M. viticulosus*, var. A; 10 - *M. viticulosus*, var. B; 11 - *M. viticulosus*, var. C; 12 - *M. viticulosus*, var. D; 13 - *M. viticulosus*, var. E 14 - *M. tetragenus*; 15 - *M. albescens*

Fig. 11 Distribution of cocci in seas and oceans

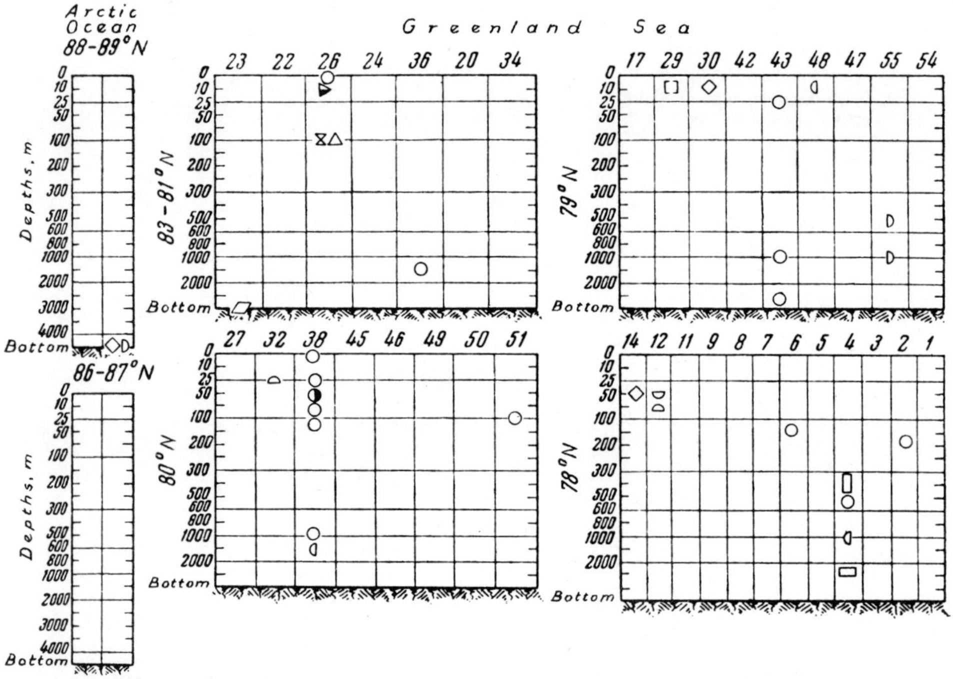

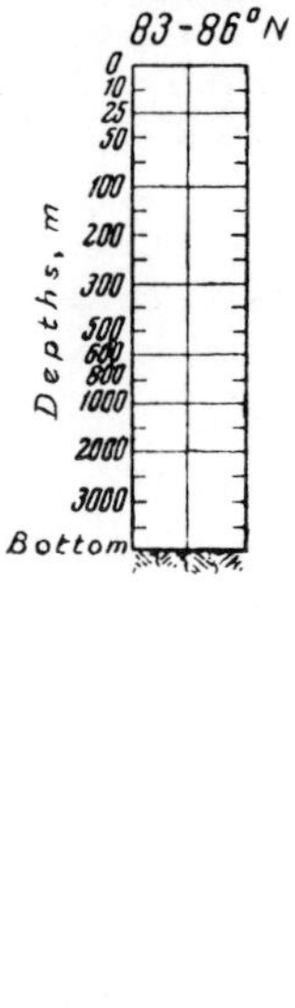

1 - *Micrococcus albicans*, var. A; 2 - *M. albicans*, var. B; 3 - *M. albicans*, var. C; 4 - *M. albicans*, var. D; 5 - *M. albicans*, var. E 6 - *M. albicans*, var. F; 7 - *M. albicans*, var. G; 8 - *M. albicans*, var. H; 9 - *M. viticulosus*, var. A; 10 - *M. viticulosus*, var. B 11 - *M. viticulosus*, var. C; 12 - *M. viticulosus*, var. D; 13 - *M. viticulosus*, var. E; 14 - *M. tetragenus*; 15 - *M. albescens*

Fig. 11a Distribution of cocci in seas and oceans

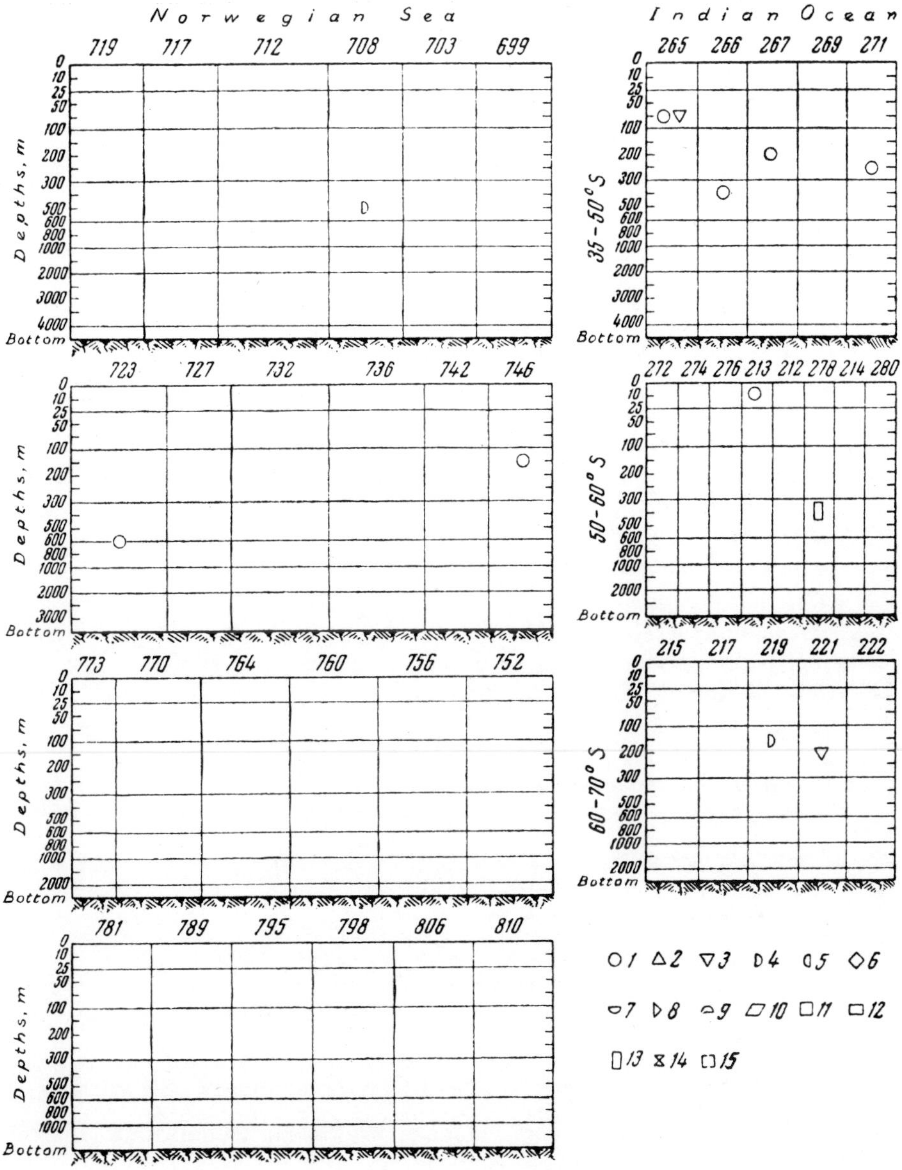

Norwegian Sea
719 717 712 708 703 699
723 727 732 736 742 746
773 770 764 760 756 752
781 789 795 798 806 810
Depths, m
0
10
25
50
100
200
300
500
600
800
1000
2000
3000
4000
Bottom
Indian Ocean
265 266 267 269 271
35-50° S
272 274 276 213 212 278 214 280
50-60° S
215 217 219 221 222
60-70° S
1 2 3 4 5 6
7 8 9 10 11 12
13 14 15

On meat-peptone broth – growth poor, turbidity, some cultures form ammonia.
Milk not peptonized. Gelatine not liquefied. Peptone water with mannitol, glucose, sucrose, maltose or lactose not acidified. Starch not hydrolysed. Mineral nitrogen assimilated. Nitrates not reduced.
From: Greenland Sea, (st. **26**), 100 m;
Indian Ocean and Antarctic seas (st. **240**), 104 m; (st. **246**), 133 m.

Assigned to aggregate species ***Micrococcus tetragenus*** **Gaffky, 1883.**

Cocci 0.7 – 1.7 μ, single and paired, sometimes forming tetrads. Gram-positive.
On nutrient agar with sea salt – growth in the form of individual, small, whitish, semitransparent colonies with even margin.
On nutrient agar without sea salt – growth in the form of small, whitish-beige convex colonies.
On meat-peptone agar with 1% glucose – greyish-white, semitransparent streak.
On potato and wort agar – no growth.
On meat-peptone broth – growth poor, turbidity, some cultures form ammonia.
Milk not peptonized. Gelatine liquefied. Peptone water with glucose, sucrose, maltose or lactose acidified, with mannitol not acidified. Starch not hydrolysed. Mineral nitrogen assimilated. Nitrates not reduced.
From: Atlantic Ocean, (st. **354**), 466 m;
Greenland Sea, (st. **29**), 10 m;
Pacific Ocean, (st. **3791**), 424 and 979 m; (st. **3825**), 188 m; (st. **3843**), 380, 744 m.

Assigned to aggregate species ***Micrococcus albescens*** **Henrici, 1894.**

Cocci 0.5 – 1.5 μ, mainly paired or in the form of tetrads. Gram-positive.
On nutrient agar with sea salt – yellowish-green streak with humpy, shiny surface.
On nutrient agar without sea salt – yellow, semitransparent streak with mat surface; agar turns brown.
On meat-peptone agar with 1% glucose – yellowish-greenish streak with even margin and shiny surface.
On potato – streak canary-coloured, pasty consistency, with even margin and mat, humpy surface. Potato becomes slightly darkened.
On wort agar – streak bright yellow with mat surface and coarsely incised margin.
On meat-peptone broth – turbidity, film.
Milk not peptonized. Gelatine liquefied. Peptone water with mannitol, glucose, sucrose, maltose or lactose not acidified. Starch hydrolysed. Mineral nitrogen assimilated. Nitrates not reduced.
From: Indian Ocean, (st. 252), 2806 m.

Assigned to aggregate species *Micrococcus chlorinus* Cohn, 1872.

Cocci 0.8 – 1.8 μ, paired and in the form of tetrads. Gram-positive.

On nutrient agar: with sea salt – abundant growth of yellowish-green colour, slimy consistency, humpy surface; without sea salt – semitransparent, yellow streak, with mat fine-grained surface, agar turns brown.

On meat-peptone agar with 1% glucose – greenish-yellow, light streak with even margin with shiny surface.

On potato – modest growth of slimy, yellowish-white streak.

On wort agar – no growth.

On meat-peptone broth – turbidity.

Milk not peptonized. Gelatine not liquefied. Peptone water with mannitol, glucose, sucrose, maltose or lactose not acidified. Starch hydrolysed. Mineral nitrogen assimilated. Nitrates reduced.

From: Indian Ocean, (st. **316**), 2870 m.

Assigned to aggregate species *Micrococcus granulosus* Kern, 1897.

Cocci 1.0 – 2.3 μ, often in pairs, short chains or clusters. Gram-positive.

On nutrient agar with or without sea salt – whitish-grey with yellowish-greenish tint, slimy, semitransparent streak with humpy surface.

On meat-peptone, agar with 1% glucose – growth weak, greyish film.

On potato – no growth or very poor growth of individual, yellowish colonies.

On wort agar – no growth or very poor growth, whitish-cream colonies.

On meat-peptone broth – turbidity.

Milk not peptonized. Gelatine not liquefied. Peptone water with glucose, sucrose or maltose acidified, with mannitol or lactose not acidified. Starch hydrolysed. Mineral nitrogen assimilated. Nitrates reduced.

From: Greenland Sea, (st. **46**), 2000 m;
Indian Ocean, (st. **219**), 715 m; (st. **251**), 2312 m;
Pacific Ocean, (st. **3876**), 50 m.

Assigned to aggregate species *Micrococcus subflavus* Migula, 1900, var. A.

Cocci 1.0 – 1.5 μ, single, in short chains and clusters. Gram-positive.

On nutrient agar with sea salt – yellowish-cream streak, smooth, shiny, with ribbed margin. Greenish colour at base of streaks. Agar becomes slightly darkened.

On nutrient agar without sea salt – greyish-beige streak with pink tinge; medium turns brown.

On meat-peptone agar with 1% glucose – slimy, whitish-grey streak.

On potato and wort agar – no growth.

On meat-peptone broth – turbidity, film, ammonia formed.

Milk not peptonized. Gelatine not liquefied. Peptone water with glucose or sucrose acidified; with mannitol, maltose or lactose not acidified. Starch not hydrolysed. Mineral nitrogen assimilated. Nitrates reduced.

From: Greenland Sea, (st. **6**), 0, 150, 200, 250 m.

Assigned to aggregate species *M. subflavus* Migula, 1900, var. B.

Cocci distinguished from var. A by ability to acidify peptone water with mannitol or lactose and inability to hydrolyse starch.

From: Greenland Sea, (st. **4**), 2500 m.

Assigned to aggregate species *M. subflavus* Migula, 1900, var. C.

Cocci distinguished from var. A by inability to acidify peptone water with glucose, sucrose or maltose.

From: Norwegian Sea, (st. **1719**), 400 m.

Assigned to aggregate species *M. subflavus* Migula, 1900, var. E.

Cocci distinguished from var. B by ability to peptonize milk and inability to reduce nitrates.

From: Greenland Sea, (st. **6**), 10 m.

Assigned to aggregate species *M. subflavus* Migula, 1900, var. F.

Cocci 1.1 – 1.5 μ; single or in small clusters. Gram-positive.

On nutrient agar with sea salt – white, semitransparent streak with shiny, slightly humpy surface and even, transparent margin.

On nutrient agar without sea salt – white streak, with shiny surface.

On meat-peptone agar with 1% glucose – greyish-white, shiny streak with even margin.

On potato – slimy, semitransparent streak with white margin and yellowish-greenish centre.

On wort agar – growth in individual, greyish-white colonies.

On meat-peptone broth – uniform turbidity; in the majority of cultures ammonia is formed.

Milk not peptonized. Gelatine liquefied. Peptone water with mannitol, glucose, sucrose, maltose or lactose acidified. Starch not hydrolysed. Mineral nitrogen assimilated. Nitrates not reduced.

From: Atlantic Ocean, (st. **350**), 94 m;
Greenland Sea, (st. **24**), 1290 m;
Indian Ocean, (st. **243**), 2360 m.

Assigned to aggregate species *Micrococcus conglomeratus* Migula, 1900, var. A.

Cocci distinguished from var. A by ability to reduce nitrates and inability to form acid in peptone water with mannitol.

From: Greenland Sea, (st. **29**), 50, 100 m.

Assigned to aggregate species *M. conglomeratus* Migula, 1900, var. B.

Cocci 0.6 – 1.6 μ, single, forming short chains and clusters. Gram-positive.
On nutrient agar with or without sea salt – streak slimy, semitransparent, with yellowish-green tint.
On meat-peptone agar with 1% glucose–growth in yellow streak with shiny surface.
On potato – no growth.
On wort agar – growth in whitish, cream colonies.
On meat-peptone broth – no growth.
Milk not peptonized. Gelatine not liquefied. Peptone water with mannitol, glucose, sucrose, maltose or lactose not acidified. Starch not hydrolysed. Mineral nitrogen assimilated. Nitrates not reduced.
From: Pacific Ocean, (st. **3782**), 2782 m.

Assigned to aggregate species *Micrococcus citreus* Migula, 1900, var. A.

Cocci distinguished from var. A by presence of growth on meat-peptone broth and ability to acidify peptone water with mannitol, glucose, sucrose or maltose.
From: Indian Ocean, (st. **291**), 430 m.

Assigned to aggregate species *M. citreus* Migula, 1900, var. B.

Cocci 0.8 – 1.2 μ, often joined into tetrads. Gram-positive.
On nutrient agar with sea salt – yellowish cinnamon-coloured, opaque streak with humpy, shiny surface.
On nutrient agar without sea salt – yellowish-beige, dense streak with mat surface and even margin; the agar becomes reddish-brown in colour.
On meat-peptone agar with 1% glucose – light yellow streak with mat surface.
On potato – no growth or growth in individual, yellowish-white colonies.
On wort agar – growth of canary-yellow colour with shiny surface and even margin.
On meat-peptone broth – slight turbidity, dense sediment.
Milk not peptonized. Gelatine liquefied. Peptone water with mannitol, glucose, sucrose, maltose or lactose not acidified. Starch not hydrolysed. Mineral nitrogen assimilated. Nitrates not reduced.
From: Arctic Ocean mud (st. 88°04′ N, 151°16′ W);
Atlantic Ocean, (st. **354**), 0 m;
Indian Ocean, (st. **260**), 438 m;
Pacific Ocean, (st. **3814**), 605, 1472 m; (st. **3844**), 282 m.

Assigned to aggregate species *Micrococcus luteolus* Henrici, 1894, var. A.

Cocci distinguished from var. A by good growth on potato; streak of canary colour with mat surface.
From: Pacific Ocean, (st. **3850**), 500 m; (st. **3854**), 25, 298, 397, 595 m;

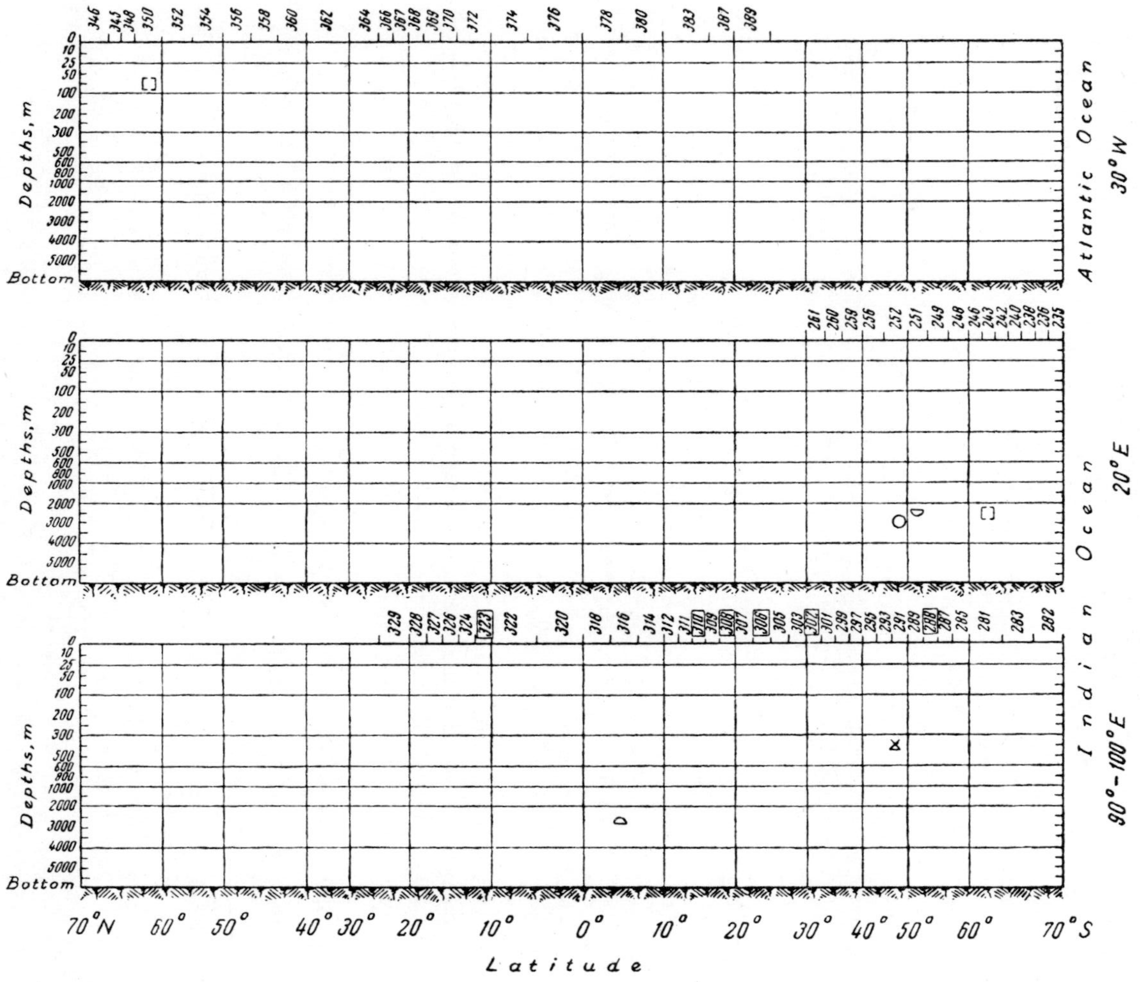

Atlantic Ocean
30°W
Indian Ocean
20°E
90°-100°E
Depths, m
0
10
25
50
100
200
300
500
600
800
1000
2000
3000
4000
5000
Bottom
70°N
60°
50°
40°
30°
20°
10°
0°
10°
20°
30°
40°
50°
60°
70°S
Latitude
346 345 348 350 352 354 356 358 360 362 364 366 367 368 369 370 372 374 376 378 380 383 387 389
261 260 259 256 252 251 249 248 246 243 242 240 238 236 235
329 328 327 326 324 323 322 320 318 316 314 312 311 310 309 308 307 306 305 303 302 301 299 297 295 293 291 289 288 287 285 281 283 282

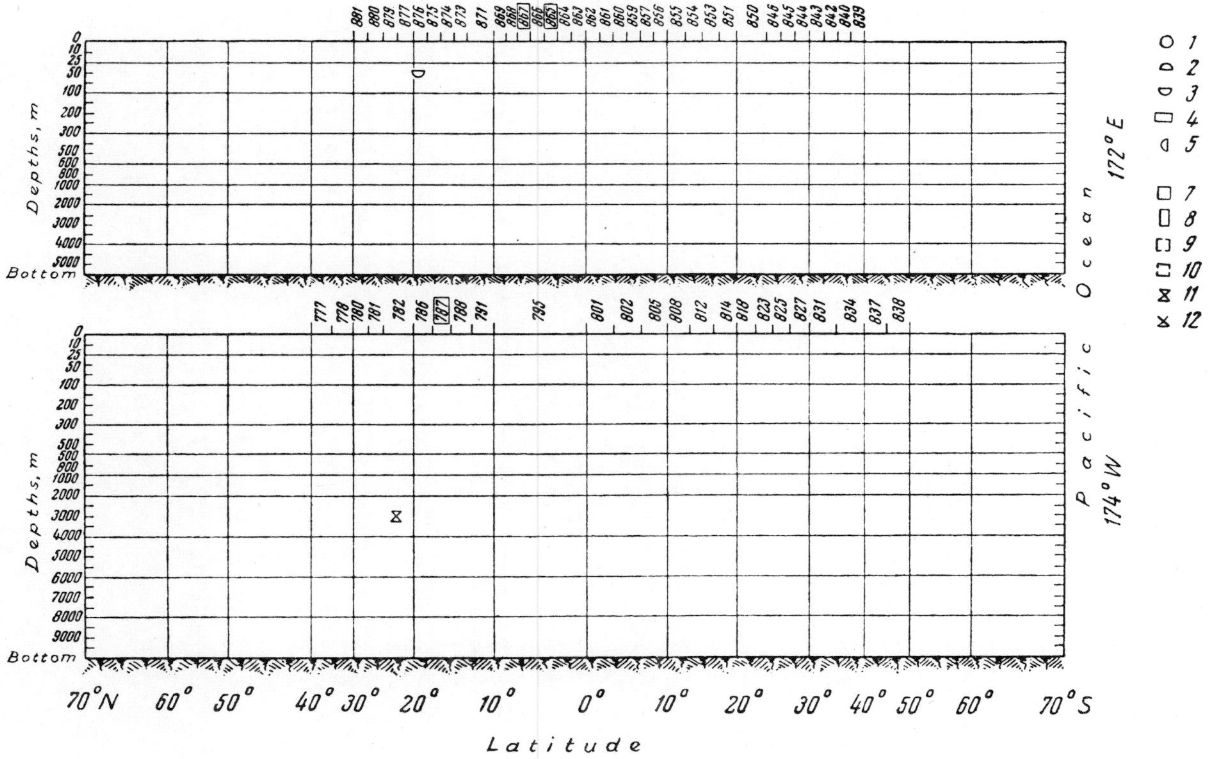

1 - *M. chlorinus*; 2 - *M. granulosus*; 3 - *M. subflavus*, var. A; 4 - *M. subflavus*, var. B; 5 - *M. subflavus*, var. C
7 - *M. subflavus*, var. E; 8 - *M. subflavus*, var. F; 9 - *M. conglomeratus*, var. A; 10 - *M. conglomeratus*, var. B
11 - *M. citreus*, var. A; 12 - *M. citreus*, var. B

Fig. 12 Distribution of cocci in seas and oceans

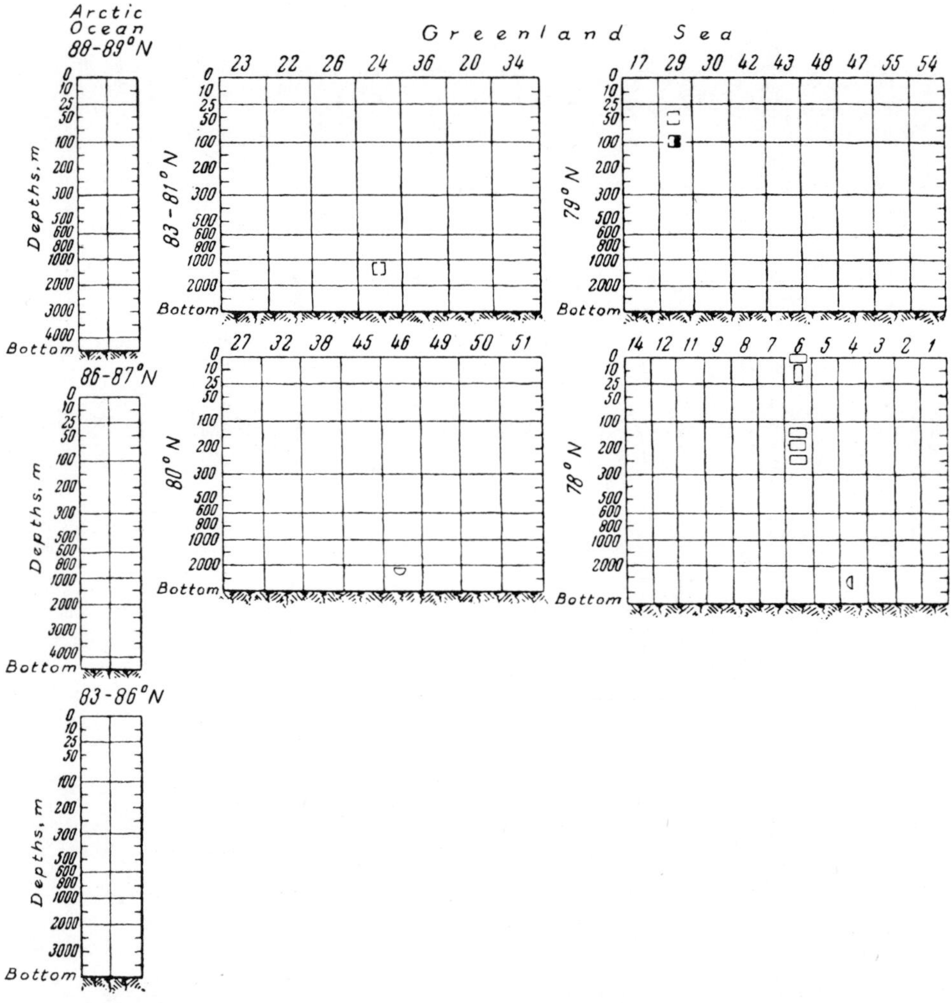

1 - *M. chlorinus*; 2 - *M. granulosus*; 3 - *M. subflavus*, var. A; 4 - *M. subflavus*, var. B; 5 - *M. subflavus*, var. C; 7 - *M. subflavus*, var. E; 8 - *M. subflavus*, var. F 9 - *M. conglomeratus*, var. A; 10 - *M. conglomeratus*, var. B; 11 - *M. citreus*, var. A 12 - *M. citreus*, var. B

Fig. 12a Distribution of cocci in seas and oceans

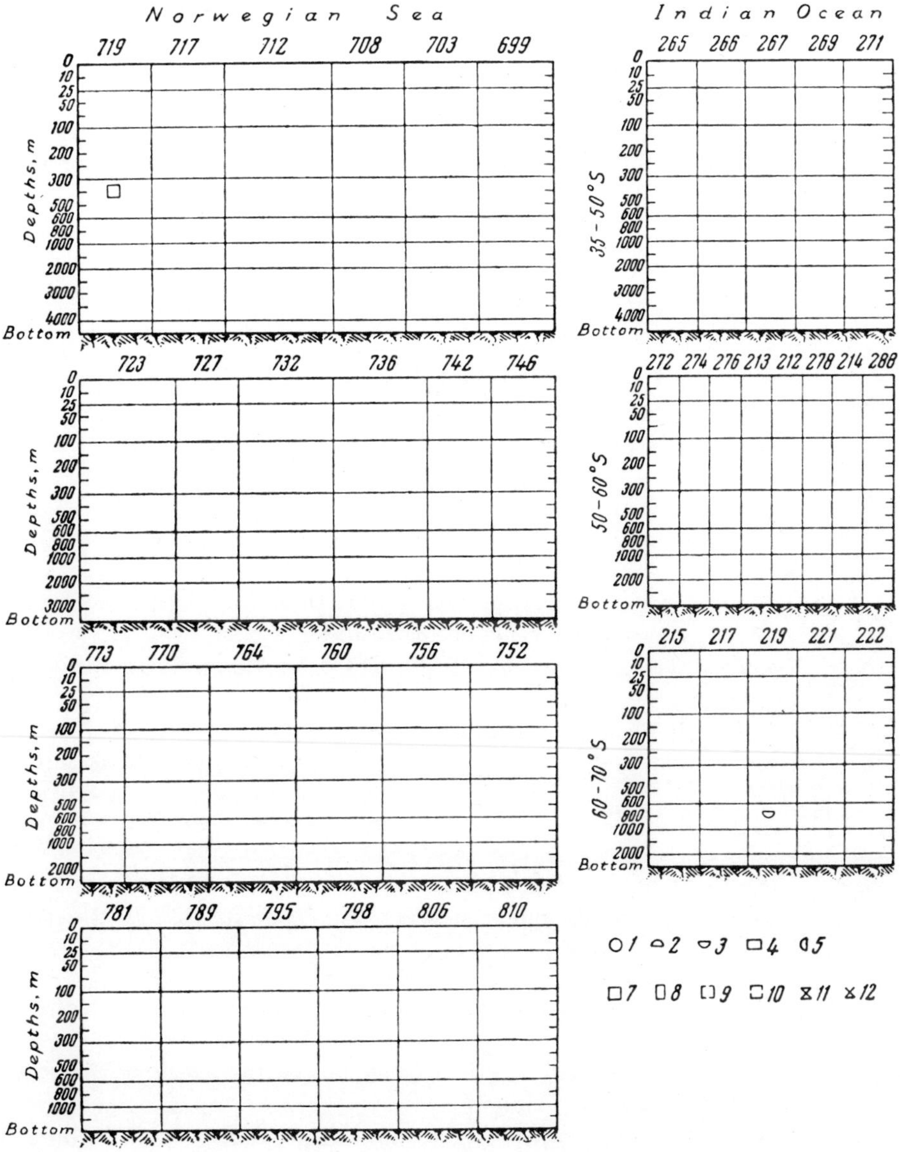

Norwegian Sea
719 717 712 708 703 699
723 727 732 736 742 746
773 770 764 760 756 752
781 789 795 798 806 810
Depths, m
0 10 25 50 100 200 300 500 600 800 1000 2000 3000 4000
Bottom
Indian Ocean
265 266 267 269 271
272 274 276 213 212 278 214 288
215 217 219 221 222
35-50° S
50-60° S
60-70° S
1 2 3 4 5
7 8 9 10 11 12

(st. **3856**), 300, 2960 m.

Assigned to aggregate species *M. luteolus* Henrici, 1894, var. B.

Cocci distinguished from var. A by character of streak on nutrient agar without sea salt and on meat-peptone agar with 1% glucose; streak coloured yellow and transparent.

From: Indian Ocean, (st. **256**), 173 m.

Assigned to aggregate species *M. luteolus* Henrici, 1894, var. C.

Cocci distinguished from var. A by good growth on potato; streak greenish-yellow with mat surface. Starch hydrolysed.

From: Pacific Ocean, (st. **3854**), 397 m.

Assigned to aggregate species *M. luteolus* Henrici, 1894, var. D.

Cocci 0.8–1.4 μ, single, tetrads and clusters. Gram-positive.

On nutrient agar with sea salt – whitish-creamy, opaque colonies with shiny surface.

On meat-peptone agar with 1% glucose – whitish-yellowish, shiny streak.

On potato – growth poor, in the form of a yellowish streak.

On wort agar – streak transparent with secondary growth of small, whitish-cream colonies.

On meat-peptone broth – ring, turbidity.

Milk not peptonized. Gelatine not liquefied. Peptone water with mannitol, glucose, sucrose or maltose acidified; with lactose not acidified. Starch not hydrolysed. Mineral nitrogen assimilated. Nitrates not reduced.

From: Greenland Sea, (st. **32**), 250 m.

Assigned to aggregate species *Micrococcus pallidus* Henrici, 1894.

Cocci 1.3–2.6 μ, often paired or in tetrads, giant cells occur. Gram-positive.

On nutrient agar with sea salt – yellowish-cinnamon streak with small humps on mat surface and even margin.

On nutrient agar without sea salt – yellowish-beige, dense streak with mat surface and even margin. The agar becomes coloured red-brown.

On meat-peptone agar with 1% glucose – yellowish-grey, semitransparent streak.

On potato – weak growth of yellowish coating.

On wort agar – streak reddish-yellow.

On meat-peptone broth – slight turbidity.

Milk not peptonized. Gelatine not liquefied. Peptone water with mannitol, glucose, sucrose, maltose or lactose not acidified. Starch hydrolysed. Mineral nitrogen assimilated. Nitrates not reduced.

From: Greenland Sea, (st. **34**), 75 m; from mud (st. **47**).

Assigned to aggregate species *Micrococcus rugatus* Migula, 1900, var. A.

Cocci distinguished from var. A by inability to hydrolyse starch.
From: Greenland Sea, (st. 34), 400 m.

Assigned to aggregate species *M. rugatus* Migula, 1900, var. B.

Cocci 1.1 – 1.4 μ, single, paired and in small clusters. Gram-positive.
On nutrient agar with sea salt – yellowish straw-coloured, shiny streak with even margin.
On nutrient agar without sea salt – greyish-beige, shiny streak with slight hint of yellow. Medium turns dark.
On meat-peptone agar with 1% glucose – whitish-grey streak with mat surface.
On potato – no growth.
On wort agar – growth weak.
On meat-peptone broth – turbidity, ring, some cultures form ammonia.
Milk not peptonized. Gelatine not liquefied. Peptone water with mannitol, glucose, sucrose, maltose acidified; with lactose not acidified. Starch hydrolysed. Mineral nitrogen assimilated. Nitrates reduced.
From: Indian Ocean, (st. 251), 2788 m.

Assigned to aggregate species *Micrococcus luteus* Cohn 1872, var. A.

Cocci 1.1 – 1.4 μ, single or in short chains. Gram-positive.
On nutrient agar with sea salt – beige, semitransparent streak.
On nutrient agar without sea salt – growth transparent, poor.
On meat-peptone agar with 1% glucose – transparent yellowish, diffused growth.
On potato – slimy, yellowish streak.
On wort agar and meat-peptone broth – no growth.
Milk slightly peptonized. Gelatine not liquefied. Peptone water with glucose, sucrose or maltose acidified; with mannitol or lactose not acidified. Starch hydrolysed. Mineral nitrogen assimilated. Nitrate reduction poor.
From: Greenland Sea, (st. 23), 1000 m.

Assigned to aggregate species *M. luteus* Cohn, 1872, var. B.

Cocci distinguished from var. A by growth on potato in the form of a mat, folded streak of beige colour.
From: Indian Ocean, (st. 274), 175 m.

Assigned to aggregate species *M. luteus* Cohn, 1872, var. C.

Cocci distinguished from var. A by presence of greyish-orange growth with mat surface on wort agar and by inability to acidify peptone water with mannitol.

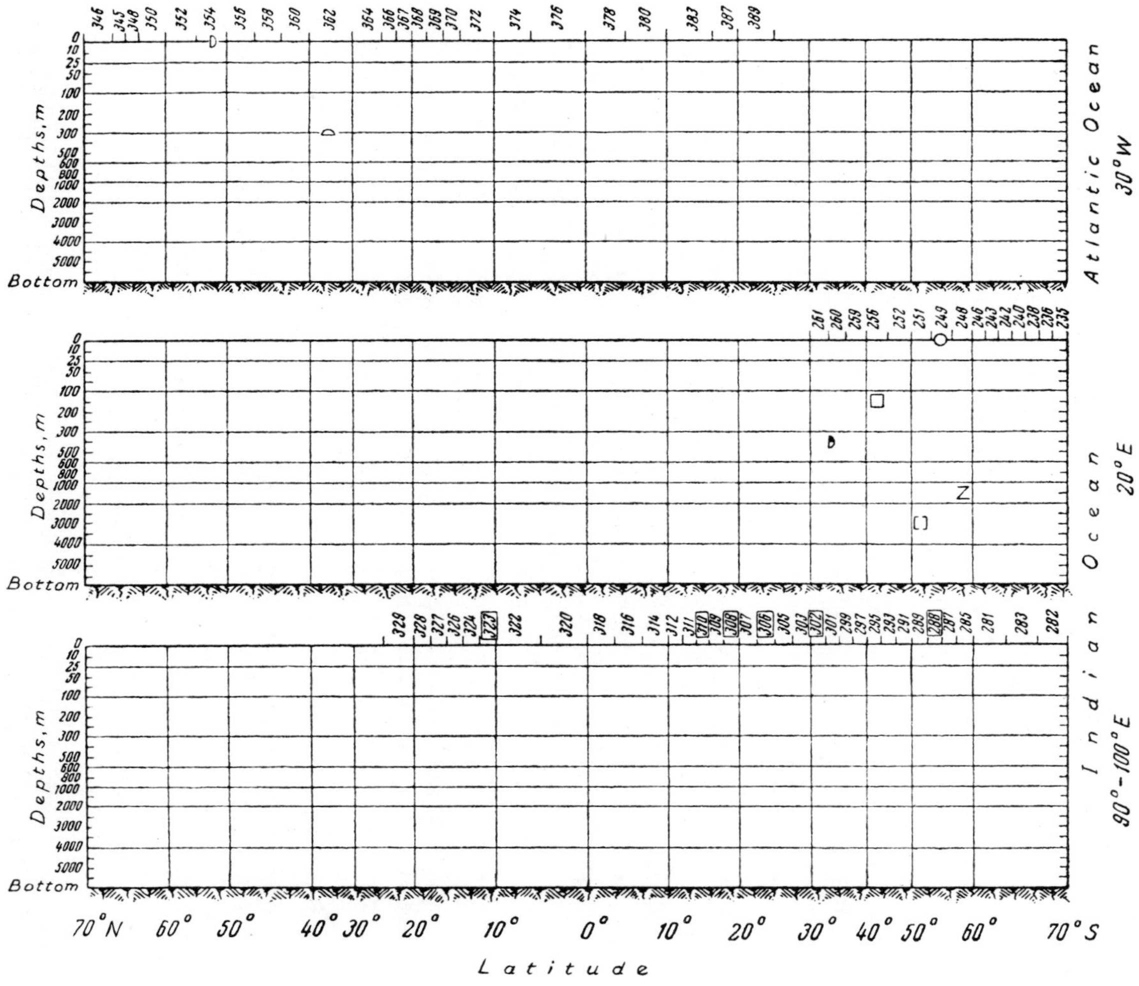
Atlantic Ocean 30°W
Ocean 20°E
Indian 90°-100°E
Depths, m
0 10 25 50 100 200 300 500 600 800 1000 2000 3000 4000 5000 Bottom
70°N 60° 50° 40° 30° 20° 10° 0° 10° 20° 30° 40° 50° 60° 70°S
Latitude

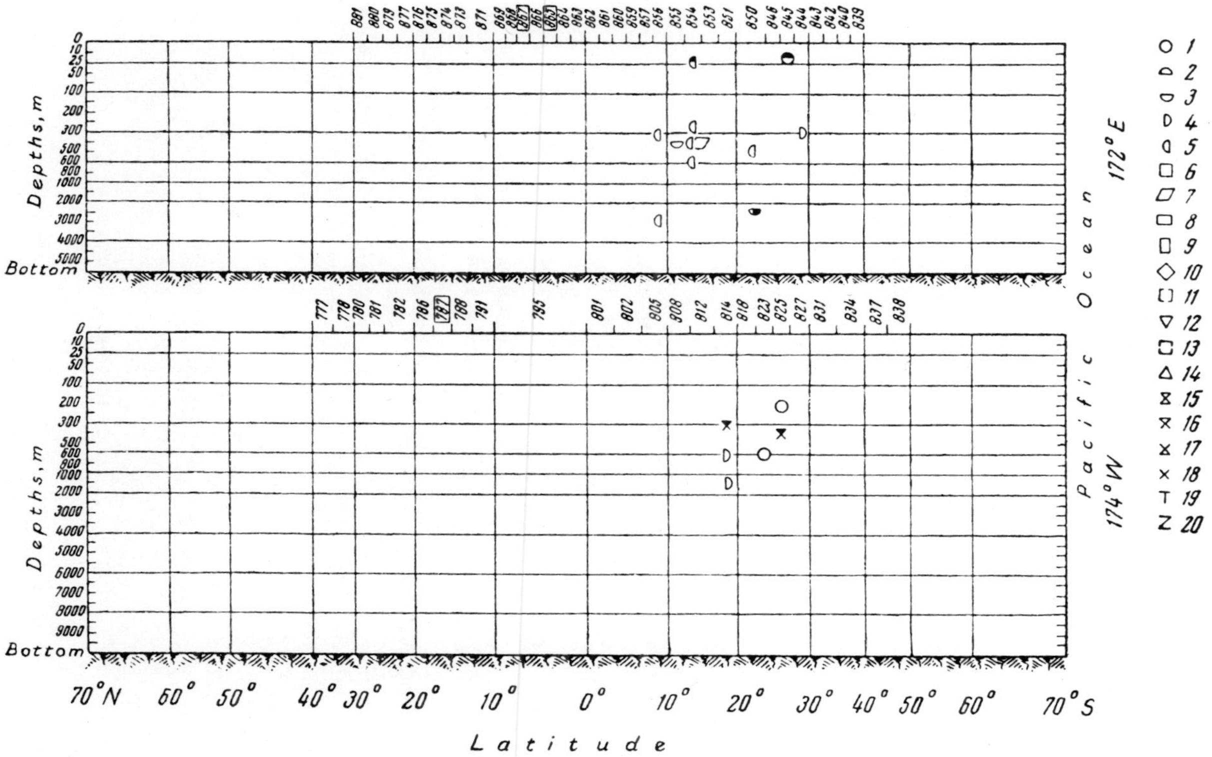

1 - *Sarcina subflava*, var. A; 2 - *Sarcina subflava*, var. B; 3 - *Sarcina luteola*; 4 - *M. luteolus*, var. A; 5 - *M. luteolus*, var. B; 6 - *M. luteolus*, var. C; 7 - *M. luteolus*, var. D; 8 - *M. pallidus*; 9 - *M. rugatus*, var. A; 10 - *M. rugatus*, var. B; 11 - *M. luteus*, var. A; 12 - *M. luteus*, var. B; 13 - *M. luteus*, var. C; 14 - *M. luteus*, var. D; 15 - *M. ochraceus*, var. A; 16 - *M. ochraceus*, var. B; 17 - *M. ochraceus*, var. C; 18 - *M. ochraceus*, var. D; 19 - *M. ochraceus*, var. E; 20 - *M. sulfureus*

Fig. 13 Distribution of cocci in seas and oceans

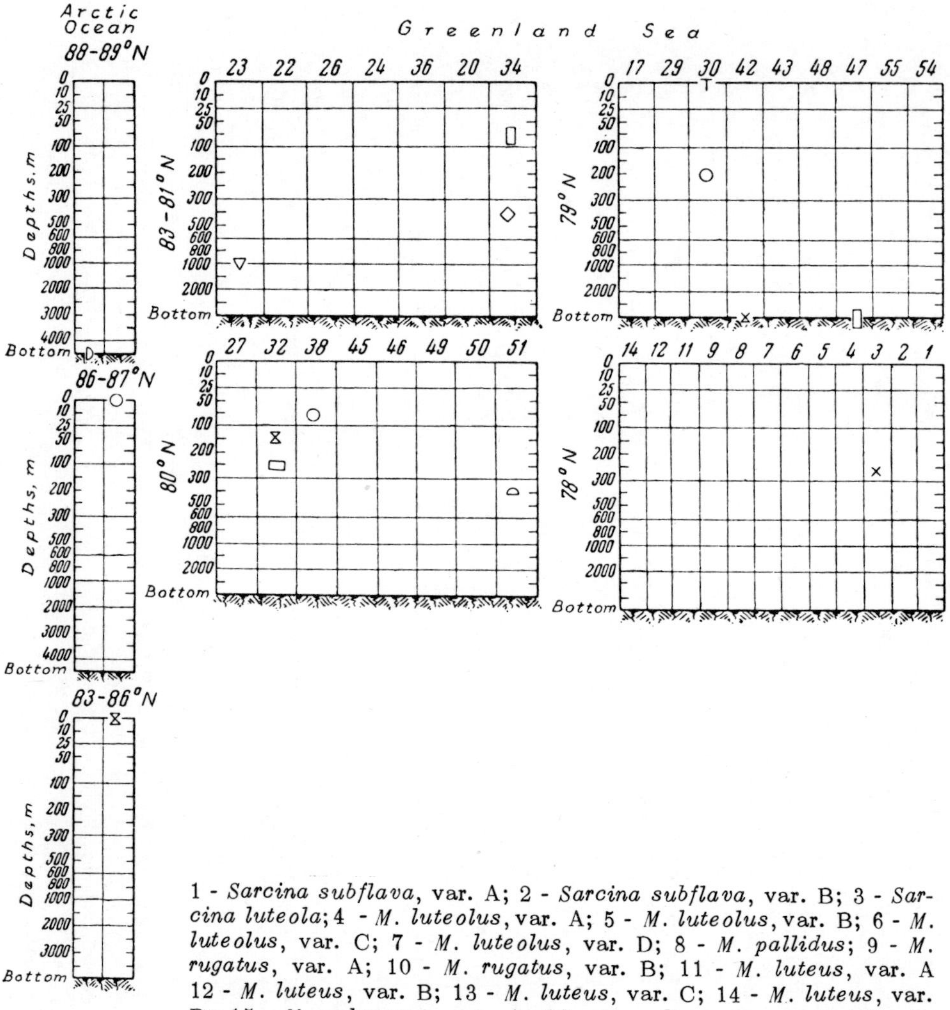

1 - *Sarcina subflava*, var. A; 2 - *Sarcina subflava*, var. B; 3 - *Sarcina luteola*; 4 - *M. luteolus*, var. A; 5 - *M. luteolus*, var. B; 6 - *M. luteolus*, var. C; 7 - *M. luteolus*, var. D; 8 - *M. pallidus*; 9 - *M. rugatus*, var. A; 10 - *M. rugatus*, var. B; 11 - *M. luteus*, var. A 12 - *M. luteus*, var. B; 13 - *M. luteus*, var. C; 14 - *M. luteus*, var. D; 15 - *M. ochraceus*, var. A; 16 - *M. ochraceus*, var. B; 17 - *M. ochraceus*, var. C; 18 - *M. ochraceus*, var. D; 19 - *M. ochraceus*, var. E; 20 - *M. sulfureus*

Fig. 13a Distribution of cocci in seas and oceans

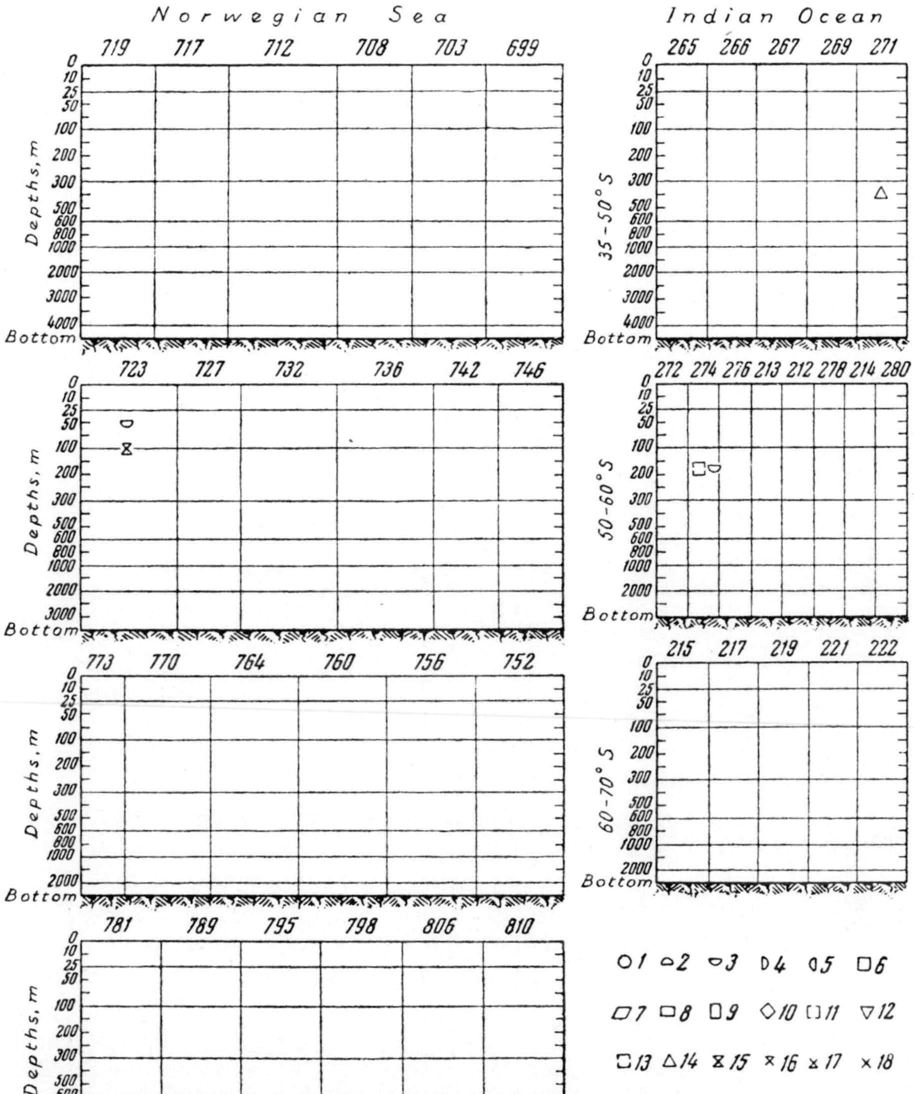
Norwegian Sea
Indian Ocean
Depths, m
Bottom
35-50° S
50-60° S
60-70° S
O 1 2 3 4 5 6
7 8 9 10 11 12
13 14 15 16 17 18
19 20

From: Indian Ocean, (st. 271), 396 m.

Assigned to aggregate species *M. luteus* **Cohn, 1872, var. D.**

Cocci 1.5–2.7 μ, single, in pairs or in small clusters. Gram-positive.

On nutrient agar with sea salt – streak has at first a yellowish-beige and then on ageing a yellow colour. Surface of streak uneven, shiny. Margin even, semitransparent.

On nutrient agar without sea salt – yellowish-beige, dense streak, with even margin and mat surface. A reddish-brown pigment is secreted into the agar.

On meat-peptone agar with 1% glucose – light yellow streak with mat surface.

On potato and wort agar – canary-yellow growth with mat surface.

On meat-peptone broth – turbidity.

Milk not peptonized. Gelatine not liquefied. Peptone water with mannitol, glucose, sucrose, maltose or lactose not acidified. Starch hydrolysed. Mineral nitrogen assimilated. Nitrates not reduced.

From: Arctic Ocean, (st. 85°53′ N, 27°30′ W), 0 m;
Greenland Sea, (st. 32), 150 m;
Norwegian Sea, (st. 723), 100 m.

Assigned to aggregate species *Micrococcus ochraceus* **Rosenthal, 1893, var. A.**

Cocci distinguished from var. A by inability to hydrolyse starch.

From: Pacific Ocean, (st. 3814), 300 m; (st. 3825), 390 m.

Assigned to aggregate species *M. ochraceus* **Rosenthal, 1893, var. B.**

Cocci distinguished from var. A by causing blackening of nutrient agar without sea salt. Acid in peptone water with glucose, sucrose or maltose.

From: Greenland Sea mud, (st. 42).

Assigned to aggregate species *M. ochraceus* **Rosenthal, 1893, var. C.**

Cocci distinguished from var. A by causing blackening of nutrient agar without sea salt. Acid in peptone water with glucose, sucrose, maltose or lactose. Nitrates reduced.

From: Greenland Sea, (st. 3), 250 m.

Assigned to aggregate species *M. ochraceus* **Rosenthal, 1893, var. D.**

Cocci distinguished from var. A by forming acid in peptone water with mannitol, glucose, sucrose, maltose or lactose, reducing nitrates and not hydrolysing starch.

From: Greenland Sea, (st. 30), 0 m.

Assigned to aggregate species *M. ochraceus* Rosenthal, 1893, var. E.

Cocci 0.6 – 1.2 μ, single, in pairs or in small clusters. Gram-positive.

On nutrient agar with sea salt – streak at first yellow-beige, then yellow on ageing. Surface of streak uneven, shiny. Margin even, semitransparent.

On nutrient agar without sea salt – yellowish-beige, dense streak, with even margin and mat surface. Agar acquires red-brown coloration.

On meat-peptone agar with 1% glucose – streak light yellow, with mat surface.

On potato and wort agar – canary-coloured growth with mat surface.

On meat-peptone broth – turbidity.

Milk not peptonized. Gelatine not liquefied. Peptone water with mannitol, glucose, sucrose, maltose or lactose not acidified. Starch not hydrolysed. Mineral nitrogen not assimilated. Nitrates not reduced.

From: Indian Ocean, (st. 248), 1572 m.

Assigned to aggregate species *Micrococcus sulfureus* Zimmermann, 1890.

Cocci 0.6 – 1.0 μ, single, paired or in short chains. Gram-positive.

On nutrient agar with sea salt – cinnamon-coloured, semitransparent streak with even, shiny surface and scalloped margin.

On nutrient agar without sea salt – streak of individual, grey, flat colonies, with a pinkish-cinnamon tinge.

On meat-peptone agar with 1% glucose – creamy-pink, shiny, transparent streak.

On potato – transparent, flat streak, rust-coloured, with uneven margin.

On wort agar – growth poor.

On meat-peptone broth – turbidity.

Milk not peptonized. Gelatine liquefied. Peptone water with mannitol, glucose, sucrose, maltose or lactose acidified. Starch not hydrolysed. Mineral nitrogen poorly assimilated. Nitrates not reduced.

From: Arctic Ocean, (st. 86°26′N, 79°19′E), 50, 100, 150 m;
Indian Ocean, (st. 271), 0 m.

Assigned to aggregate species *Micrococcus roseus* Flügge, 1886, var. A.

Cocci 0.7 – 1.5 μ, single, paired or in short chains. Gram-positive.

On nutrient agar with sea salt – shiny, flat streak, white with yellowish-cinnamon tint. Margin of streak undulate. Agar tinged pink.

On nutrient agar without sea salt – shiny streak with characteristic markings of lighter colour and middle part tinged pink.

On meat-peptone agar with 1% glucose – whitish straw-coloured streak.

On potato and wort agar – no growth.

On meat-peptone broth – turbidity, ring, ammonia formed.

Milk not peptonized. Gelatine liquefied. Peptone water with glucose, sucrose or maltose acidified, with mannitol or lactose not acidified. Starch not hydrolysed. Mineral nitrogen assimilated. Nitrates not reduced.

From: Indian Ocean, (st. **219**), 471 m; (st. **251**), 820 m;
Norwegian Sea, (st. **1703**), 0 m.

Assigned to aggregate species *M. roseus* Flügge, 1886, var. B.

Cocci 0.4 – 0.9 μ, single and paired. Gram-positive.

On nutrient agar with sea salt – slimy, creamy-white, abundant streak. Agar tinged pink.

On nutrient agar without sea salt – streak pinkish-grey, with humpy surface; agar turns brown.

On meat-peptone agar with 1% glucose – slimy, white, shiny streak.

On potato – slimy, semitransparent streak with white, even margin and yellowish-greenish middle.

On wort agar – streak grey, flat.

On meat-peptone broth – turbidity.

Milk not peptonized. Gelatine liquefied. Peptone water with mannitol, glucose, sucrose, maltose or lactose not acidified. Starch not hydrolysed. Mineral nitrogen assimilated. Nitrates reduced.

From: Indian Ocean, (st. **287**), 461 m.

Assigned to aggregate species *M. roseus* Flügge, 1886, var. C.

Cocci distinguished from var. A by character of growth on meat-peptone agar with 1% glucose, where the streak is yellowish-creamy, and by absence of growth on potato.

From: Greenland Sea, (st. **46**), 250 m.

Assigned to aggregate species *M. roseus* Flügge, 1886, var. D.

Cocci distinguished from var. A by character of growth on nutrient agar with or without sea salt, where streak is tinged yellow. Milk peptonized. Starch hydrolysed. Peptone water with mannitol not acidified.

From: Greenland Sea, (st. **43**), 0 m.

Assigned to aggregate species *M. roseus* Flügge, 1886, var. E.

Cocci distinguished from var. A by absence of acid formation on peptone water with mannitol.

From: Greenland Sea, (st. **29**), 100 m;
Indian Ocean mud, (st. **251**);
Pacific Ocean, (st. **3843**), 195 m; (st. **3851**), 635 m.

Assigned to aggregate species *M. roseus* Flügge, 1886, var. F.

Cocci distinguished from var. B by good growth on potato, where streak has pinkish-yellow tinge and potato starts turning black. Peptone water with mannitol acidified. Nitrates reduced.

From: Indian Ocean, (st. **297**), 2910 m; (st. **299**), 3930 m.

Assigned to aggregate species *M. roseus* Flügge, 1886, var. G.

Cocci distinguished from var. B by good growth on potato, where streak has pinkish-yellow tinge and potato starts to blacken. Peptone water with mannitol acidified.

From: Pacific Ocean, (st. **3856**), 400 m.

Assigned to aggregate species *M. roseus* Flügge, 1886, var. H.

Cocci 0.7–1.6 μ, single, paired and in short chains. Gram-positive.

On nutrient agar with sea salt – shiny, flat streak, white with yellowish-cinnamon tinge. Margin of streak undulate. Pink pigment secreted into agar.

On nutrient agar without sea salt – shiny streak with characteristic markings on lighter margin and with the middle tinged pink.

On meat-peptone agar with 1% glucose – whitish straw-coloured streak.

On potato – orange streak.

On wort agar – growth poor, individual, greyish-white colonies.

On meat-peptone broth – turbidity, ring, majority of cultures form ammonia.

Milk not peptonized. Gelatine not liquefied. Peptone water with mannitol, glucose, sucrose or maltose acidified; with lactose not acidified. Starch not hydrolysed. Mineral nitrogen assimilated. Nitrates not reduced.

From: Greenland Sea, (st. **38**), 50 m;
Indian Ocean, (st. **212**), 75, 100 m; (st. **236**), 249 m; (st. **312**), 220 m.

Assigned to aggregate species *Micrococcus aurantiacus* Cohn, 1872, var. A.

Cocci 1.3–1.8 μ, single, paired and in short chains, sometimes joined into tetrads. Gram-positive.

On nutrient agar with sea salt – orange streak with humpy, shiny surface.

On nutrient agar without sea salt – cinnamon-orange streak, semitransparent, with shiny surface.

On potato, wort agar, meat-peptone broth – no growth.

Milk not peptonized. Gelatine not liquefied. Peptone water with mannitol, glucose, sucrose, maltose or lactose acidified. Starch not hydrolysed. Mineral nitrogen assimilated. Nitrates poorly reduced.

From: Greenland Sea, (st. **51**), 10 m.

Assigned to aggregate species *M. aurantiacus* Cohn, 1872, var. B.

Cocci distinguished from var. A by character of growth on potato, where streak is of a cinnamon-brown colour.

From: Greenland Sea, (st. **32**), 25 m;
Pacific Ocean, (st. **3850**), 212 m.

Assigned to aggregate species *M. aurantiacus* Cohn, 1872, var. C.

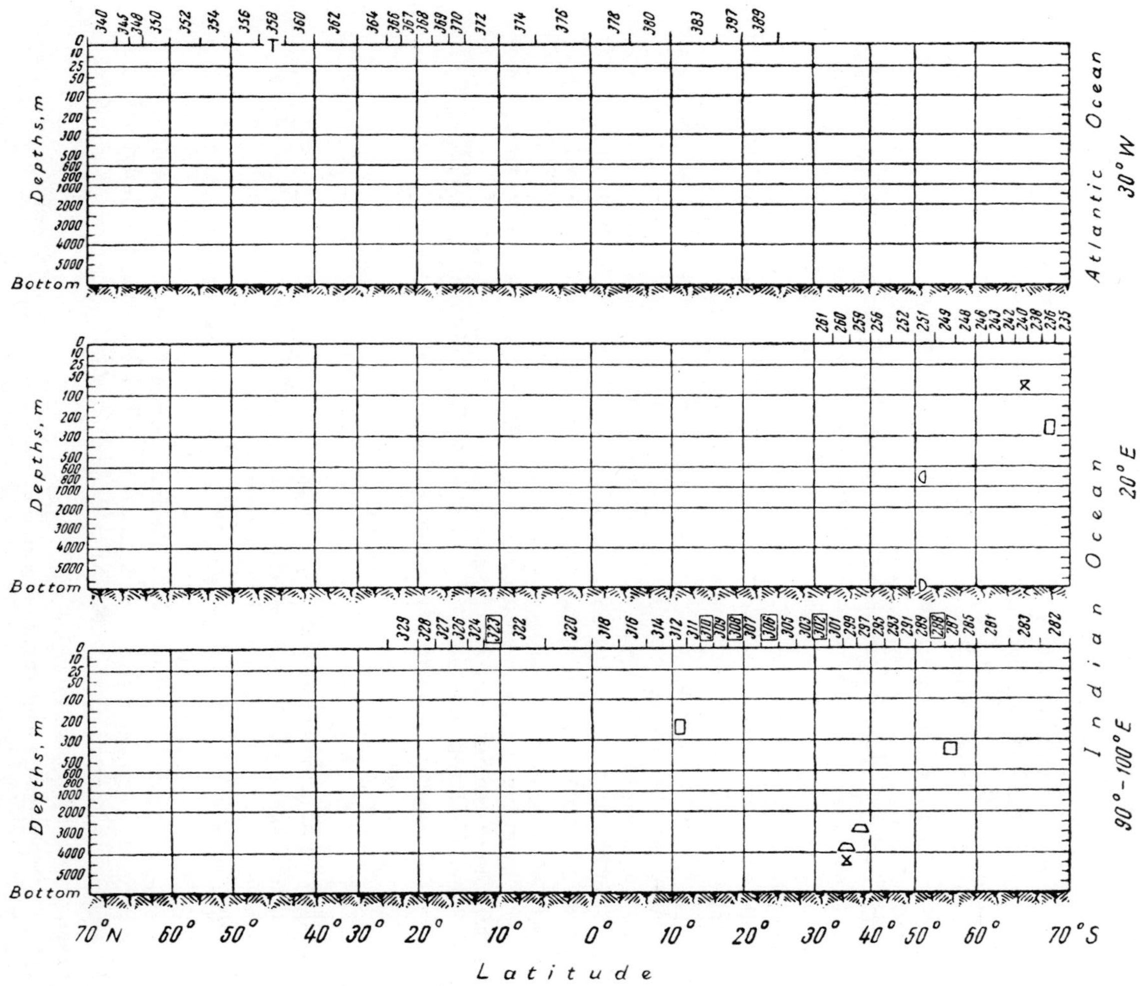
Atlantic Ocean
30° W
Indian Ocean
20° E
90°-100° E
Depths, m
Bottom
Latitude
70° N
70° S

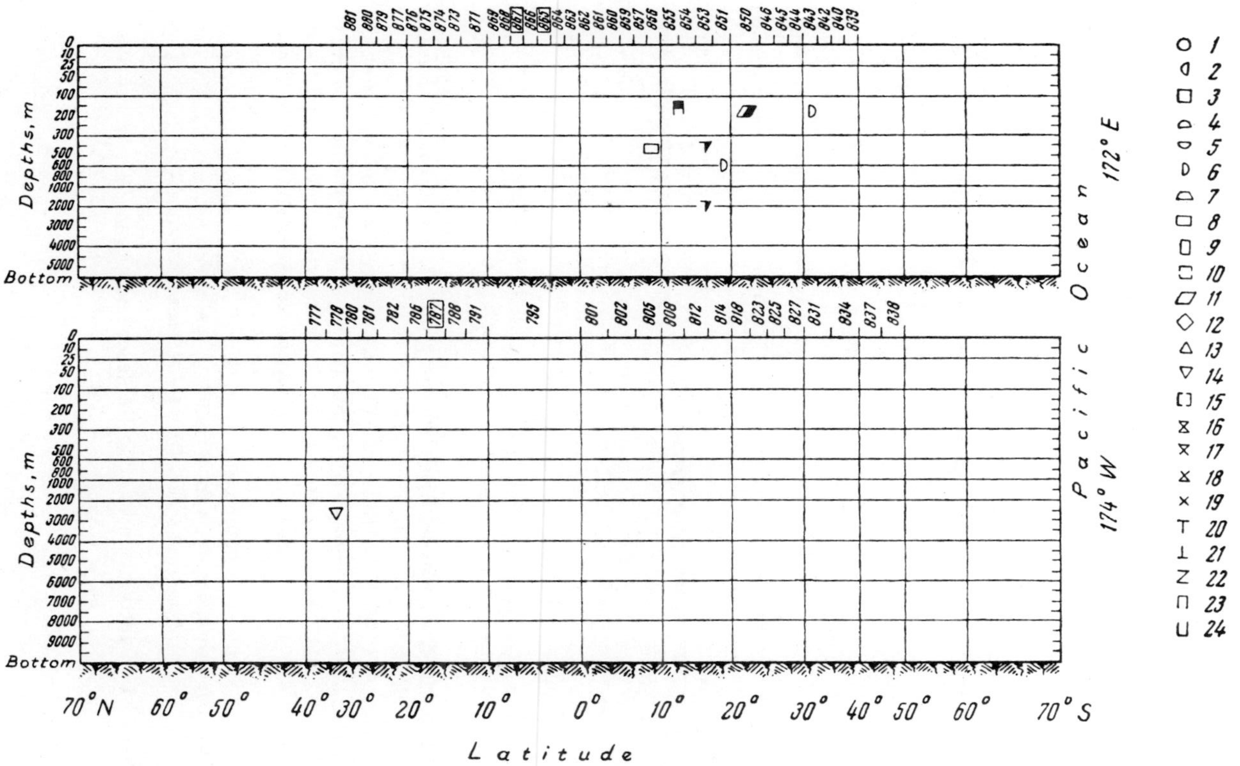

1 - *M. roseus*, var. A; 2 - *M. roseus*, var. B; 3 - *M. roseus*, var. C; 4 - *M. roseus*, var. D; 5 - *M. roseus*, var. E 6 - *M. roseus*, var. F; 7 - *M. roseus*, var. G; 8 - *M. roseus*, var. H; 9 - *M. aurantiacus*, var. A; 10- *M. aurantiacus*, var. B; 11 - *M. aurantiacus*, var. C; 12 - *M. aurantiacus*, var. D; 13 - *M. aurantiacus*, var. E; 14 - *M. aurantiacus*, var. F; 15 - *M. aurantiacus*, var. G; 16 - *M. cinnabareus*, var. A; 17 - *M. cinnabareus*, var. B; 18 - *M. cinnabareus*, var. C; 19 - *M. cinnabareus*, var. D; 20 - *M. cinnabareus*, var. E; 21 - *M. cinnabareus*, var. F; 22 - *M. cinnabareus*, var. G; 23 - *M. cinnabareus*, var. H; 24 - *M. cinnabareus*, var. I

Fig. 14 Distribution of cocci in seas and oceans

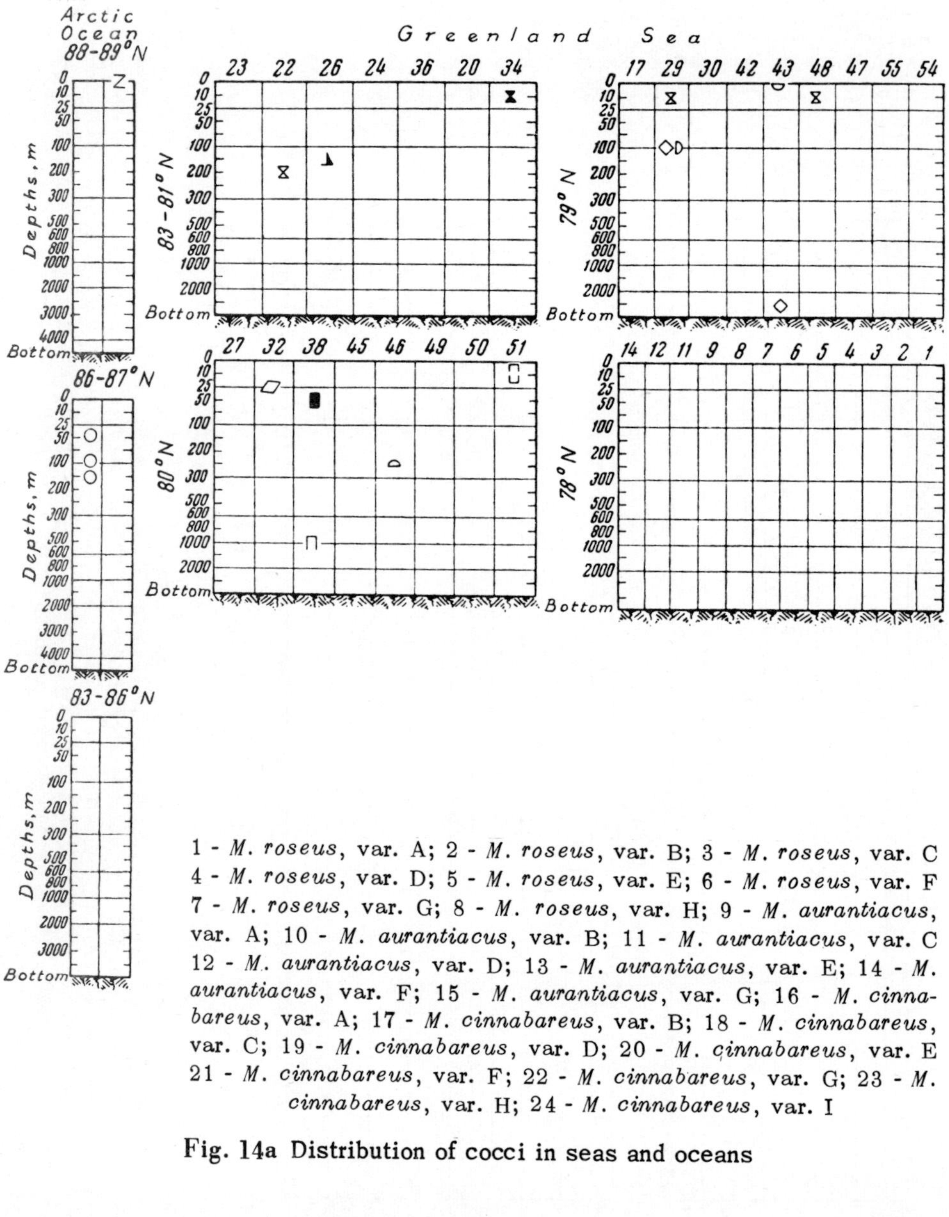

1 - *M. roseus*, var. A; 2 - *M. roseus*, var. B; 3 - *M. roseus*, var. C 4 - *M. roseus*, var. D; 5 - *M. roseus*, var. E; 6 - *M. roseus*, var. F 7 - *M. roseus*, var. G; 8 - *M. roseus*, var. H; 9 - *M. aurantiacus*, var. A; 10 - *M. aurantiacus*, var. B; 11 - *M. aurantiacus*, var. C 12 - *M. aurantiacus*, var. D; 13 - *M. aurantiacus*, var. E; 14 - *M. aurantiacus*, var. F; 15 - *M. aurantiacus*, var. G; 16 - *M. cinnabareus*, var. A; 17 - *M. cinnabareus*, var. B; 18 - *M. cinnabareus*, var. C; 19 - *M. cinnabareus*, var. D; 20 - *M. cinnabareus*, var. E 21 - *M. cinnabareus*, var. F; 22 - *M. cinnabareus*, var. G; 23 - *M. cinnabareus*, var. H; 24 - *M. cinnabareus*, var. I

Fig. 14a Distribution of cocci in seas and oceans

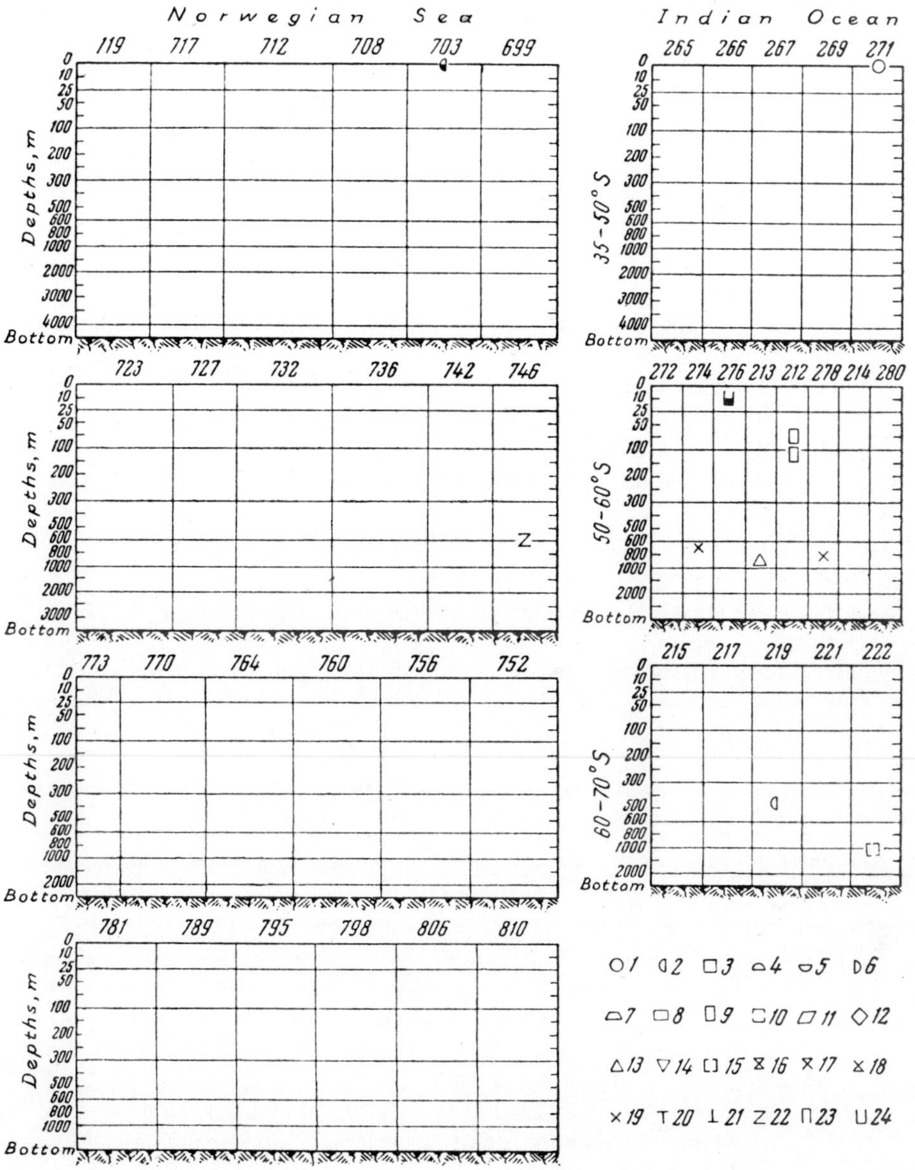
Norwegian Sea
Indian Ocean
119 717 712 708 703 699
723 727 732 736 742 746
773 770 764 760 756 752
781 789 795 798 806 810
265 266 267 269 271
272 274 276 213 212 278 214 280
215 217 219 221 222
Depths, m
0 10 25 50 100 200 300 500 600 800 1000 2000 3000 4000
Bottom
35–50° S
50–60° S
60–70° S
1 2 3 4 5 6 7 8 9 10 11 12 13 14 15 16 17 18 19 20 21 22 23 24

Cocci distinguished from var. A by absence of growth on potato.
From: Greenland Sea, (st. 29), 100 m; (st. 43), 2600 m.

Assigned to aggregate species *M. aurantiacus* Cohn, 1872, var. D.

Cocci distinguished from var. A by absence of growth on potato and meat-peptone agar with 1% glucose and also by inability to form acid in peptone water with mannitol, glucose, sucrose or maltose.
From: Indian Ocean, (st. 213), 906 m.

Assigned to aggregate species *M. aurantiacus* Cohn, 1872, var. E.

Cocci distinguished from var. A by ability to form acid in peptone water with lactose, to hydrolyse starch and reduce nitrates.
From: Pacific Ocean, (st. 3778), 2703 m.

Assigned to aggregate species *M. aurantiacus* Cohn, 1872, var. F.

Cocci distinguished from var. A by ability to reduce nitrates.
From: Indian Ocean, (st. 222), 1000 m.

Assigned to aggregate species *M. aurantiacus* Cohn, 1872, var. G.

Cocci 0.6 – 1.4 μ, single, paired and in short chains. Gram-positive.
On nutrient agar with sea salt – streak shiny, white, with yellowish-cinnamon tinge. Margin of streak undulate. Pinkish pigment secreted into agar.
On nutrient agar without sea salt – streak shiny, beige, with characteristic marginal markings in the form of flounces and middle part tinged pink.
On meat-peptone agar with 1% glucose – whitish straw-coloured streak.
On potato – shiny streak of brownish colour.
On wort agar – poor growth of individual, greyish-white colonies.
On meat-peptone broth – turbidity, ring, most cultures form ammonia.
Milk not peptonized. Gelatine not liquefied. Peptone water with mannitol, glucose, sucrose or maltose acidified; with lactose not acidified. Starch not hydrolysed. Mineral nitrogen not assimilated or poorly assimilated. Nitrates not reduced.
From: Greenland Sea, (st. 22), 200 m; (st. 29, 34 and 48), 10 m.

Assigned to aggregate species *Micrococcus cinnabareus* Flügge, 1886, var. A.

Cocci distinguished from var. A by absence of growth on potato
From: Indian Ocean, (st. 240), 76 m.

Assigned to aggregate species *M. cinnabareus* Flügge, 1886, var. B.

Cocci distinguished from var. A by ability to liquefy gelatine and by character of growth on potato, where streak is slimy, semitransparent and has a yellowish-greenish tinge.

From: Indian Ocean, (st. **299**), 4200 m.

Assigned to aggregate species *M. cinnabareus* **Flügge, 1886, var. C.**

Cocci distinguished from var. A by absence of growth on potato and by ability to liquefy gelatine and form acid in peptone water with lactose.

From: Indian Ocean, (st. **274**), 730 m; (st. **278**), 861 m.

Assigned to aggregate species *M. cinnabareus* **Flügge, 1886, var. D.**

Cocci distinguished from var. A by absence of growth on potato, ability to liquefy gelatine and form acid in peptone water with lactose and absence of acid formation in peptone water with mannitol.

From: Atlantic Ocean, (st. **358**), 0 m;
Pacific Ocean, (st. **3853**), 386, 2124 m.

Assigned to aggregate species *M. cinnabareus* **Flügge, 1886, var. E.**

Cocci distinguished from var. A by absence of acid formation in peptone water with mannitol.

From: Greenland Sea, (st. **26**), 150 m.

Assigned to aggregate species *M. cinnabareus* **Flügge, 1886, var. F.**

Cocci distinguished from var. A by acidification of peptone water with lactose.

From: Arctic Ocean, (st. 89°29′ N, 65°43′ W), 0 m;
Norwegian Sea, (st. **1746**), 600 m.

Assigned to aggregate species *M. cinnabareus* **Flügge, 1886, var. G.**

Cocci distinguished from var. A by orange tinge of streak on potato agar, acidification of peptone water with lactose and absence of acid formation in peptone water with mannitol.

From: Greenland Sea, (st. **38**), 1000 m;
Pacific Ocean, (st. **3855**), 154 m.

Assigned to aggregate species *M. cinnabareus* **Flügge, 1886, var. H.**

Cocci distinguished from var. A by absence of growth on potato and meat-peptone agar with 1% glucose and absence of acid formation in peptone water with mannitol, glucose, sucrose or maltose.

From: Indian Ocean, (st. **276**), 10 m.

Assigned to aggregate species *M. cinnabareus* **Flügge, 1886, var. I.**

Cocci 1.1 – 1.8 μ, forming packets of 16 or more cells. Gram-positive.

On nutrient agar with sea salt – light yellow streak, pasty consistency, with mat, slightly humpy surface, and opaque, even margin.

On nutrient agar without sea salt – yellowish-beige streak with mat surface. Agar turns red and brown.

On meat-peptone agar with 1% glucose – streak light yellow, convex, with even margin and shiny surface,

On potato and wort agar – canary-coloured growth.

On meat-peptone broth – slight turbidity.

Milk not peptonized. Gelatine liquefied. Peptone water with mannitol, glucose, sucrose, maltose or lactose not acidified. Starch not hydrolysed. Mineral nitrogen assimilated. Nitrates not reduced.

From: Arctic Ocean, (st. 87°28′N, 177°12′W), 5 m;
Greenland Sea, (st. **30**), 200 m; (st. **38**), 75 m;
Indian Ocean, (st. **249**), 0 m;
Pacific Ocean, (st. **3823**), 578 m; (st. **3825**), 188 m; (st. **3845**), 15 m.

Assigned to aggregate species *Sarcina subflava* Ravenel, 1896, var. A.

Cocci distinguished from var. A by producing pinkish-yellow streak with shiny surface on wort agar and by ability to hydrolyse starch.

From: Atlantic Ocean, (st. **362**), 300 m;
Greenland Sea, (st. **51**), 400 m.

Assigned to aggregate species *S. subflava* Ravenel, 1896, var. B.

Cocci 1.1 – 1.7 μ, forming packets of 8, 16 or more cells. Gram-positive.

On nutrient agar with sea salt – growth greenish-yellow, margin even, semi-transparent.

On nutrient agar without sea salt – yellowish-beige, dense streak with mat surface. Agar turns red and brown.

On meat-peptone agar with 1% glucose – whitish-yellowish streak, semi-transparent, with mat surface.

On potato – no growth.

On wort agar – growth in the form of individual, cinnamon-yellow, shiny colonies.

On meat-peptone broth – slight turbidity.

Milk not peptonized. Gelatine not liquefied. Peptone water with mannitol, glucose, sucrose, maltose or lactose unchanged. Starch not hydrolysed. Mineral nitrogen assimilated. Nitrates not reduced.

From: Indian Ocean, (st. **274**), 175 m;
Norwegian Sea, (st. **1723**), 50 m;
Pacific Ocean, (st. **3850**), 2518 m; (st. **3855**), 412 m.

Assigned to aggregate species *Sarcina luteola* Gruber 1895.

9

Species of mycobacteria

Rod-shaped cells of irregular contour, curved, 0.3 – 0.7 × 1.8 – 5 μ, with rudimentary branching, which become slightly shortened on ageing. Gram-positive.

On nutrient agar with sea salt – abundant, white streak with uneven, mat surface; on ageing the streak becomes flatter and acquires a beige colour.

On meat-peptone agar and meat-peptone agar with 1% glucose – a white, slimy streak; growth modest.

On wort agar – growth of a white, slimy consistency.

On potato – colonies white, shiny.

On meat-peptone broth – slight turbidity, sediment.

Milk not peptonized. Gelatine not liquefied. Peptone water with mannitol, glucose, sucrose or maltose acidified; peptone water with lactose not acidified. Starch not hydrolysed. Mineral nitrogen not assimilated. Nitrates not reduced.

From: Greenland Sea, (st. 12), 10 m.

Assigned to aggregate species *Mycobacterium filiforme* Krasil'nikov, 1941, var. A.

Mycobacteria distinguished from var. A by inability to acidify peptone water with mannitol, glucose, sucrose or maltose and by ability to hydrolyse starch.

From: Greenland Sea, (st. 50), 0 m.

Assigned to aggregate species *Mycob. filiforme* Krasil'nikov, 1941, var. B.

Rod-shaped cells and filaments without clear branching, 0.5 – 0.9 × 2.6 – 5.3 μ; on ageing the cells become slightly shorter, acquiring the shape of oval rods and granulated-plasma cocci. Gram-positive.

On nutrient agar with sea salt – whitish-orange growth, mat, pasty consistency.

On meat-peptone agar – abundant whitish-yellow growth with mat surface;

sometimes streak basally slimy.

On meat-peptone agar with 1% glucose – streak bright straw-coloured, with mat surface, pasty consistency.

On wort agar – modest growth of a whitish streak with mat surface.

On potato – convex colonies of bright straw colour.

On meat-peptone broth – turbidity and a light film which crawls up the walls of the test tube.

Milk not peptonized. Gelatine liquefied. Peptone water with mannitol, glucose, sucrose, maltose or lactose not acidified. Starch hydrolysed. Mineral nitrogen assimilated. Nitrates reduced.

From: Indian Ocean mud (st. 288).

Assigned to aggregate species ***Mycobacterium lacticolum*** **Lehmann et Neumann, 1899.**

Rod-shaped cells 0.2 – 0.6 × 1.2 – 2.0 μ, joined into conglomerates. On ageing the rods become slightly shortened. Gram-positive.

On nutrient agar with sea salt – yellowish cinnamon-coloured, shiny streak with slight transverse striation.

On meat-peptone agar and meat-peptone agar with 1% glucose – streak slimy, straw-coloured.

On wort agar and potato – slimy, yellowish straw-coloured growth.

On meat-peptone broth – ring, film, slight turbidity, ammonia formed.

Milk peptonized. Gelatine liquefied. Peptone water with mannitol, glucose, sucrose, maltose, or lactose not acidified. Starch not hydrolysed. Mineral nitrogen assimilated. Nitrates not reduced.

From: Indian Ocean, (st. 266), 0 m.

Assigned to aggregate species ***Mycobacterium mucosum*** **Krasil'nikov, 1941, var. A.**

Mycobacteria distinguished from var. A by folding of colonies on meat-peptone agar with 1% glucose, on wort agar and on potato. Milk not peptonized. Starch hydrolysed. Nitrates reduced.

From: Indian Ocean, (st. 266), 1983 m.

Assigned to aggregate species ***Mycob. mucosum*** **Krasil'nikov, 1941, var. B.**

Mycobacteria distinguished from var. A by poor growth on meat-peptone broth, inability to peptonize milk or liquefy gelatine, poor assimilation of mineral nitrogen, ability to acidify peptone water with mannitol, glucose, sucrose or maltose.

From: Indian Ocean, (st. 249), 210 m.

Assigned to aggregate species ***Mycob. mucosum*** **Krasil'nikov, 1941, var. C.**

Mycobacteria distinguished from var. A by inability to peptonize milk or liquefy gelatine. Acid in peptone water with glucose. Nitrates reduced.

From: Pacific Ocean, (st. **3877**), 305 m.

Assigned to aggregate species *Mycob. mucosum* **Krasil'nikov, 1941, var. D.**

Mycobacteria distinguished from var. A by inability to peptonize milk or liquefy gelatine.

From: Indian Ocean, (st. **265**), 294 m; (st. **314**), 158 m.

Assigned to aggregate species *Mycob. mucosum* **Krasil'nikov, 1941, var. E.**

Rod-shaped cells 0.4 – 0.8 × 0.9 – 3.0 μ, with rounded ends, single, paired or in clusters. In old cultures, almost coccoidal cells, sometimes forming chainlets. Gram-positive.

On nutrient agar – yellow streak of various hues; smooth, with even margin.

On meat-peptone broth – ring, turbidity, yellow sediment, hydrogen sulphide evolved.

Gelatine liquefied. Milk not peptonized. Peptone water with mannitol, glucose, sucrose, maltose or lactose unchanged. Starch not hydrolysed. Mineral nitrogen assimilated. Nitrogen not reduced.

From: Pacific Ocean, (st. **3854**), 0 m; (st. **3861**), 0 m.

Assigned to aggregate species *Mycobacterium luteum* **(Söhngen) Krasil'nikov, 1941, var. A.**

Mycobacteria distinguished from var. A by ability to reduce nitrates.

From: Pacific Ocean, (st. **3778**), 2703 m.

Assigned to aggregate species *Mycob. luteum* **(Söhngen) Krasil'nikov, 1941, var. B.**

Mycobacteria distinguished from var. A by ability to peptonize milk, hydrolyse starch and reduce nitrates.

From: Arctic Ocean mud, (st. 88°04′ N, 151°16′ W)

Assigned to aggregate species *Mycob. luteum* **(Söhngen) Krasil'nikov, 1941, var. C.**

Rod-shaped cells 2.5 – 5.5 × 0.5 – 1.1 μ, polymorphous, thickening and shortening to coccoidal shape on ageing. Gram-positive.

On nutrient agar with sea salt – streak creamy, shiny, smooth; margins even.

On meat-peptone broth – flocculent turbidity, sediment.

Gelatine not liquefied. Milk unchanged. Peptone water with mannitol, glucose, sucrose, maltose or lactose, not changed. Starch not hydrolysed. Mineral nitrogen poorly assimilated. Nitrates not reduced.

From: Pacific Ocean, (st. **3853**), 146 m.

Assigned to aggregate species *Mycobacterium album* **Söhngen, 1913.**

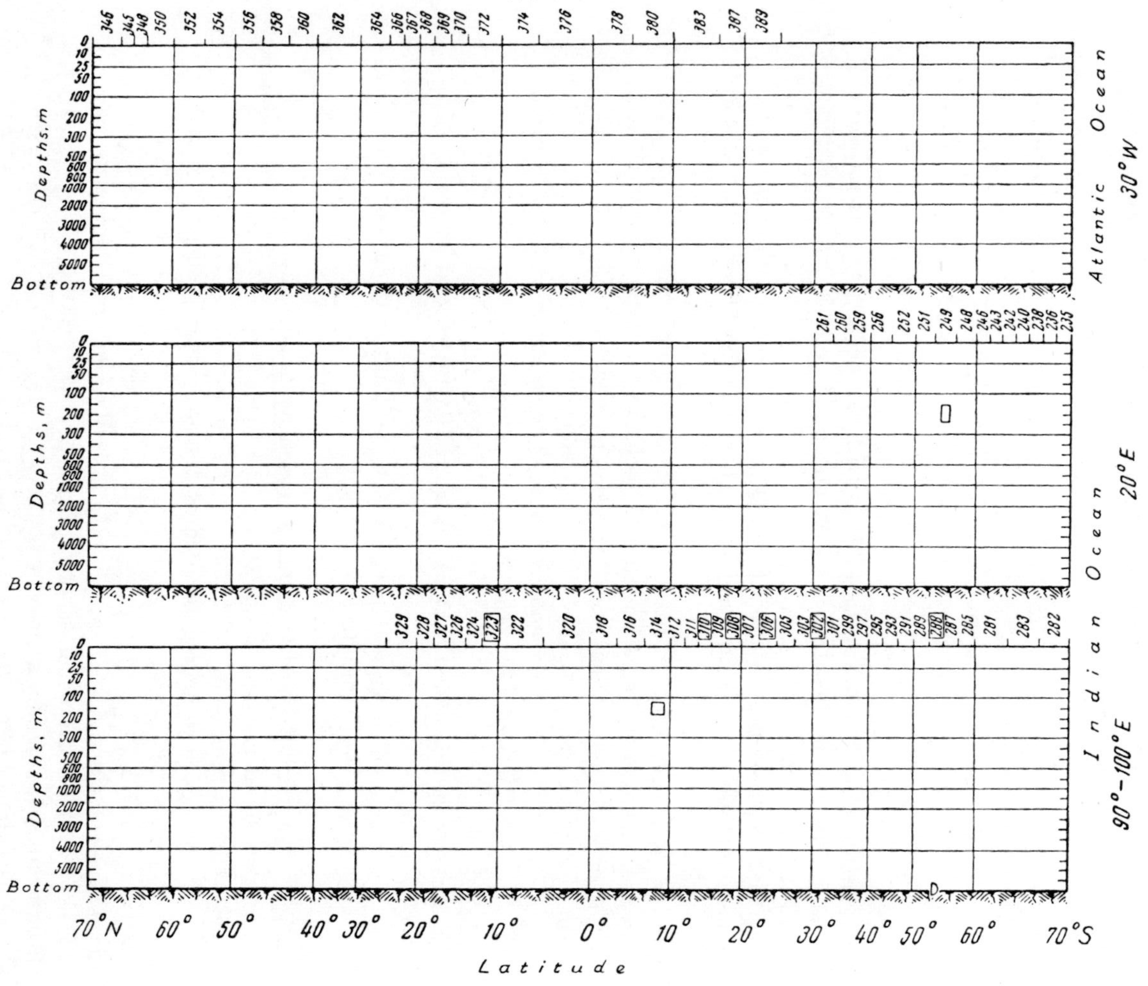

Atlantic Ocean
30°W
Ocean
20°E
Indian
90°–100°E
Depths, m
0
10
25
50
100
200
300
500
600
800
1000
2000
3000
4000
5000
Bottom
346 345 348 350 352 354 356 358 360 362 364 366 367 368 369 370 372 374 376 378 380 383 387 389
261 260 259 256 252 251 249 248 246 243 242 240 238 236 235
329 328 327 326 324 323 322 320 318 316 314 312 311 310 309 308 307 306 305 303 302 301 299 297 295 293 291 289 288 287 285 281 283 282
70°N 60° 50° 40° 30° 20° 10° 0° 10° 20° 30° 40° 50° 60° 70°S
Latitude

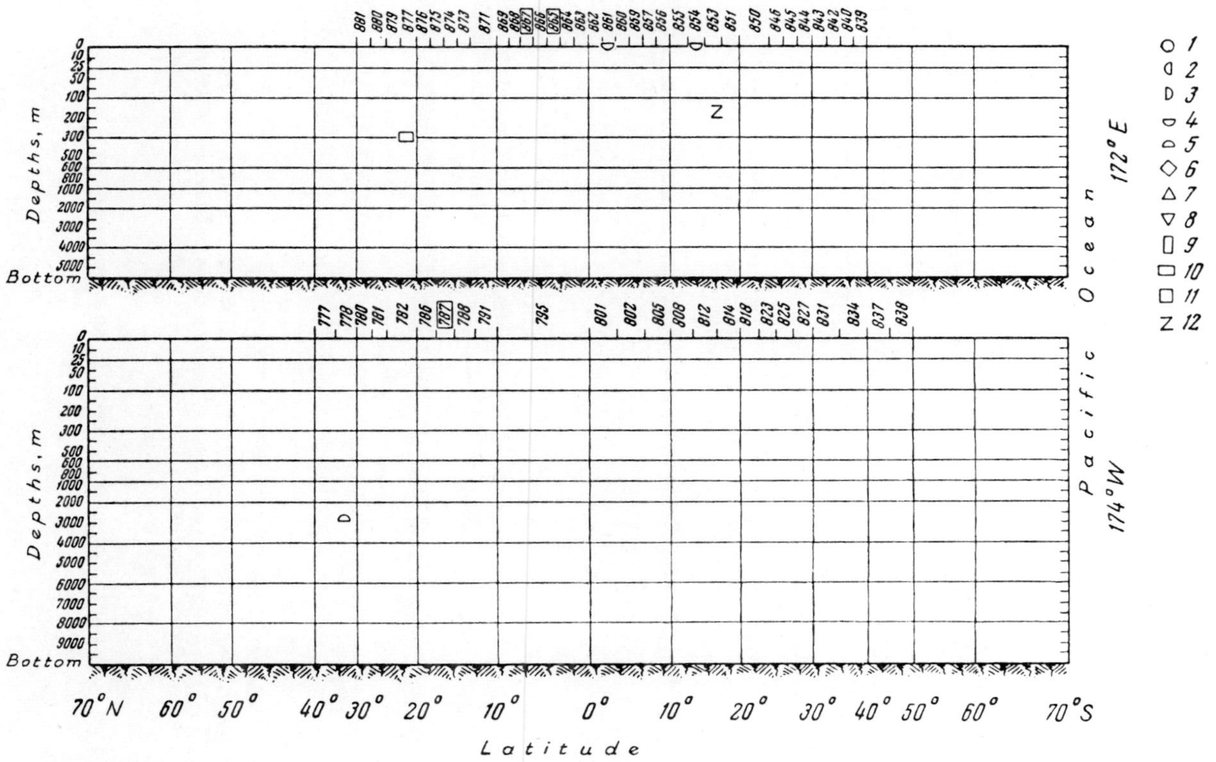

1 - *Mycobacterium filiforme*, var. A; 2 - *Mycob. filiforme*, var. B; 3 - *Mycob. lacticolum*; 4 - *Mycob. luteum*, var. A
5 - *Mycob. luteum*, var. B; 6 - *Mycob. luteum*, var. C; 7 - *Mycob. mucosum*, var. A; 8 - *Mycob. mucosum*, var. B
9 - *Mycob. mucosum*, var. C; 10 - *Mycob. mucosum*, var. D; 11 - *Mycob. mucosum*, var. E; 12 - *Mycob. album*

Fig. 15 Distribution of mycobacteria in seas and oceans

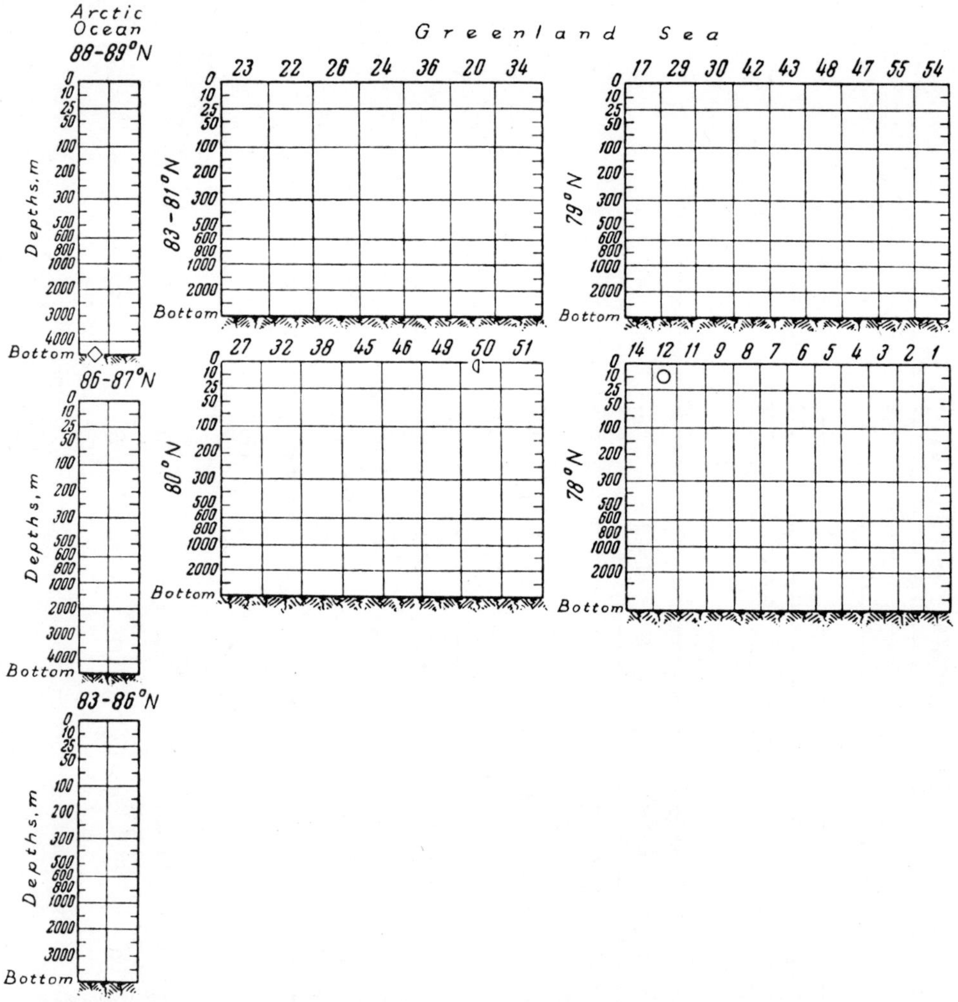

1 - *Mycobacterium filiforme*, var. A; 2 - *Mycob. filiforme*, var. B; 3 - *Mycob. lacticolum*; 4 - *Mycob. luteum*, var. A; 5 - *Mycob. luteum*, var. B; 6 - *Mycob. luteum*, var. C; 7 - *Mycob. mucosum*, var. A; 8 - *Mycob. mucosum*, var. B; 9 - *Mycob. mucosum*, var. C; 10 - *Mycob. mucosum*, var. D; 11 - *Mycob. mucosum*, var. E 12 - *Mycob. album*

Fig. 15a Distribution of mycobacteria in seas and oceans

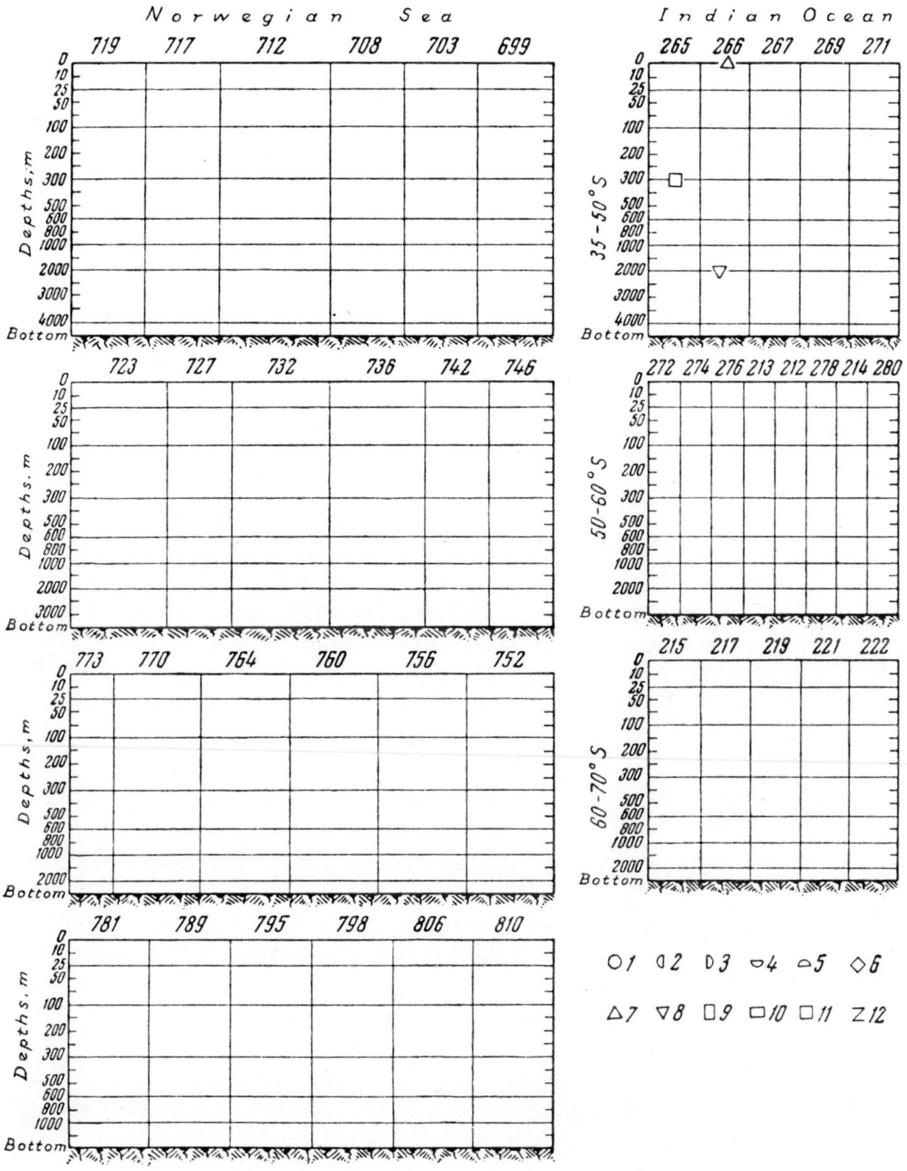
Norwegian Sea
719 717 712 708 703 699
723 727 732 736 742 746
773 770 764 760 756 752
781 789 795 798 806 810
Depths, m
0 10 25 50 100 200 300 500 600 800 1000 2000 3000 4000
Bottom
Indian Ocean
265 266 267 269 271
35 - 50° S
272 274 276 213 212 278 214 280
50-60° S
215 217 219 221 222
60-70° S
1 2 3 4 5 6
7 8 9 10 11 12

10

Species of actinomycetes and proactinomycetes

Mycelial growth with monopodial branching; hyphae from 0.4 to 0.9 μ thick. Sporophores straight or slightly contorted. Spores polymorphous – spheroid, spheroid-oval, oval or cylindrical, $0.6-0.9 \times 0.6-1.5$ μ.

On synthetic agar the culture develops well, secreting a yellowish pigment into the medium; the colonies are flat and whitish. Aerial mycelium mealy, snow-white.

On other media (nutrient agar, potato agar, wort agar) the colour is dirty-white or greyish and the colonies are humpy, sometimes flat, mat and shiny.

On nutrient agar and wort agar the aerial mycelium develops poorly. On potato agar the culture secretes a pigment of lilac to cinnamon-like colour into the medium. Aerial mycelium well developed. On meat-peptone broth slight turbidity occurs at the bottom and a white, mealy film on the surface of the broth.

Gelatine liquefied. Milk peptonized and alkalinized. Starch hydrolysed. Nitrates not reduced. Peptone water with sucrose alkalinized. Peptone water with glucose, lactose, maltose or mannitol, acidified.

From: Greenland Sea, (st. **49**), surface; (st. **50**), 100 m;
Indian Ocean, (st. **246**), 250 m; (st. **248**), 300 m.

Assigned to aggregate species *Actinomyces globisporus* Krasil'nikov.

In the early stages of growth a substrate mycelium forms, which decays within 2 to 4 days into rod-like elements $2-10 \times 0.7-0.9$ μ. No formation of aerial mycelium or sporophores. Greatly distended, spheroid and retort-like cells occur in old cultures.

On nutrient media the colonies are white, of pasty consistency and easily picked up with a loop; they are humpy, folded, mat and sometimes shiny.

On meat-peptone broth a light, flocculent turbidity forms at the bottom.

Gelatine poorly liquefied, only after 10 – 20 days. Milk coagulates and is slightly peptonized. Starch hydrolysed. Nitrated not reduced. Peptone water with sucrose, glucose, lactose, maltose or mannitol acidified.

From: Greenland Sea, (st. 14), 10 m; (st. 8), 75 m.

Assigned to aggregate species *Proactinomyces albus* Krasil'nikov.

11

Species of yeasts

Cells oval, 4.5 – 8.7 × 2.6 – 5.3 μ, budding, no spore formation.

On wort agar – cream-coloured streak, slimy, running.

Glucose, galactose, lactose, sucrose, maltose not fermented. Nitrate nitrogen, asparagine, peptone assimilated; ammonium sulphate and urea not assimilated. Of carbon sources, glucose, galactose, lactose, sucrose and maltose assimilated. Ethyl alcohol not assimilated.

From: Arctic Ocean, (st. 88°04′ N, 151°16′ W), 10 m; (st. 87°28′ N, 177°12′ W), 3950 m.

Assigned to *Torulopsis aeria* (Saito) **Lodder, var. A.**

Asporogenous yeast distinguished from var. A by assimilating ethyl alcohol.

From: Arctic Ocean, (st. 88°04′ N, 151°16′ W), 250 m.

Assigned to *T. aeria* (Saito) **Lodder, var. B.**

Asporogenous yeast distinguished from var. A by not assimilating nitrate nitrogen and by assimilating ethyl alcohol.

From: Indian Ocean, (st. 252), 1500 m;
Norwegian Sea, (st, 1727), 30 m.

Assigned to *T. aeria* (Saito) **Lodder, var. C.**

Cells oval, 3.4 – 6.7 × 1.3 – 5.1 μ, budding, not spore-forming.

On wort agar – streak yellowish-white, mat, smooth, margins slightly scalloped in old cultures. Ferments glucose, sucrose and raffinose but not galactose, lactose or maltose. Assimilates asparagine, peptone, but not nitrate nitrogen, ammonium sulphate or urea. Assimilates glucose, galactose, sucrose and maltose but not lactose as sources of carbon. Assimilates ethyl alcohol.

From: Greenland Sea, (st. 23), 3306 m; (st. 24), 1304 m.

Assigned to *Torulopsis dattila* (Kluyver) **Lodder.**

Cells oval, 3.6 – 7.7 × 2.7 – 6.8 μ, budding, not spore-forming.

On wort agar – streak greyish-white, mat, margins even.

Glucose, galactose, lactose, sucrose and maltose not fermented. Asparagine, peptone assimilated, but not nitrate nitrogen, ammonium sulphate or urea. Of carbon sources, glucose, galactose, sucrose and maltose but not lactose assimilated. Ethyl alcohol assimilated.

From: Atlantic Ocean, (st. **350**), 150 m; (st. **356**), 200 m.

Assigned to *Torulopsis famata* (Harrison) n. comb.

Cells oval, 2.8 – 5.7 × 2.5 – 4.6 μ, budding, not spore-forming.

On wort agar – streak yellowish-white, mat, slightly rough, margins smooth.

Ferment glucose, galactose and raffinose, but not lactose, maltose or sucrose.

Assimilates asparagine and peptone but not nitrate nitrogen, ammonium sulphate or urea. Of carbon sources, assimilates glucose, galactose, sucrose, maltose but not lactose.

Assimilates ethyl alcohol.

From: Greenland Sea, (st. **6**), 2845 m.

Assigned to *Torulopsis holmii* (Jörg.) Lodder.

Cells oval, 4.0 – 6.6 × 2.0 – 6.5 μ, budding, not spore-forming.

On wort agar streak pink with orange tinge, slimy, smooth, runny growth.

Glucose, galactose, lactose, sucrose and maltose not fermented. Aspargine and peptone assimilated but not nitrate nitrogen, ammonium sulphate or urea. Of carbon sources, glucose, sucrose, maltose, galactose assimilated but not lactose. Ethyl alcohol assimilated.

From: Greenland Sea, (st. **3**), 2160 m; (st. **4**), 3040 m; (st. **5**), 3026 m; (st. **6**), 2845 m; (st. **7**), 1450 m; (st. **8**), 348 m; (st. **43**), 2656 m; (st. **45**), 2754 m;

Indian Ocean, (st. **249**), 10 m.

Assigned to *Rhodotorula mucilaginosa* (Jörg.) Harrison.

Cells oval, 4.0 – 8.4 × 2.3 – 5.4 μ, budding, not spore-forming.

On wort agar – streak pink with orange tinge, slimy, slightly spreading.

Glucose, galactose, lactose, sucrose and maltose not fermented. Nitrate nitrogen, asparagine and peptone assimilated but not ammonium sulphate of urea.* Of carbon sources glucose, galactose, sucrose, maltose but not lactose assimilated. Ethyl alcohol assimilated.

From: Greenland Sea, (st. **3**), 2160 m; (st. **4**), 3040 m; (st. **5**), 3026 m; (st. **6**), 2845 m; (st. **22**), 2581 m; (st. **24**), 1304 m;

Indian Ocean, (st. **221**), 150 m; (st. **222**), 0, 150 m.

Assigned to *Rhodotorula glutinis* (Fres.) Harrison.

*(Editor's footnote). There is some evidence that marine *Rhodotorula* spp. may be able to assimilate elementary nitrogen, N_2 (M. B. Allen, 1963, in *Symposium on Marine Microbiology*, edited by C. H. Oppenheimer, Thomas, Springfield, Illinois, pp. 85 – 92).

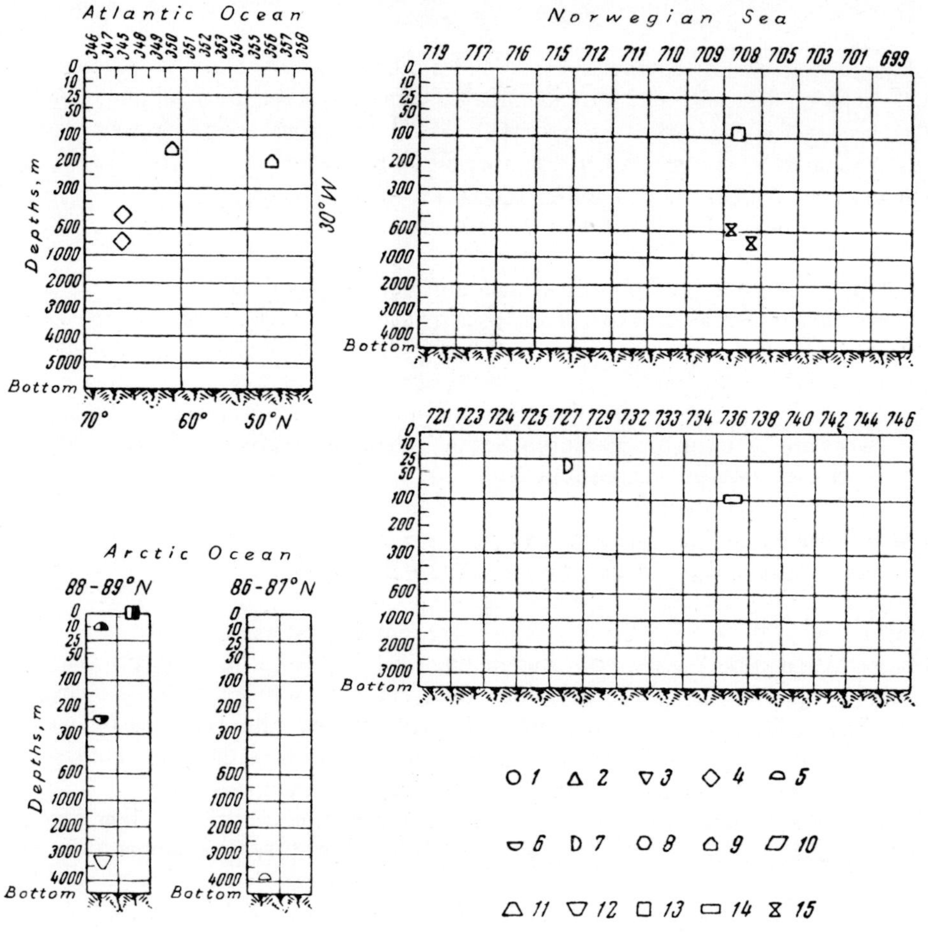

1 - *Rhodotorula mucilaginosa*; 2 - *Rh. glutinis*; 3 - *Rh. glutinis*, var. rubescens 4 - *Rh. rubra*; 5 - *Torulopsis aeria*, var. A; 6 - *T. aeria*, var. B; 7 - *T. aeria*, var. C; 8 - *T. holmii*; 9 - *T. famata*; 10 - *T. dattila*; 11 - *Sporobolomyces roseus*, var. A; 12 - *Sp. roseus*, var. B; 13 - *Debaryomyces rosei*; 14 - *Debar. globosusi* 15 - *Debar. guilliermondii*

Fig. 16 Distribution of yeast organisms in seas and oceans

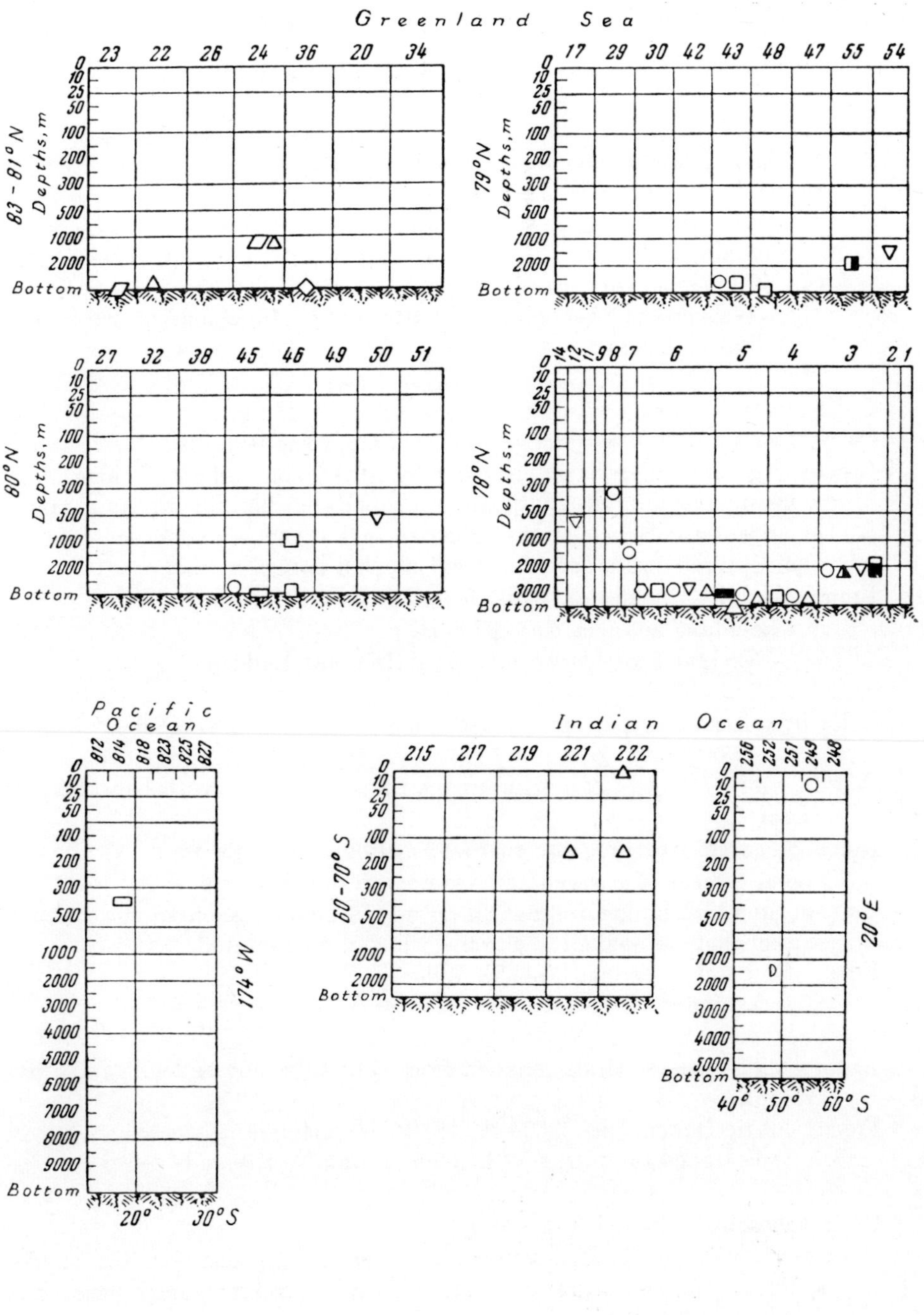
Greenland Sea
83 - 81° N
Depths, m
23 22 26 24 36 20 34
79° N
17 29 30 42 43 48 47 55 54
80° N
27 32 38 45 46 49 50 51
78° N
14 12 11 9 8 7 6 5 4 3 2 1
0 10 25 50 100 200 300 500 1000 2000 3000
Bottom
Pacific Ocean
812 814 818 823 825 827
4000 5000 6000 7000 8000 9000
174° W
20° 30° S
Indian Ocean
215 217 219 221 222
60-70° S
256 252 251 249 248
20° E
40° 50° 60° S

Cells oval, 4.0 – 8.4 × 2.3 – 5.4 μ, budding, not spore-forming.

On wort agar – streak orange, slimy, runny growth.

Glucose, galactose, lactose, sucrose or maltose not fermented. Nitrate nitrogen, asparagine and peptone assimilated but not ammonium sulphate or urea. Of carbon sources, glucose, galactose, sucrose or maltose but not lactose assimilated. Ethyl alcohol assimilated.

From: Greenland Sea, (st. **3**), 2160 m; (st. **6**), 2845 m; (st. **12**), 501 m; (st. **50**), 659 m; (st. **54**), 1280 m.

Assigned to ***Rhodotorula glutinis*** **(Fres.) Harrison var.** ***rubescens*** **(Saito) Lodder.**

Cells ovate-oblong, 4.6 – 11.0 × 2.2 – 5.3 μ, budding, not spore-forming.

On wort agar – streak red-orange, mat, smooth, sometimes slightly wrinkled.

Glucose, galactose, lactose, sucrose, maltose not fermented. Ammonium sulphate, asparagine and peptone assimilated but not nitrate nitrogen or urea. Of carbon sources, glucose, galactose, sucrose and maltose assimilated but not lactose. Ethyl alcohol assimilated.

From: Atlantic Ocean, (st. **345**), 500, 800 m;
Greenland Sea, (st. **36**), 3500 m.

Assigned to ***Rhodotorula rubra*** **(Demme) Lodder.**

Cells irregular in shape, curved, with long processes, 5.5 – 16.1 × 2.0 – 6.3 μ; not spore-forming.

On wort agar – streak pink or with orange tinge, dry, mat, with mealy coating, wrinkled.

Glucose, galactose, lactose, sucrose, maltose not fermented. Nitrate nitrogen, ammonium sulphate, asparagine and peptone assimilated but not urea. Of carbon sources, glucose, galactose, sucrose and maltose but not lactose assimilated. Ethyl alcohol assimilated.

From: Greenland Sea mud, (st. **5**), 3500 m.

Assigned to ***Sporobolomyces roseus*** **Kluyver et van Niel, var. A.**

Asporogenous yeasts distinguished from var. A by not assimilating ethyl alcohol.

From: Arctic Ocean, (st. 88°04′ N, 151°16′ W), 3400 m.

Assigned to ***Sp. roseus*** **Kluyver et van Niel, var. B.**

Cells spheroid, 3.1 – 6.1 μ, budding.

On Gorodkova's medium, meat-peptone agar and gypsum blocks, spores spheroid, formed after copulation. Spore membrane with verrucose thickenings. Cells which have not copulated turn into arthrospores. In old cultures discontinuities of the outer layers of the membranes are observed in the arthrospores.

On wort agar – streak white, mat, smooth, margins slightly scalloped in old cultures.

Glucose, sucrose, raffinose fermented but not galactose or maltose.

Arabinose, raffinose, glucose, galactose, sucrose and maltose assimilated. but not xylose or lactose.

From: Arctic Ocean, (st. 89°29′N, 65°43′W), 0 m;

Greenland Sea, (st. **3**), 2000, 2160 m; (st. **4**), 3040 m; (st. **6**), 2845 m; (st. **43**), 2656 m; (st. **46**), 1000, 2679 m; (st. **48**), 2800 m; (st. **55**), 1907 m;

Norwegian Sea, (st. **1708**), 100 m.

Assigned to *Debaryomyces rosei* Kudryavtsev, n. comb.

Cells spheroid, 2.8 – 6.6 μ, budding.

On Gorodkova's medium, meat-peptone agar and gypsum blocks spores spheroid, forming after copulation. Spore membranes with verrucose thickenings. Cells which have not copulated turn into arthrospores. In old cultures discontinuities of outer layers of membranes are observed in the arthrospores.

On wort agar – streak white, mat, smooth, margins even; in old culture, margins slightly scalloped.

Ferments glucose and sucrose but not galactose, maltose or raffinose. Assimilates arabinose, raffinose, glucose, galactose, lactose, sucrose maltose, but not xylose.

From: Greenland Sea, (st. **5**), 3026 m; (st. **45**), 2754 m;

Norwegian Sea, (st. **1736**), 100 m.

Pacific Ocean, (st. **3814**), 400 m.

Assigned to *Debaryomyces globosus* Klöcker.

Cells spheroid, 2.0 – 5.0 μ, budding.

On Gorodkova's medium, meat-peptone agar and gypsum blocks, spores spheroid, formed after copulation. Spore mantles with verrucose thickenings. Cells which have not copulated turn into arthrospores. In old cultures discontinuities of outer layers of membranes observed in the arthrospores.

On wort agar–streak white, mat, smooth, margins in old cultures slightly scalloped.

Glucose, galactose, sucrose, maltose and raffinose not fermented. Arabinose, raffinose, glucose, galactose, lactose, sucrose and maltose assimilated but not xylose.

From: Norwegian Sea, (st. **1708**), 600, 800 m.

Assigned to *Debaryomyces guilliermondii* Dekker.

12

Antagonism in marine microorganisms*

It has long been known that sea water possesses bactericidal properties (Lipman, 1926; ZoBell, 1936; Wachsman, Hotchkiss, 1937; Krasil'nikov, 1938). Not only will bacteria transported into it fail to develop, but many of them perish comparatively rapidly

We know from De Giaxa (1889), that abundant bacterial growth in untreated sea water makes it unsuitable as a culture medium for other microorganisms, probably because toxic substances are formed.

Krasil'nikov (1938) observed that prolific bacterial growth rapidly occurred in thoroughly boiled Black Sea water placed in non-sterile vessels, the water becoming very cloudy, whereas unboiled water remained transparent under the same conditions; microscopy revealed only isolated cells, or none at all.

Kiribayashi and Aida (1934) observed that bacteria lived longer in sterile than in untreated sea water. Similar effects were observed by ZoBell (1946).

Sea water becomes more suitable for bacterial growth after boiling or autoclaving, because not only microbial antagonists, but also thermolabile toxic substances, are destroyed in the process.

Waksman and Hotchkiss (1937), stressing that bacteria live longer and are more active in sterilized than in unsterilized sea water, concluded that the relatively low density of bacteria in sea water was partly due to the antagonistic action of microorganisms and also of planktonic organisms.

Another consequence of microbial antagonism is to reduce the number of bacterial species inhabiting sea water kept under laboratory conditions (ZoBell, Anderson, 1936). Bacteria of the intestinal group – *Bact. coli, Bact. typhi., Bact. dysenteriae* and others – perish after a few days in sea water. De Giaxa, in his works on factors influencing the viability of pathogenic bacteria, established that bacteria of the intestinal group were rapidly destroyed in the sea. He found more than 100 000 bacteria per ml of sea water at a distance of 50 m from a sewage outlet, against 26 000 at a distance of 350 m and less than 100 at a distance of 3000 m.

*This chapter was written by Ye. N. Krasil'nikova.

Organisms pathogenic in man live longer in freshwater than in sea water. Beard and Meadowcroft (1935) and Balasac et al. (1952) conducted experiments in which they observed rapid diminution in the number of *B. typhi* and *B. coli* in sea water, although a few of the bacilli survived for more than a month. Similar results were obtained by ZoBell (1936). In his experiments, 99.9 % of microorganisms obtained from sewage effluent perished after two days culturing in sea water and only a few survived for about a month.

Carpenter et al. (1938) found that sea water destroyed 80% of organisms isolated from sewage effluent within half an hour. Gram-positive organisms were more sensitive to the bactericidal action of sea water than Gram-negative forms (Beard, Meadowcroft, 1935; ZoBell, 1936).

The inference from the above-mentioned examples is that there must be some factor in sea water which has a marked effect on the viability of bacteria. In laboratory cultures this factor operates variously on different species of bacteria; in some it is fatal and the cells rapidly perish in sea water; in others its effect is inhibitory and the cells develop poorly or not at all. The bactericidal and bacteriostatic action of sea water is greater than could be accounted for by salinity or osmotic pressure. The bactericidal agent is non-resistant to high temperatures and is destroyed if the water is boiled.

What kind of factors are responsible for the antimicrobial action of sea water? Some authors suggest that the disappearance of bacteria in the sea is due to their being eaten by small animals such as Copepoda and others (Voroshilova, Dianova, 1937); others attribute the bactericidal effect of sea water to its chemical composition (Johannesson, 1957); but the majority finds the explanation in the phenomenon of antagonism. The phenomenon among marine microorganisms has hardly been studied at all, apart from fragmentary observations reported by ZoBell (1946) in his monograph.*

Rosenfeld and ZoBell (1947) observed that samples of sea water collected in zones of peak bacterial population contained very high concentrations of bactericidal substances. They also studied the secretion of antibiotic substances by marine microorganisms. Fifty-eight pure cultures isolated from the sea were investigated, nine of which displayed antibiotic activity in relation to non-marine forms. These species, however, had been isolated mainly from the surface layers of the water and some of them may have been of aeolian origin or have reached the sea in river discharge.

Rosenfeld and ZoBell suggest that the bacteriostatic and bactericidal effect of sea water may be due to the existence of an autochthonous microflora which produces antibiotic substances and that the sea can be regarded as a potential source of antibiotics.

*(Editor's footnote). The possibility that plankton algae produce antibacterial substances should not be overlooked. There is some evidence that this occurs (see G. E. Fogg in *Physiology and Biochemistry of Algae*, edited by R. A. Lewin, Academic Press, New York and London, 1962, p. 480).

It was of interest to discover the extent and nature of antagonism among microorganisms inhabiting open bodies of water. For this purpose we used a large collection of cultures obtained by Kriss and co-workers in various seas and oceans. The whole collection was divided into groups according to morphological, cultural and biochemical characters. Strains from each group were selected for study and care was taken that all the oceans or seas investigated should be represented. In all, 235 strains were selected: 8 yeasts, 57 coccal forms, 26 spore-forming bacteria, 143 non-sporing bacteria and one strain of *Actinomyces*.

These strains belonged to the following species (strain numbers in parentheses); *Bacterium agile,* var. A (No. 1211, 3123, 3124, 3250, 4154, 4323, 4865, 5180, 7005, 7006, 7219, 7313); *Bact. agile,* var. B (No. 2236, 2321, 2326, 2564, 2675, 2829, 2836, 2951, 3205, 3211, 4099, 4122, 4151, 4203a, 4205, 4249, 4275, 4276, 4288, 4311, 4317, 4340, 4345, 4387, 4409, 4414, 4437, 4619, 5213, 5240, 5339, 5393, 5408, 5470, 5489, 5499, 5503, 5511, 7089, 7093, 7145, 7209, 7259, 7300, 7310, 7349, 7381, 7467); *Bact. agile,* var. C (No. 4118, 7098, 7163, 7216); *Bact. agile,* var. D (No. 4078, 4091, 4100, 4325, 5407, 7016); *Bact. agile,* var. E (No. 7157); *Bact. agile,* var. F (No. 4382, 7091, 7097, 7139); *Bact. agile,* var. H (No. 7345); *Bact. agile,* var. K (No. 5245); *Bacterium candicans,* var. A (No. 1131, 4225, 5513, 5799, 7031); *Bact. candicans,* var. B (No. 5341, 7142, 7182); *Bact. candicans,* var. D (No. 4004, 4007, 4682, 5543); *Bact. candicans,* var. G (No. 6295); *Bact. candicans,* var. H (No. 1026, 1034); *Bact. candicans,* var. I (No. 1023, 1032); *Bacterium parvulum,* var. A (No. 4164); *Bact. parvulum,* var. B (No. 1022, 2006, 2855, 4075, 4143, 4183, 4769, 5289); *Bact. parvulum,* var. C (No. 4182); *Bacterium imperiale,* var. A (No. 2189, 2224, 4451); *Pseudomonas sinuosa,* var. A (No. 2009, 2013, 2148, 2173, 4133); *Ps. sinuosa,* var. B (No. 1499); *Ps. sinuosa,* var. E (No. 2682); *Ps. sinuosa,* var. F (No. 4650, 5690); *Pseudomonas caudatus,* var. B (No. 1095); *Ps. caudatus,* var. C (No. 1013); *Pseudomonas fluorescens,* var. B (No. 107. 119, 129, 209, 302); *Ps. fluorescens,* var. C (No. 1, 106); *Ps. fluorescens,* var. D (No. 7a, 9); *Pseudomonas liquida,* var. A (No. 2513); *Pseudobacterium rosea-album,* var. A (No. 1551, 2230); *Pseudobact. rosea-album,* var. B (No. 1340, 2192); *Pseudobacterium biforme* (No. 2266, 2443); *Pseudobacterium cocciformis,* var. A (No. 500, 5135, 5358); *Pseudobacterium opacum,* var. B (No. 2385, 2387); *Pseudobacterium variabilis,* var. B (No. 6120); *Pseudobact. variabilis,* var. C (No. 6072); *Pseudobact. variabilis,* var. D (No. 2457); *Bacillus catenula,* var. A (No. 2041, 3016); *Bac. catenula,* var. C (No. 1184); *Bac. catenula,* var. D (No. 2038, 2218, 4328); *Bac. catenula,* var. E (No. 1004); *Bac. catenula,* var. F (No. 3266, 3286); *Bac. catenula,* var. H (No. 3244); *Bac. catenula,* var. I (No. 136a); *Bacillus idosus,* var. A (No. 1383); *Bac. idosus,* var. B (No. 1002); *Bac. idosus,* var. E (No. 137); *Bacillus filaris,* var. B (No. 1409); *Bac. filaris,* var. E (No. 1219); *Bac. filaris,* var. F (No. 1233); *Bac. filaris,* var. I (No. 2301, 4219, 4265, 4291); *Bacillus glutinosus,* var. A (No. 28); *Bacillus brevis*

(No. 4810); *Bacillus lubinskii* (No. 4834, 7281); *Micrococcus radiatus*, var. A (No. 1286); *M. radiatus*, var. C (No. 1464); *M. radiatus*, var. F (No. 4671, 5172); *M. radiatus*, var. G (No. 7041); *M. radiatus*, var. H (No. 14); *M. radiatus*, var. K (No. 2848); *M. radiatus*, var. L (No. 1256, 4691, 4829, 5035); *Micrococcus viticulosus*, var. E (No. 2508); *M. viticulosus* (No. 1014, 2501); *Micrococcus albicans*, var. A (No. 1006, 1057, 1269, 2011, 2132, 7021); *M. albicans*, var. D (No. 135, 6044); *M. albicans*, var. F (No. 134); *M. albicans*, var. G (No. 1188); *Micrococcus albescens* (No. 4247, 4253); *Micrococcus chlorinus* (No. 2283); *Micrococcus subflavus*, var. A (No. 1449); *M. subflavus*, var. B (No. 1108, 1113, 1115); *M. subflavus*, var. E (No. 6114); *Micrococcus conglomeratus*, var. A (No. 7029); *Micrococcus luteolus*, var. A (No. 4503, 4513, 7033); *Micrococcus rugatus*, var. A (No. 1315); *Micrococcus luteus*, var. B (No. 1243); *Micrococcus ochraceus*, var. A (No. 510); *M. ochraceus*, var. B (No. 4498); *M. ochraceus*, var. D (No. 1019); *M. ochraceus*, var. E (No. 1290); *Micrococcus roseus*, var. A (No. 917); *M. roseus*, var. B (No. 6012); *Micrococcus aurantiacus*, var. A (No. 2004, 2005, 2008); *M. aurantiacus*, var. D (No. 1287); *M. aurantiacus*, var. F (No. 4076); *Micrococcus cinnabareus*, var. D (No. 2483); *M. cinnabareus*, var. F (No. 1276); *M. cinnabareus*, var. G (No. 104); *Sarcina subflava*, var. A (No. 2221, 5015); *S. subflava*, var. B (No. 1491); *Actinomyces globisporus* (No. 2185).

The following media were used: meat-peptone agar (1.0 litre of meat bouillon, 1% of peptone, 0.5% of NaCl and 2% of agar-agar), potato agar, fish agar (2% of fish extract, 2% of glucose, 0.35% of chalk, 1 litre of tap water and 1.5% of agar-agar), Czapek's medium (0.5 g of K_2HPO_4, 0.5 g of $MgSO_4$, 0.5 g of NaCl, 1.0 g of $NaNO_3$, trace of $FeSO_4$, 2 – 5 g of $CaCO_3$, 20 g of sucrose, 1 litre of distilled water and 2 g of agar-agar), seaweed agar (algal decoction containing 1.5% agar-agar) prepared in sea water, sea water solidified with agar and a medium of the following composition: 0.5% glucose, 3% sea salt, 1 litre of distilled water and 1.5% of agar-agar. The agar block method was used for computing antibiotic activity of the microorganisms (Yegorov, 1957).

In the first series of experiments all 235 strains were tested for their antibiotic activity against four test organisms: *Bacterium coli, Staphylococcus aureus* 209, *Mycobacterium luteum*, and *Saccharomyces cerevisiae*. The test strains were incubated on meat-peptone agar at 27°C. *Bact. coli, Staph. aureus* and *Mycob. luteum* were seeded on meat-peptone agar and the yeasts on wort agar. The first two test organisms were incubated at 37°C, the other two at 27°C.

No antagonists were discovered in the yeast group. *Actinomyces* displayed antagonistic activity in relation to *Mycob. luteum* and the yeasts. Of the coccal group, five cultures showed antibiotic activity against *Mycob. luteum* and two of these were active also against *Staph. aureus* (Table 28). Among the non-sporing bacteria nine antagonists were discovered out of 143 cultures (Table 29), the diameter of the sterile zones

Table 28. Antagonistic action of coccal forms incubated on meat-peptone agar against four test organisms (figures indicate diameter of sterile zones in millimeters)

Strain no.	Where obtained	Depth, m	Test organisms			
			Bact. coli	*Staph. aureus*	*Mycob. luteum*	*Sacch. cerevisiae*
	Arctic Ocean					
14	88°04′ N 151°16′ W	400	—	—	—	—
104	89°29′ N 65°43′ W	0	—	—	—	—
134	89°29′ N 65°43′ W	Bottom	—	—	—	—
135	89°29′ N 65°43′ W	Bottom	—	—	15	—
510	85°53′ N 27°30′ W	0	—	—	—	—
917	86°26′ N 79°19′ E	50	—	—	—	—
	Greenland Sea					
1006	St. 2	200	—	—	—	—
1014	St. 3	0	—	9	17	—
1019	St. 3	250	—	—	—	—
1057	St. 4	500	—	—	—	—
1108	St. 6	0	—	—	—	—
1113	St. 6	200	—	—	—	—
1115	St. 6	250	—	—	—	—
1188	St. 12	50	—	—	—	—
1243	St. 23	1000	—	—	—	—
1256	St. 24	750	—	—	—	—
1269	St. 26	0	—	—	—	—
1276	St. 26	150	—	—	—	—
1286	St. 29	50	—	—	—	—
1287	St. 29	100	—	—	—	—
1290	St. 30	0	—	—	—	—
1315	St. 34	75	—	—	—	—
1449	St. 46	2000	—	—	—	—
1464	St. 49	750	—	—	—	—
1491	St. 51	400	—	—	—	—
	Indian Ocean					
2004	St. 212	100	—	—	—	—
2005	St. 212	100	—	—	—	—
2008	St. 212	75	—	—	—	—
2011	St. 213	10	—	—	—	—
2132	St. 238	121	—	—	—	—
2145	St. 240	104	—	—	—	—
2221	St. 249	0	—	—	—	—
2283	St. 252	2806	—	—	—	—
2483	St. 274	730	—	—	—	—
2501	St. 278	11	—	—	15	—
2508	St. 278	425	—	12	8	—

Table 28 (continued)

Strain no.	Where obtained	Depth, m	Test organisms			
			Bact. coli	*Staph. aureus*	*Mycob. luteum*	*Sacch. cerevisiae*
2848	St. 305	2450	—	—	—	—
	Pacific Ocean					
4076	St. 3778	2703	—	—	—	—
4247	St. 3791	424	—	—	20	—
4253	St. 3791	979	—	—	—	—
4266	St. 3795	0	—	—	—	—
4498	St. 3814	300	—	—	—	—
4503	St. 3814	605	—	—	—	—
4513	St. 3814	1472	—	—	—	—
4671	St. 3831	69	—	—	—	—
4691	St. 3831	1334	—	—	—	—
4829	St. 3839	48	—	—	—	—
5015	St. 3845	15	—	—	—	—
5035	St. 3845	482	—	—	—	—
5172	St. 3853	50	—	—	—	—
	Norwegian Sea					
6012	St. 1703	0	—	—	—	—
6044	St. 1708	500	—	—	—	—
6114	St. 1719	400	—	—	—	—
	Atlantic Ocean					
7021	St. 348	78	—	—	—	—
7029	St. 350	94	—	—	—	—
7033	St. 354	0	—	—	—	—
7041	St. 356	0	—	—	—	—

Table 29. Antagonistic action of non-sporing bacteria incubated on meat-peptone agar against four test organisms (figures indicate diameter of sterile zones in millimetres)

Strain no.	Where obtained	Depth, m	Test organisms			
			Bact. coli	*Staph. aureus*	*Mycob. luteum*	*Sacch. cerevisiae*
	Arctic Ocean					
1	88°04′ N 151°16′ W	10	—	—	10	—
7a	» »	100	—	—	15	—
9	» »	150	—	—	—	—
106	89°29′ N 65°43′ W	10	—	—	—	—
107	» »	25	—	—	—	—
119	» »	250	—	—	—	—
129	» »	2500	—	—	12	—
209	88°04′ N 151°16′ W	50	—	—	12	—
302	89°29′ N 65°43′ W	10	—	—	14	—

Table 29 (continued)

Strain no.	Where obtained	Depth, m	Test organisms			
			Bact. coli	*Staph. aureus*	*Mycob. luteum*	*Sacch. cerevisiae*
500	86°26′ N 79°19′ E	0	—	—	—	—
	Greenland Sea					
1013	St. 3	0	—	—	—	—
1022	» »	400	—	—	15	—
1023	» »	400	—	—	10	—
1026	» »	750	—	—	—	—
1032	» »	2000	—	—	—	—
1034	» »	2000	—	—	12	—
1095	St. 5	400	—	—	—	—
1131	St. 6	750	—	—	—	—
1211	St. 17	200	—	—	—	—
1340	St. 36	2500	—	—	—	—
1499	St. 54	600	—	—	—	—
1551	St. 23	Bottom	—	—	—	—
	Indian Ocean and Antarctic seas					
2006	St. 212	100	—	—	—	—
2009	» »	75	—	—	—	—
2013	St. 213	197	—	—	—	—
2148	St. 240	319	—	—	—	—
2173	St. 243	3330	—	—	—	—
2189	St. 246	362	—	—	—	—
2192	» »	362	—	—	—	—
2224	St. 249	77	—	—	—	—
2230	» »	380	—	—	—	—
2236	» »	1930	—	—	—	—
2266	St. 251	2788	—	—	—	—
2321	St. 259	1305	—	—	—	—
2326	St. 260	25	—	—	—	—
2385	St. 265	716	—	—	—	—
2387	» »	1430	—	—	—	—
2443	St 271	200	—	—	—	—
2457	» »	300	—	—	—	—
2513	St. 280	0	—	—	—	—
2564	St. 283	25	—	—	—	—
2675	St. 295	410	—	—	—	—
2682	» »	3000	—	—	—	—
2829	St. 305	150	—	—	—	—
2836	» »	425	—	—	—	—
2855	» »	4420	—	—	—	—
2951	St. 311	830	—	—	—	—
3123	St. 322	101	—	—	—	—
3124	» »	152	—	—	—	—
3205	St. 328	197	—	—	—	—
3211	St. 329	10	—	—	—	—

Table 29 (continued)

Strain no.	Where obtained	Depth, m	Test organisms			
			Bact. coli	*Staph. aureus*	*Mycob. luteum*	*Sacch. cerevisiae*
3250	St. 274	Bottom	—	—	—	—
	Pacific Ocean					
4004	St. 3777	0	—	—	—	—
4007	» »	11	—	—	—	—
4075	St. 3778	2150	—	—	—	—
4078	St. 3780	0	—	—	—	—
4091	» »	46	—	—	—	—
4098	» »	192	—	—	—	—
4099	» »	192	—	—	—	—
4100	St. 3780	192	—	—	—	—
4118	St. 3781	72	—	—	—	—
4122	» »	72	—	—	—	—
4133	St. 3782	61	—	—	—	—
4143	» »	1979	—	—	—	—
4151	St. 3786	10	—	—	—	—
4154	» »	45	—	—	—	—
4164	» »	195	—	—	—	—
4182	St. 3788	0	—	—	—	—
4183	» »	0	—	—	—	—
4203a	» »	304	—	—	—	—
4205	» »	304	—	—	—	—
4225	St. 3791	10	—	—	—	—
4249	» »	640	—	—	—	—
4275	St. 3795	41	—	—	—	—
4276	» »	41	—	—	—	—
4288	» »	422	—	—	—	—
4311	St. 3801	35	—	—	—	—
4317	» »	103	—	—	—	—
4323	» »	272	—	—	—	—
4325	» »	340	—	—	—	—
4340	St. 3802	50	—	—	—	—
4345	» »	75	—	—	—	—
4382	St. 3805	0	—	—	—	—
4387	» »	24	—	—	—	—
4409	» »	974	—	—	—	—
4414	» »	1950	—	—	—	—
4437	St. 3808	95	—	—	—	—
4451	St. 3812	2456	—	—	—	—
4619	St. 3825	290	—	—	—	—
4650	St. 3827	1508	—	—	—	—
4682	St. 3831	183	—	—	—	—
4769	St. 3837	248	—	—	—	—
4865	St. 3840	10	—	—	—	—
5135	St. 3851	45	—	—	—	—
5180	St. 3853	146	—	—	—	—
5213	St. 3854	10	—	—	—	—

Table 29 (continued)

Strain no.	Where obtained	Depth, m	Test organisms			
			Bact. coli	*Staph. aureus*	*Mycob. luteum*	*Sacch. cerevisiae*
5240	St. 3854	962	—	—	—	—
5245	St. 3855	0	—	—	—	—
5289	St. 3856	0	—	—	—	—
5339	St. 3857	98	—	—	—	—
5341	» »	117	—	—	—	—
5358	St. 3859	10	—	—	—	—
5393	St. 3860	107	—	—	—	—
5407	» »	1717	—	—	—	—
5408	» »	1717	—	—	—	—
5470	St. 3863	107	—	—	—	—
5489	St. 3864	26	—	—	—	—
5499	St. 3864	308	—	—	—	—
5503	» »	821	—	—	—	—
5511	St. 3866	50	—	—	—	—
5513	» »	100	—	—	—	—
5543	St. 3868	212	—	—	—	—
5690	St. 3875	406	—	—	—	—
5799	St. 3879	675	—	—	—	—
	Norwegian Sea					
6059	St. 1712	10	—	—	10	—
6072	» »	300	—	—	—	—
6120	St. 1719	800	—	—	—	—
6295	St. 1764	1500	—	—	—	—
	Atlantic Ocean					
7005	St. 345	76	—	—	—	—
7006	» »	95	—	—	—	—
7016	St. 346	0	—	—	—	—
7031	St. 352	10	—	—	—	—
7089	St. 364	10	—	—	—	—
7091	» »	31	—	—	—	—
7093	» »	101	—	—	—	—
7097	» »	607	—	—	—	—
7139	St. 367	100	—	—	—	—
7142	» »	200	—	—	—	—
7145	» »	400	—	—	—	—
7157	» »	4678	—	—	—	—
7163	St. 368	48	—	—	—	—
7182	St. 368	990	—	—	—	—
7209	St. 369	780	—	—	—	—
7216	» »	2990	—	—	—	—
7219	St. 370	0	—	—	—	—
7259	St. 372	189	—	—	—	—
7300	St. 374	314	—	—	—	—
7310	» »	2098	—	—	—	—
7313	» »	3086	—	—	—	—
7345	St. 378	146	—	—	—	—
7349	» »	388	—	—	—	—
7381	St. 380	1483	—	—	—	—
7467	St. 389	1260	—	—	—	—

being small. Antibiotic activity was displayed only against *Mycob. luteum.*

A large proportion of active forms was found in the spore-forming bacteria: of the 26 cultures, antagonistic activity was displayed by 11 strains, or roughly 42% of the total number of cultures tested (Table 30). Active forms made up roughly 9% of the cocci and 6% of the non-sporing bacteria.

In the next series of tests 26 strains which had proved to be antagonists were investigated in greater detail. The spectrum of their antibiotic action against *Bacterium coli, Staphylococcus aureus* 209, *Bacillus subtilis, Pseudomonas aurantiaca, Mycobacterium* sp. B – 5, *Mycob. luteum, Sarcina lutea, Actinomyces* sp. 2911, *Proactinomyces albus, Saccharomyces cerevisiae, Candida albicans, Monilia* sp., *Torulopsis lactis, Fusarium vasinfectum, Botrytis alii, Penicillium chrysogenum* was studied.

The bacterial cultures were incubated on meat-peptone agar and the yeasts and fungi on wort agar.

It can be seen from Table 31 that the action spectrum is much wider in the case of spore-forming bacteria than for other microorganisms and that the activity of the former is greater. The non-sporing bacteria are less active and their antibiotic spectrum is narrow, comprising mainly *Mycob. luteum, Sarcina lutea* and *Proact. albus*. In the coccal forms the spectrum of antibiotic action, very slightly wider than for non-sporing bacteria, is again narrow: the antibiotic activity is directed mainly against bacteria and does not inhibit the growth of yeasts and fungi. No antagonists of *B. coli* or of *Torulopsis lactis* were discovered in any of the groups studied.

In view of the fact that antibiotic properties are often determined by the composition of the medium in which the antagonists are incubated, 26 of the active organisms indicated above were inoculated into various media: potato agar, fish agar and Czapek's medium. In the main, all the bacteria and *Actinomyces* grew well on these media, whereas the coccal forms developed very poorly; in some cases hardly any growth could be detected in the Petri dishes.

The non-sporing Gram-negative bacteria (Table 32) showed slight antagonistic action against the test organisms investigated in the abovementioned media. Only in meat-peptone agar did all the antagonistic strains give sterile zones; but the same antagonistic strains incubated on fish agar, potato agar and Czapek's medium behaved differently.

The micrococci displayed antimicrobial activity against a number of test organisms on meat-peptone agar (Table 33). On fish agar and Czapek's medium the antibiotic spectrum was restricted to a small number of species; these showed no activity on potato agar.

Actinomyces developed well on all media but displayed antagonism to bacteria and fungi when incubated on meat-peptone agar and to yeasts when incubated on fish agar (Table 34). Despite abundant growth on Czapek's medium, this culture did not inhibit the growth of the test organisms.

Spore-forming bacteria grew well on meat-peptone agar, fish agar, potato

Table 30. Antagonistic action of spore-forming bacteria incubated on meat-peptone agar against four test organisms (figures indicate diameter of sterile zones in millimeters)

Strain no.	Where obtained	Depth, m	Test organisms			
			Bact. coli	*Staph. aureus*	*Mycob. luteum*	*Sacch. cerevisiae*
	Arctic Ocean					
28	88°04′ N 151°16′ W	Bottom	—	—	—	—
136a	89°29′ N 65°43′ W	Bottom	—	—	15	—
137	89°29′ N 65°43′ W	2500	—	—	12	22
	Greenland Sea					
1002	St. 1	50	—	—	10	—
1004	St. 2	10	—	—	—	—
1184	St. 12	0	—	—	17	—
1219	St. 22	750	—	—	10	—
1233	St. 23	75.	—	—	—	—
1383	St. 43	10	—	—	—	20
1409	St. 45	75	—	—	—	—
	Indian Ocean					
2038	St. 215	27	—	—	—	—
2041	St. 215	81	—	—	15	22
2218	St. 249	0	—	—	15	—
2301	St. 256	1018	—	—	—	—
3016	St. 314	3270	—	10	—	—
3244	St. 271	Bottom	—	—	—	—
3266	St. 302	Bottom	—	—	—	—
3281	St. 323	Bottom	—	—	10	—
3286	St. 326	Bottom	—	—	—	—
	Pacific Ocean					
4219	St. 3788	2034	—	—	—	—
4265	St. 3795	0	—	—	—	—
4291	St. 3795	518	—	—	—	—
4328	St. 3801	340	—	—	10	—
4810	St. 3838	560	—	—	—	—
4834	St. 3839	71	—	—	—	—
	Atlantic Ocean					
7281	St. 372	3946	—	—	—	—

Table 31. Antagonistic action of cultures incubated on meat-peptone agar (figures indicate diameter of sterile zones in millimetres)

Test organism	Strain no.																										Total no. of active strains
	Spore-forming bacteria											Non-sporing bacteria									Coccal forms					Actinomycetes	
	136a	137	1002	1184	1219	1383	2041	2218	3016	3281	4328	1	7a	129	209	302	1022	1023	1034	6059	135	2501	2508	4247	1014	2185	
Bact. coli	—	—	—	—	—	—	—	—	—	—	—	—	—	—	—	—	—	—	—	—	—	—	—	—	—	—	—
Staph. aureus	—	—	—	—	—	—	—	—	9	—	—	—	—	—	—	—	—	—	—	—	—	—	12	—	9	—	3
Bac. subtilis	—	—	—	9	—	—	—	—	—	—	—	—	—	—	—	—	—	—	—	—	—	—	—	—	—	—	1
Ps. aurantiaca	—	—	—	—	—	—	—	—	—	—	—	—	—	—	—	—	9	—	9	—	—	9	—	—	—	—	3
Bact. prodigiosum	—	—	—	—	—	—	—	—	—	—	—	—	—	—	—	—	—	—	—	—	—	—	—	—	—	—	—
Mycob. sp.	—	—	—	—	—	—	—	—	—	—	—	—	—	—	—	—	15	—	—	—	—	9	—	—	16	—	3
Mycob. luteum	15	12	10	17	10	—	15	15	—	10	10	10	15	12	12	14	15	10	12	8	15	15	18	20	17	11	24
Sarcina lutea	9	20	—	—	11	20	16	25	18	—	9	—	12	—	—	—	—	—	—	—	—	10	11	16	10	9	14
Proact. albus	8	—	—	10	25	—	16	23	20	13	14	—	—	—	—	—	9	—	8	—	—	15	18	17	18	—	14
Act. sp.	—	—	—	18	—	20	—		—	—	—	—	—	—	—	—	—	—	—	—	—	—	—	—	—	—	2
Sacch. cerevisiae	—	22	—	—	—	20	22	—	—	—	—	—	—	—	—	—	—	—	—	—	—	—	—	—	—	—	3
Candida albicans	—	15	—	—	—	19	14	—	—	—	—	—	—	—	—	—	—	—	—	—	—	—	—	—	—	—	3
Monilia sp.	—	—	—	—	—	16	—	—	—	—	—	—	—	—	—	—	—	—	—	—	—	—	—	—	—	—	1
Torulopsis lactis	—	—	—	—	—	—	—	—	—	—	—	—	—	—	—	—	—	—	—	—	—	—	—	—	—	—	—
Botrytis alii	—	16	—	16	—	16	—	—	—	—	—	—	—	—	—	—	—	—	—	—	—	—	—	—	—	—	3
Fusarium vasinfectum	—	—	—	20	—	—	—	—	—	—	—	—	—	—	—	—	—	—	—	—	—	—	—	—	—	16	2
Penicillium chrysogenum	—	18	13	18	—	20	9	—	9	—	10	—	—	—	14	—	—	—	—	—	—	—	—	—	—	14	9

Table 32. Influence of composition of nutrient medium on spectrum of antibiotic action of non-sporing gram-negative bacteria (figures indicate diameter of sterile zones in millimeters).

Strain no.	Meat-peptone agar	Fish agar	Potato agar		Czapek's medium		Seaweed agar	Sea water plus 5% agar	Saline agar with glucose
			Without salt	With 3% sea salt	Without salt	With 3% sea salt			
1	*Mycob. luteum* – 10	–	*Mycob. luteum* – 11	*Act.* sp.–11	–	*Mycob. luteum* – 14 *Sarcina lutea* – 11	–	–	–
7a	*Mycob. luteum* – 15 *Sarcina lutea* – 12	*Proact. albus* – 12	–	–	–	–	–	–	–
129	*Mycob. luteum* – 12	–	*Mycob. luteum* – 10 *Proact. albus* – 8	–	–	*Mycob. luteum* – 15	–	–	–
209	*Mycob. luteum* – 12 *Penicillium chrysogenum* – 10	–	–	–	–	–	–	–	–
302	*Mycob. luteum*–14	–	–	*Act.* sp.–20	–	*Act.* sp.–20	–	–	–

Table 32 (continued)

Strain no.	Meat-peptone agar	Fish agar	Potato agar		Czapek's medium		Seaweed agar	Sea water plus 1.5% agar	Saline agar with glucose
			Without salt	With 3% sea salt	Without salt	With 3% sea salt			
1022	*Ps. aurantiaca* – 9 *Mycob. sp.* – 15 *Mycob. luteum* – 12 *Proact. albus* – 9	–	–	*Mycob. luteum* – 8 *Sarcina lutea*–12	–	–	–	–	–
1023	*Mycob. luteum* – 10	*Act.* sp.– 12	–	–	*Mycob. luteum* – 10	*Mycob. luteum* –10 *Sarcina lutea* –8 *Act.* sp.–9	–	–	–
1034	*Ps. aurantiaca* – 9 *Mycob. luteum* – 12 *Proact. albus* – 8	*Mycob. luteum* – 10	*Staph. aureus* – 11 *Mycob. luteum* – 15 *Sarcina lutea* – 11 *Proact. albus* – 14 *Sacch. cerevisiae* – 12	–	–	–	*Mycob.* sp.– 9 *Mycob. luteum* – 9	*Mycob. luteum* – 8	–
6059*	*Mycob. luteum* – 8	–	–	–	*Proact. albus* –8	–	–	–	–

*Species affinity not determined.

Table 33. Influence of nutrient medium on spectrum of antibiotic action of micrococci (figures indicate diameter of sterile zones in millimetres)

Strain no.	Meat-peptone agar	Fish agar	Potato agar		Czapek's medium		Seaweed agar	Sea water plus 1.5% agar	Saline agar with glucose
			Without salt	With 3% sea salt	Without salt	With 3% sea salt			
135	*Mycob. luteum* – 15	*Mycob. luteum* – 11 *Sarcina lutea*–11	–	–	–	–	–	–	–
1014	*Staph. aureus* – 9 *Ps. aurantiaca* – 8 *Mycob.* sp. – 16 *Mycob. luteum* – 17 *Sarcina lutea* – 10 *Proact. albus* – 18	*Mycob. luteum* – 12	–	–	*Proact. albus* – 13	*Mycob. luteum* – 10 *Act.* sp.–9	–	–	–
2501	*Ps. aurantiaca* – 9 *Mycob.* sp. – 9 *Mycob. luteum* – 15 *Sarcina lutea* – 10 *Proact. albus* – 15	*Mycob. luteum* – 12	–	*Mycob. luteum* – 8	*Mycob. luteum* – 9 *Sarcina lutea* – 8 *Proact. albus* – 9	*Mycob. luteum* – 11 *Act.* sp.–10	–	–	*Mycob.* sp.– 11
2508	*Staph. aureus* – 12 *Mycob. luteum* – 18 *Sarcina lutea* – 11 *Proact. albus* – 18	*Mycob. luteum* – 12	–	*Act.* sp.– 17	*Mycob. luteum* – 10 *Proact. albus* – 11	*Mycob. luteum* – 11 *Act.* sp.–10	*Mycob. luteum* – 12 *Staph. aureus* – 8	–	*Mycob.* sp.– 9
4247	*Mycob. luteum* – 20 *Sarcina lutea* – 16 *Proact. albus* – 17	*Mycob. luteum* – 12	–	–	–	–	–	–	–

Table 34. Influence of nutrient medium on spectrum of antibiotic action of actinomycetes (figures indicate diameter of sterile zones in millimetres)

Strain no.	Meat-peptone agar	Fish agar	Potato agar		Czapek's medium		Seaweed agar	Sea water plus 1.5% agar	Saline agar with glucose
			Without salt	With 3% sea salt	Without salt	With 3% sea salt			
2185	*Mycob. luteum* – 11 *Sarcina lutea* – 9 *Botrytis alii* – 12 *Penicillium chrysogenum* – 11	*Mycob. luteum* – 12 *Sacch. cerevisiae* – 12 *Candida albicans* – 15 *Monilia* sp. – 8 *Torulopsis lactis* – 10	*Candida albicans* – 8	*Mycob. luteum* – 17 *Act.* sp – 15 *Sacch. cerevisiae* – 11 *Candida albicans* – 9 *Monilia* sp. – 8 *Torulopsis lactis* – 11	–	*Mycob. luteum* – 14 *Sacch. cerevisiae* – 11 *Candida albicans* – 9 *Monilia* sp. – 8 *T. lactis* – 8	*Proact. albicans* – 8 *Sacch. cerevisiae* – 11 *Candida albicans* – 9 *Monilia* sp. – 8 *T. lactis* – 12 *Penicillium chrysogenum* – 11	*Proact. albus* – 8 *Candida albicans* – 8 *Penicillium chrysogenum* – 11	*Act.* sp. – 8

Table 35. Influence of composition of nutrient medium on spectrum
indicate diameter of ster

Strain no.	Meat-peptone agar	Fish agar	Potato agar	
			Without salt	With 3% sea s
136a	*Mycob. luteum*–15 *Sarcina lutea*–9 *Proact. albus*–8	*Staph. aureus*–20 *Mycob. luteum*–15 *Sarcina lutea*–9 *Proact. albus*–16 *Sacch. cerevisiae* –27 *Candida albicans* –16	*Staph. aureus*–12 *Mycob. luteum*–12 *Proact. albus*–12 *Sacch. cerevisiae* –15 *Candida albicans* –14	*Staph. aureus*- *Mycob. luteum*- *Sarcina lutea*- *Act.* sp. – 10 *Sacch. cerevis* –15 *Candida albica* –16
1184	*Bac. subtilis*–9 *Mycob. luteum*–17 *Proact. albus*–10 *Act.* sp. – 18 *Fusarium vasinfectum*– 12 *Botrytis alii*–14 *Penicillium chrysogenum*–12	*Mycob. luteum*–20 *Sarcina lutea*–9 *Act.* sp. – 22	*Mycob. luteum*–11 *Sarcina lutea*–12 *Proact. albus* –16 *Act.* sp.–27 *Fusarium vasinfectum*–11	*Mycob. luteum*- *Proact. albus*- *Act.* sp. – 26
2041	*Mycob. luteum*–15 *Sarcina lutea*–16 *Proact. albus*–16 *Sacch. cerevisiae* –22 *Candida albicans* –14 *Penicillium chrysogenum*–9	*Staph. aureus*–12 *Mycob. luteum*–15 *Sarcina lutea*–10 *Sacch. cerevisiae* –17 *Candida albicans* –16	*Sarcina lutea*–8 *Proact. albus*–10 *Candida albicans* –11	*Candida albica* –8
2218	*Mycob. luteum*–15 *Sarcina lutea*–25 *Proact. albus*–23	*Staph. aureus*–14 *Mycob. luteum*–11 *Sarcina lutea*–18 *Sacch. cerevisiae* –16 *Candida albicans* –16	*Staph. aureus*–9 *Sarcina lutea*–12 *Proact. albus*–23 *Candida albicans* –8	*Staph. aureus*– *Mycob. luteum*- *Candida albica* –10
3016	*Staph. aureus*–9 *Sarcina lutea*–18 *Proact. albus*–20 *Sacch. cerevisiae* –13 *Penicillium chrysogenum*–9	*Bact. coli*–10 *Staph. aureus*–16 *Mycob. luteum*–16 *Sarcina lutea*–12 *Sacch. cerevisiae* –23 *Candida albicans* –18	*Staph. aureus*–16 *Sarcina lutea*–10 *Proact. albus*–27 *Sacch. cerevisiae* –19 *Candida albicans* –17	*Mycob. luteum*- *Candida albica* –9
4328	*Mycob. luteum*–10 *Sarcina lutea*–9 *Proact. albus*–14	*Staph. aureus*–12 *Proact. albus*–17 *Sacch. cerevisiae* –11 *Candida albicans* –16	*Staph. aureus*–17 *Sarcina lutea*–9 *Proact. albus*–18 *Sacch. cerevisiae* –18 *Candida albicans* –13	*Staph. aureus*– *Proact. albus*– *Candida albica* –12

iotic action of spore-forming bacteria (*Bacillus catenula*) (figures
s in millimetres)

Czapek's medium		Seaweed agar	Sea water plus 1.5% agar	Saline agar with glucose
thout salt	With 3% sea salt			
h. aureus–23 *b. luteum*–12 *ct. albus*–20 *h. cerevisiae* 8 *lida albicans* 0 *lia* sp. – 11	*Staph. aureus*–18 *Mycob. luteum*–15 *Sarcina lutea*–11 *Act.* sp. – 16 *Sacch. cerevisiae* –24 *Candida albicans* –22	*Mycob. luteum* –10 *Proact. albus* –10	*Mycob. luteum* –9 *Proact. albus* –12	
h. aureus–8 *subtilis*–9 *b. luteum*–12 *ct. albus*–15 sp. – 24 *h. cerevisiae*	*Staph. aureus*–9 *Bac. subtilis*–9 *Mycob. luteum*–12 *Proact. albus*–10 *Act.* sp. – 27 *Sacch. cerevisiae* –10	*Staph. aureus* –8 *Bac. subtilis* –8 *Mycob. luteum* –9 *Sarcina lutea* –8 *Act.* sp. – 12 *Fusarium vasinfectum*–10	*Bac. subtilis* –9 *Mycob. luteum* –8 *Act.* sp.– 12 *Fusarium vasinfectum*–8	*Staph. aureus* –8 *Bac. subtilis* –8 *Mycob. luteum* –10 *Act.* sp.–11 *Fusarium vasinfectum*–11 *Penicillium chrysogenum*–9
h. aureus–24 *ct. albus*–14 *h. cerevisiae* 0 *dida albicans* 1	*Sarcina lutea*–12 *Sacch. cerevisiae* –16 *Candida albicans* –18	*Sarcina lutea* –8	–	*Proact. albus* –9
h. aureus–16 *ct. albus*–15 *h. cerevisiae* 1 *lida albicans* 7	*Mycob. luteum*–11 *Sarcina lutea*–18 *Candida albicans* –8	–	–	*Proact. albus* –8 *Fusarium vasinfectum*–9
t. coli–8 *h. aureus*–18 *ct albus*–22 *h. cerevisiae* 2 *dida albicans* 2	*Staph. aureus*–8 *Sarcina lutea*–10 *Sacch. cerevisiae* –17 *Candida albicans* –13	*Mycob.* sp.– 9	*Mycob.* sp.– 9	*Mycob.* sp.–11 *Proact. albus* –8 *Fusarium vasinfectum*–10
h. aureus–9 *ob. luteum*–8 *cina lutea*–8 *act. albus*–11 *dida albicans* 9	*Mycob. luteum*–8	*Sarcina lutea* –9 *Proact. albus* –8	*Sarcina lutea* –8 *Proact. albus* –8	*Proact. albus* –9

Table 36. Influence of composition of nutrient medium on spectrum
filaris) (figures indicate diamete

Strain no.	Meat-peptone agar	Fish agar	Potato agar	
			Without salt	With 3% sea s
137	*Mycob. luteum*–12 *Sarcina lutea*–20 *Sacch. cerevisiae* –22 *Candida albicans* –15 *Fusarium vasinfectum*–16 *Penicillium chrysogenum*–18	*Staph. aureus* –12 *Sarcina lutea*–15 *Proact. albus*–12 *Sacch. cerevisiae* –18 *Candida albicans* –16 *Fusarium vasinfectum*–10	*Mycob. luteum*–9 *Sarcina lutea*–22 *Proact. albus*–17 *Sacch. cerevisiae* –11 *Candida albicans* –11 *Fusarium vasinfectum* –10	*Mycob. luteum* *Proact. albus*- *Candida albic* –9
1002	*Mycob. luteum*–10 *Penicillium chrysogenum*–12	*Staph. aureus*–20 *Mycob. luteum*–12 *Sarcina lutea*–10 *Act.* sp.–22 *Sacch. cerevisiae* –25 *Candida albicans* –20 *Fusarium vasinfectum* – 12	*Staph. aureus*–12 *Mycob. luteum*–16 *Act.* sp.–20 *Sacch. cerevisiae* –16 *Candida albicans* –16 *Fusarium vasinfectum*–10	*Mycob. luteum* *Act.* sp.–22
1219	*Mycob. luteum*–10 *Sarcina lutea*–11 *Proact. albus*–25	*Mycob. luteum*–16 *Sarcina lutea*–12 *Proact. albus*–24	*Sarcina lutea*–8 *Proact. albus*–18	*Mycob. luteum* *Act.* sp.–12
1383	*Sarcina lutea*–20 *Act.* sp.–20 *Sacch. cerevisiae* –12 *Candida albicans* –19 *Monilia* sp.–16 *Fusarium vasinfectum*–12 *Penicillium chrysogenum*–12	*Bact. coli*–8 *Staph. aureus*–22 *Mycob. luteum*–22 *Sarcina lutea*–20 *Act.* sp.–22 *Sacch. cerevisiae* –27 *Candida albicans* –22 *Fusarium vasinfectum*–14	*Staph. aureus*–20 *Mycob. luteum*–9 *Sarcina lutea*–18 *Act.* sp.–22 *Sacch. cerevisiae* –26 *Candida albicans* –20 *Fusarium vasinfectum*–10	*Staph. aureus*- *Mycob. luteum* *Act.* sp.–26 *Sacch. cerevis* –14 *Candida albic* –9
3281*	*Mycob. luteum*–10 *Proact. albus*–13	–	–	*Mycob. luteum* –10 *Sarcina lutea*-

*Species affinity not determined

ɔiotic action of spore-forming bacteria (*Bacillus idosus, Bacillus*
.le zones in millimetres)

Czapek's medium		Seaweed agar	Sea water plus 1.5% agar	Saline agar with glucose
ithout salt	With 3% sea salt			
h. aureus–23 *ɔb. luteum*–10 *ina lutea*–22 *ct. albus*–14 *h. cerevisiae* 6 *lida albicans* 8 *ilia* sp.–12 *arium vasin-tum*–11	*Mycob. luteum*–10 *Sarcina lutea*–12 *Candida albicans* –12	*Staph. aureus*–8 *Mycob. luteum*–9 *Proact. albus*–9 *Fusarium vasinfectum*–8	*Mycob. luteum* –9 *Proact. albus* –8 *Fusarium vasinfectum*–8	*Mycob. luteum*–9 *Proact. albus*–8 *Fusarium vasinfectum*–8 *Penicillium chrysogenum*–10
h. aureus–23 *ob. luteum*–24 *ina lutea*–13 sp.–24 *ch. cerevisiae* 4 *dida albicans* 2 *ilia* sp.–11 *arium vasin-ctum*–10	*Staph. aureus*–9 *Mycob. luteum*–25 *Sarcina lutea*–8 *Act.* sp.–26 *Sacch. cerevisiae* –14 *Candida albicans* –12	*Mycob. luteum*–9 *Act.* sp.–14 *Candida albicans* –9 *Fusarium vasinfectum*–8	*Proact. albus* –8 *Fusarium vasinfectum*–9	*Candida albicans* –12 *Fusarium vasinfectum*–10 *Penicillium chrysogenum*–9
. subtilis–9 *ina lutea*–13 *act. albus*–16 . sp.–10	*Bac. subtilis*–9 *Sarcina lutea*–11 *Proact. albus*–11 *Act.* sp.–12	*Mycob.* sp.–9 *Act.* sp.–12	*Act.* sp.–12	*Proact. albus*–14 *Act.* sp. –10
t. coli–12 *h. aureus*–24 *ob. luteum*–10 . sp.–22 *ch. cerevisiae* 28 *dida albicans* 20 *ilia* sp.–16 *arium vasin-tum*–10	*Staph. aureus*–15 *Mycob. luteum*–12 *Sarcina lutea*–18 *Act.* sp.–20 *Sacch. cerevisiae* –24 *Candida albicans* –18	*Mycob. luteum* –8 *Proact. albus*–9 *Act.* sp.–10 *Fusarium vasinfectum*–8	*Mycob. luteum* –8 *Proact. albus* –8 *Fusarium vasinfectum*–8	*Mycob. luteum*–9 *Sacch. cerevisiae* –9 *Candida albicans* –8 *Fusarium vasinfectum*–10
–	–	*Mycob. luteum* –9	–	–

agar and Czapek's medium and displayed more or less strong antibiotic action against a large number of the test cultures; their activity was expressed in varying degrees, depending on the composition of the medium (Tables 35 and 36).

The influence of sea salt on the antibiotic properties of 26 strains of marine antagonists was studied in a further set of experiments, in which 3% of salt were added to Czapek's medium and to potato agar. *Actinomyces* and most of the spore-forming bacteria grew well on these media. Non-sporing bacteria and micrococci grew poorly on the saline potato agar and hardly any growth was perceptible on the saline Czapek's medium.

The difference in *Actinomyces* behaviour after the addition of sea salt to the media can be seen from Table 34: there is only one instance of inhibiting action displayed by *Actinomyces* on the salt-free potato agar and none on Czapek's medium, but with the addition of sea salt the antimicrobial spectrum widens.

In other groups of microorganisms no such phenomenon was observed, with the exception of a few cases in which micrococci started to behave more actively against some of the test organisms after the addition of salt to the potato agar (Table 33). Gram-negative non-sporing bacteria (strains Nos. 1, 129, 302) became active on saline Czapek's medium against one or two species, whereas they had been inactive on the salt-free medium. Strains 1 and 302 suppressed the growth of *Actinomyces* species on potato agar only after salt had been added (Table 32).

In the spore-forming bacterial cultures (Tables 35 and 36) the antimicrobial spectrum narrowed in most cases after the addition of salt to the media and activity also was found to diminish.

It was of interest to test also algae with sea water added as a nutrient medium and salt agar with glucose. Cultures were incubated in these media and the rate of growth and antimicrobial activity were observed. The former was determined from the turbidity of the liquid medium, measured with an electronephelometer, and the latter from the inhibition of growth in the test organisms. Better growth was observed in all microorganisms in the algal decoction.*

The micrococci (Table 33) showed no activity when incubated on these media, with the exception of strains 2501 and 2508, which caused very weak inhibition zones on the algal and saline agars with glucose.

With one exception, strain 1034, the Gram-negative bacteria also were inactive on these media (Table 32). In the majority of the spore-forming bacteria activity was in all cases low on incubation in algal agar and saline agar with glucose (Tables 35 and 36).

* (Editor's footnote). It is unfortunate that the species of alga and the method of preparation of the decoction are not stated. Antibiotics have been extracted from many kinds of seaweed (see R. A. Lewin in *Physiology and Biochemistry of Algae*, edited by R. A. Lewin, Academic Press, New York and London, 1962, p. 841).

The spectrum of antibiotic action of *Actinomyces* on algal agar was wide, but the zones formed were themselves small (Table 34).

The strains tested were found to include eight cultures obtained from Arctic Ocean, Greenland Sea and Indian Ocean mud. In the general test for antagonistic properties these organisms displayed no activity at all. Assuming that they were adapted to mud, we tested the possibility of incubating them on a medium prepared from mud (1 litre of sea water, 50 ml of mud decoction and 15 g of agar-agar). On this medium all eight cultures developed comparatively well, but were not capable of forming antibiotic substances.

In conclusion, it should be noted that the majority of the active forms with which the work was performed had been isolated at high-latitude stations. Whether this was the result of random selection of the strains or indicates a definite pattern we cannot tell, since our material was insufficient to permit a conclusion.

13

Bacteriophages in cultures of marine micro-organisms

The earliest data on bacteriophages in sea water date from the 1930's and relate to lytic agents attacking bacteria mainly of faecal origin.

Arloing and Sempé (1926) added sea-water filtrate to cultures of *Bact. paratyphi* A, *Bact. typhi* and *Bact. dysenteriae* Shiga. Samples of surface water were taken at South American ports, from the Atlantic Ocean, the Indian Ocean, the Red Sea and the Suez canal. Distinct lysis of these cultures was observed in the case of water taken from harbours contaminated with waste. In the open sea the presence of phage was doubtful, possibly because the cultures were of bacteria not indigenous to the sea. In contaminated water from the Monaco marine aquarium, Fejgin (1926) detected a polyvalent phage active against *Bact. dysenteriae* Shiga and *Bact. dysenteriae* Flexner. Asheshova (1926) isolated a phage active against *Ps. pyocyanea* from water in the harbour of Dubrovnik.

The first work in which deep-sea microbes were used as test organisms was the research on bacteriophages in the Black Sea described by Kriss and Rukina in 1947. The phages lysed cocci, non-sporing and spore-forming bacteria of various species. Smith and Krueger (1954) isolated a vibrio and a phage active against it from mud in San Francisco Bay.

Spencer (1960) made an interesting attempt to determine the concentration of phage particles in water samples from the North Sea, 10 miles from the Scottish coast. The test material consisted of 40 strains of bacteria isolated from fish and sea water. According to Spencer's data, from 1 to 5 particles of phage were found in 10 ml of water, although in one sample the concentration reached 100 particles to 10 ml of water.*

In studying the microflora of the seas and oceans it is essential to allow for the possible presence of phage in cultures of marine micro-organisms.

In the course of five years inspection of microbial cultures obtained

*(Editor's footnote). For a further account of work on this subject see R. Spencer, 1963, in *Symposium on Marine Microbiology*, edited by C. H. Oppenheimer, Thomas, Springfield, Illinois, pp. 350-65.

during ocean voyages (1954 – 9) we recorded occurrences of zones of lysis of the tâches vierges type in certain cultures. On routine reinoculation in April 1960, however, the lysis effect took on a mass character and clear zones of lysis were observed in 752 cultures (Table 37). The same medium as before had been used for the reinoculation (tryptic hydrolysate of fish meal), but the pH was now 7.2, whereas the pH of the medium previously used for reinoculation had been 7.8.

No instance of lysis was observed in the Arctic Ocean cultures, which were always reinoculated on nutrient agar of pH 7.2. The fact that lysis occurred simultaneously in a large number of cultures may possibly have been due to the sharp change in the pH of the medium; for it was not observed subsequently in cultures seeded on nutrient agar of pH 7.2. The cultures which displayed zones of lysis included non-sporing rods, cocci and spore-forming bacteria.

Table 38 shows the number of water samples collected in various geographical zones of the sea and oceans from which microbial cultures with zones of lysis were obtained. It can be seen that the incidence of cultures with zones of lysis becomes more frequent with proximity to the tropics.

In order to obtain confirmation of the presence of phage in the zones of lysis the cultures were prepared for electron microscopy by the following method.* The material, which was washed off in a drop of distilled water on a grid carrying the film, was carefully picked up with a platinum needle from sterile zones. After the drop had dried, the preparations were shadowed with chromium. The preparations thus obtained proved to be heavily contaminated. In order to avoid contamination, we used the following method of attaching the particles to the film (Stefanov, 1962). Drops of distilled water were placed in a dish floating on the surface of water. The temperature of the water was 45 – 50°C. The grid with the preparation was lowered on to the drop, with the film downwards. After 10 to 30 minutes of exposure the grids with the preparation were removed and the liquid was soaked up from the grids with filter paper. The preparations were shadowed with tungsten oxide. Bacterial cells and flagella were detected in them but no particles of phage were found.

A different method yielded better results. Into all the test tubes in which zones of lysis were observed in the cultures were poured 2 ml of 1% formalin solution and 5 ml of distilled water. The test tubes were then agitated for a long time and after this the suspensions were transferred to centrifuge tubes and centrifuged, first for 10 minutes at 7000 rpm and then at 10 000 rpm for 15 minutes. A sample was taken from the middle layer of the liquid with a pipette. The hot fixation method was then applied in a slightly modified form. The dish was placed on the surface of water which had been poured into a Dewar flask. The water temperature was 50 – 55°C and

*These investigations were performed by Ye. I. Smirnova and L. N. Khadzhi-Murat.

Table 37. Lysis in cultures of marine microorganisms

Provenance of culture	Total no. of microbial cultures	No. of cultures with zones of lysis	Cultures with zones of lysis as %age of total no. of cultures
Pacific Ocean	1104	293	26
Indian Ocean and seas adjoining Antarctica . . .	805	302	38
Atlantic Ocean	412	91	22
Norwegian Sea	88	18	20
Greenland Sea	188	48	25
Arctic Ocean . . .	177	Nil	—

Table 38. Geographical distribution of marine microorganisms yielding cultures in which zones of lysis were detected

Latitude	Pacific Ocean			Indian Ocean			Atlantic Ocean		
	Total no. of water samples	No. of samples from which bacterial cultures with zones of lysis were obtained	% age of total no. of samples	Total no. of water samples	No. of samples from which bacterial cultures with zones of lysis were obtained	% age of total no. of samples	Total no. of water samples	No. of samples from which bacterial cultures with zones of lysis were obtained	% age of total no. of samples
66—60°N	—	—	—	—	—	—	49	2	2
60—50°N	—	—	—	—	—	—	29	2	7
50—40°N	—	—	—	—	—	—	52	3	6
40—23°N	152	17	11	—	—	—	58	11	19
23—10°N	165	37	22	74	27	36	100	33	33
10°N —10°S	278	97	35	106	35	33	75	17	23
10—23°S	160	45	28	89	49	55	61	10	16
23—40°S	236	44	18	176	54	31	—	—	—
40—50°S	36	10	27	135	35	26	—	—	—
50—60°S	—	—	—	213	43	20	—	—	—
60—70°S	—	—	—	273	32	12	—	—	—

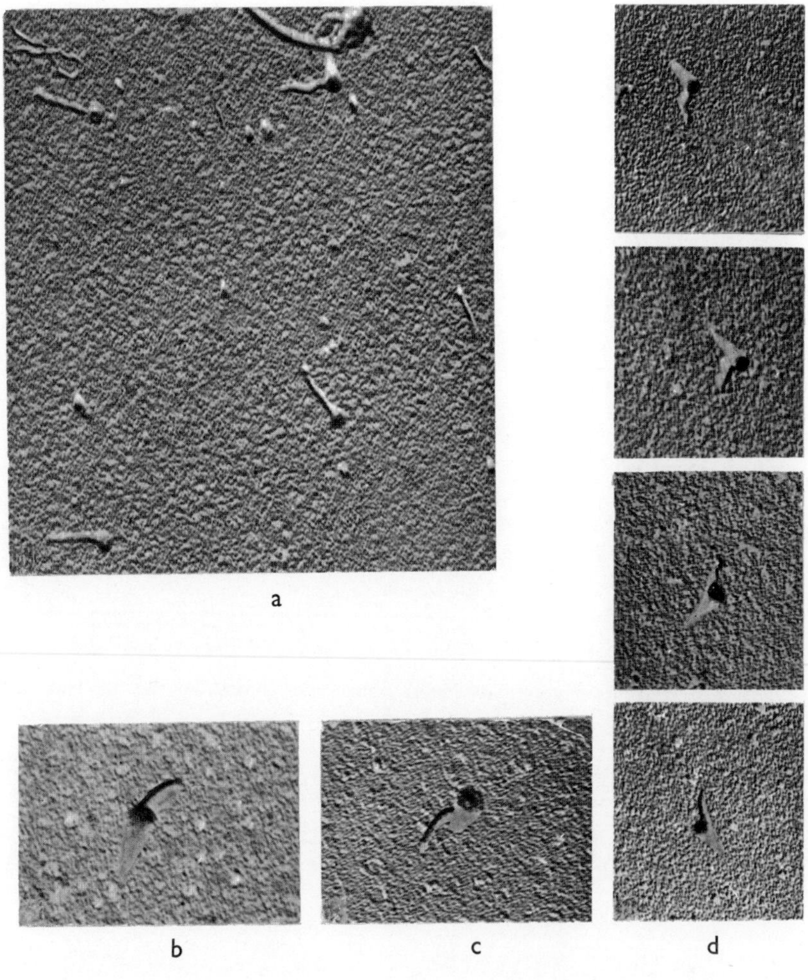

a - *Pseudobacterium cocciformis*, var. A, culture obtained from Pacific Ocean, depth 68 m; b - *Bact. candicans*, var. B, culture obtained from Pacific Ocean, depth 263 m; c - *Bact. agile*, var. A, culture obtained from Atlantic Ocean, depth 886 m; d - *Bact. agile*, var. B, culture obtained from Indian Ocean, depth 26 m

Fig. 17 Phage corpuscles in cultures with zones of lysis

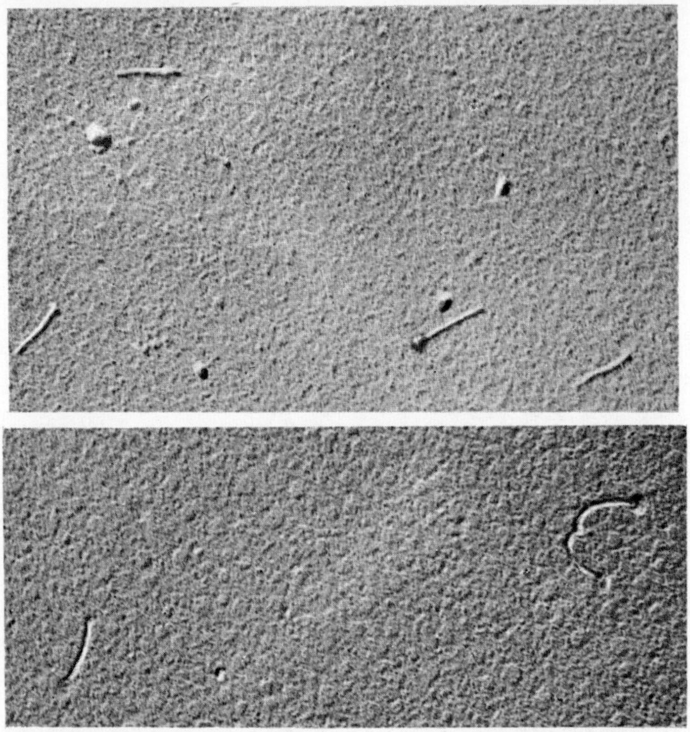

a

b

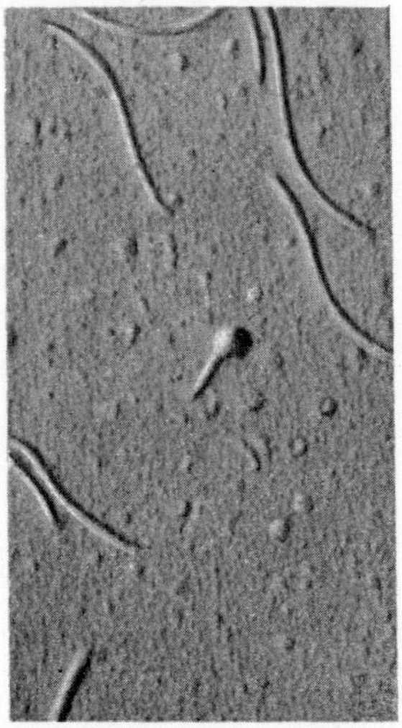

c

a - *Micrococcus radiatus*, Indian Ocean, 2884 m; b - *Bact. agile*, var. B, Indian Ocean, 275 m; c - *Bact. agile*, var. B, Pacific Ocean, surface

Fig. 18 Phage corpuscles in cultures with zones of lysis

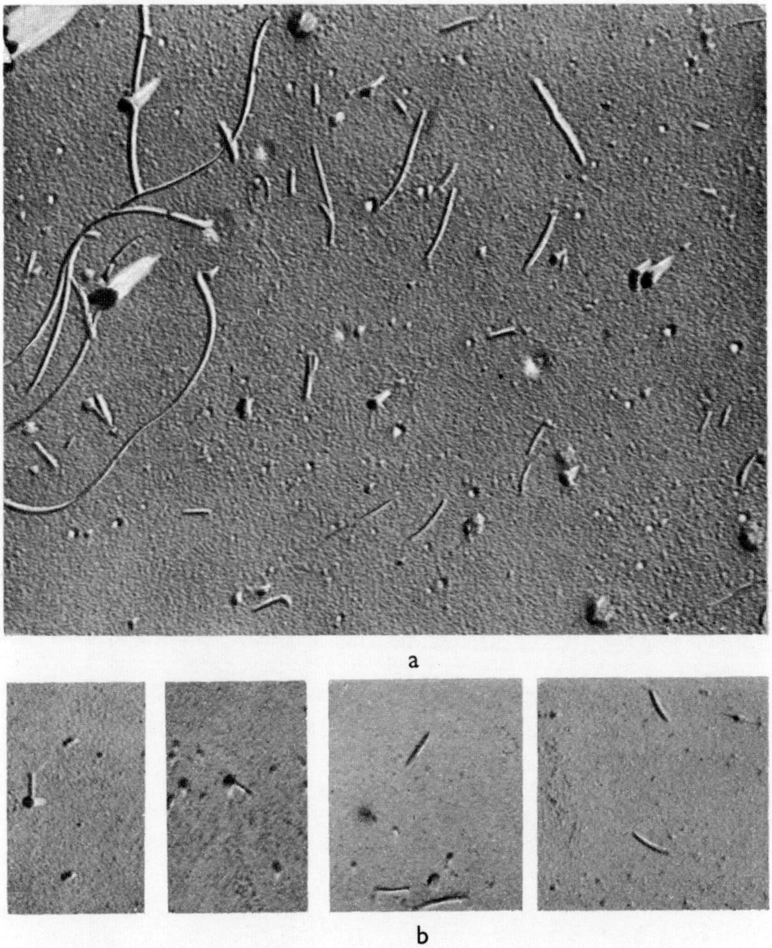

a - *Bacillus catenula*, var. D, Indian Ocean, surface; b - *Bact. agile*, var. B, Indian Ocean, 1026 m

Fig. 19 Phage corpuscles in cultures with zones of lysis

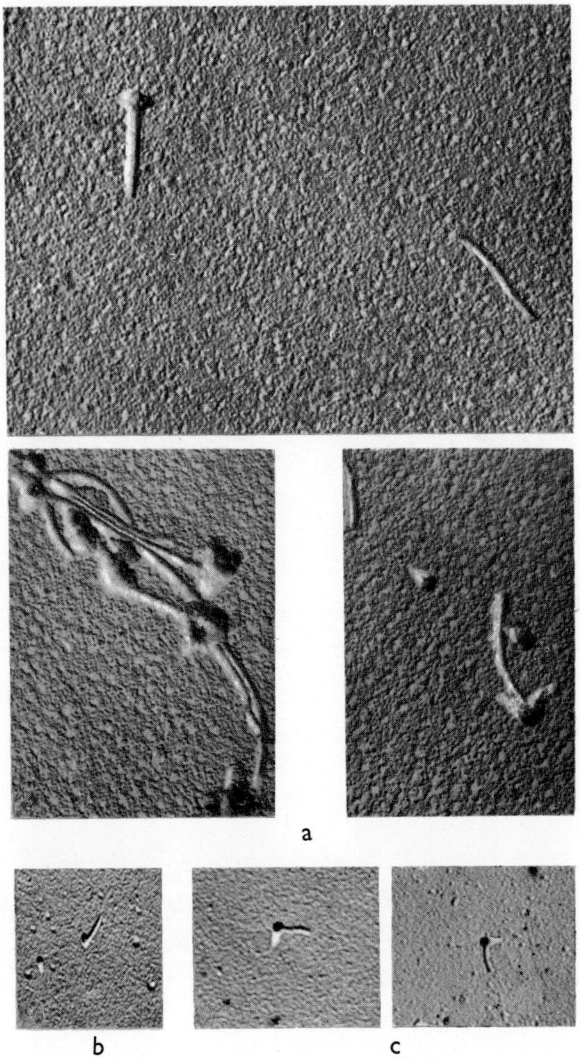

a - *Bact. agile*, var. B, Indian Ocean, 25 m; b - *Micrococcus albicans*, var. A, Indian Ocean, 409 m; c - *Pseudobacterium rosea-album*, var. B, Indian Ocean, 361 m

Fig. 20 Phage corpuscles in cultures with zones of lysis

the air temperature 5°C. After 5 minutes exposure the grids carrying the preparations were removed and washed with distilled water. Washing was repeated 3 to 5 times, after which the liquid was completely dried off the film with filter paper. The preparations were shadowed with chromium.

Using this method, we inspected 250 cultures with zones of lysis, but only in 12 of them did we detect typical bacteriophage particles in the preparations (Figs. 17 – 20).

In view of the difficulty of detecting particles of phage in low concentration in a mass of bacterial culture on a dense medium we cannot be sure that the zones of lysis in the remaining cultures, in which no phage corpuscles were found, were in fact phage-free. In nearly all the cultures the zones of lysis were monotypic and resembled tâches vierges. Lysogeny is evidently a phenomenon to a large extent characteristic also of deep-sea organisms, despite the nature of their habitat.

III

GEOGRAPHY OF MARINE MICROORGANISMS

14

Density of heterotrophic microbial population in various geographical zones of the sea and ocean

The geography of microorganisms, unlike that of animals and plants, has not been the subject of much research. It is only in the last two decades that information on the pattern of geographical distribution of microorganisms in the soil has begun to accumulate, thanks to the work of Mishustin and his school (1947, 1953, 1958).

Our own research on marine microbiology (1954 – 9), which has covered extensive areas of the ocean, has yielded comparative data on the population and species composition of microbial heterotrophs in various geographical zones of the eastern and western hemispheres, from the Central Arctic to the seas of Antarctica.

The data contained in this section give an idea of the quantitative distribution of microbial forms capable of multiplying in organic media of proteinaceous composition in oceanic areas of various geographical zones. Since these heterotrophic microorganisms assimilate readily available organic matter, they are indicators of the marine distribution of organic material which has undergone little transformation, is in the initial stages of decomposition and has not yet been subjected to humification.

In the Pacific Ocean there are distinct differences between the subtropical, tropical and equatorial zones in regard to the concentration of heterotrophic microorganisms (Table 39). The concentration was found to be lowest in the subtropical zones and highest in the equatorial region. In the subtropical areas the percentage of water samples yielding 0 – 9 colonies from 40 ml of water was 44% (40° – 23°N) and 38% (23° – 40°S). The percentage of samples yielding more than 100 colonies varied from 14 in the south to 23 in the north subtropical zone.

By the time we reach the tropics the ratio alters in favour of samples containing a large quantity of heterotrophs and in the region of the Equator the percentage of such samples is more than three times higher than that of samples containing a very small number of heterotrophic microorganisms (52% with more than 100 colonies, against 17% with only 0 – 9 colonies).

It must be remembered that these overall figures for the Pacific to some

Table 39. Quantitative ratio of heterotrophic microorganisms in various geographical zones of the Pacific

Latitude	No. of water samples investigated	% age of water samples investigated yielding various nos. of colonies on filters		
		0 – 9	10 – 99	More than 100
40—23° N	152	44.4	32.5	23.1
23—10° N	165	18.4	41.2	40.4
10° N —10° S	278	16.6	31.3	52.1
10—23° S	160	24.7	48.7	26.6
23—40° S	272	37.6	48.5	13.9

extent conceal differences in particular areas of the ocean due to the proximity of land, the influence of currents and other factors. We have already described the sharp vertical fluctuations in the distribution of heterotroph concentrations in the oceanic water column, due to currents carrying Antarctic and Arctic water into tropical regions and equatorial-tropical water to the high latitudes (Kriss, Lebedeva et al., 1958).

These differences can be very striking, as can be seen from comparison of two sections in the central part of the Pacific (Table 40). North of the Equator the stations in the 172°E section were situated in the sphere of influence of the powerful Japan current, a branch of the North Equatorial Current enriched in organic material. This must account for the astonishingly low percentage of water samples containing not more than 9 colonies and the very high percentage yielding more than 100 in the 172°E section in the north tropical and subtropical zones, in comparison with the results obtained in the southern part of this section and at stations in the same zones in the 174°W section (Table 40).

Table 40. Quantitative ratio of heterotrophic microorganisms at various latitudes of the Pacific along meridians 172°E and 174°W

Latitude	Section 172°E				Section 174°W			
	No. of water samples investigated	% age of samples yielding various nos. of colonies on filters			No. of water samples investigated	% age of samples yielding various nos. of colonies on filters		
		0 – 9	10 – 99	More than 100		0 – 9	10 – 99	More than 100
40—23° N	54	9.3	44.4	46.3	98	79.5	20.5	0
23—10° N	111	3.6	37.8	58.6	54	33.3	44.5	22.2
10° N —10° S	196	4.1	32.1	63.8	82	29.2	30.5	40.3
10—23° S	96	22.9	49.0	28.1	64	26.6	48.4	25.0
23—40° S	123	34.2	48.8	17.0	149	40.9	48.3	10.8

In the Indian Ocean the microbiological stations in the eastern section were situated in all geographical zones, from Antarctica to the Tropic of Cancer; those in the western part were situated south of the zone of subtropical convergence.

As in the Pacific, there was a pattern of diminishing density of heterotroph population with distance from the Equator and proximity to the Antarctic regions. As can be seen from Table 41, the percentage of samples yielding 0 – 9 colonies from 40 ml of water increased from 7.5 in the equatorial zone to 73 – 74% in Antarctic waters; the percentage of samples yielding more than 100 colonies corresponding fell from 89 at the Equator to 13 near Antarctica. The distinct differences between the eastern and western parts of the Indian Ocean south of latitude 35°S in regard to the concentration of heterotrophs in the oceanic water column should be noted: the percentage of samples containing a small number of heterotrophs proved lower

Table 41. Quantitative ratio of heterotrophic microorganisms in various geographical zones of the Indian Ocean

Latitude	No. of water samples investigated	% age of samples yielding various nos. of colonies on filters		
		0 – 9	10 – 99	More than 100
21—10° N	74	1.4	5.4	93.2
10° N —10° S	106	7.5	3.8	88.7
10—23° S	89	11.2	14.6	74.2
23—35° S	58	17.2	36.2	46.6
35—50° S	254	58.2	20.1	21.7
50—60° S	213	73.9	12.6	13.5
60—70° S	273	72.8	14.1	13.1

in the eastern part, whereas the percentage of samples with a high content of heterotrophs was higher than in the 35 – 70°S zone in the western part of the Indian Ocean (Table 42).

In the Atlantic, where the microbiological stations were situated in a section along 30°W, from Iceland to the Tropic of Capricorn, a similar picture of diminishing concentration of heterotrophs with distance from the equatorial-tropical regions was observed (Table 43). At latitudes 40 – 66°N the percentage of water samples with a low content of heterotrophs was as high as 90 – 99 and there were no samples at all with more than 100 heterotrophs.

The Greenland Sea and the Central Arctic, where investigations on heterotroph distribution were carried out between the Pole and latitude 83°N, were found to be poor in heterotrophic microorganisms assimilating readily available organic matter. The concentration was very low in most of the samples (79 – 85%), with only 0 – 9 colonies developing from 35 – 40 ml of water (Table 43).

Compared with the sub-Arctic part of the Atlantic Ocean (along 30°W)

Table 42. Quantitative ratio of heterotrophic microorganisms at various latitudes in the eastern and western halves of the Indian Ocean

Latitude	80 - 90 – 100°E				20 - 40 – 60°E			
	No. of water samples investigated	% age of samples yielding various nos. of colonies on filters			No. of water samples investigated	% age of samples yielding various nos. of colonies on filters		
		0 - 9	10-99	More than 100		0 - 9	10–99	More than 100
35—50°S	97	46.5	22.7	30.8	157	70.0	17.3	12.7
50—60°S	106	63.1	20.8	16.1	157	84.7	4.5	10.8
60—70°S	45	60.0	20.0	20.0	228	85.6	8.3	6.1

and the sub-Antarctic areas, the Norwegian Sea is something of an exception in regard to its content of heterotrophic microorganisms. A relatively high number of heterotrophs was found in 65% of the samples. In this respect the Norwegian Sea resembled the subtropical area of the North Atlantic. There was a difference, however, between its southern and northern halves; only 2% of the water samples from sections in the southern part were found to be rich in heterotrophs. These peculiarities of the Norwegian Sea are undoubtedly due to the considerable influence of the Gulf Stream on the hydrographic régime.

The results obtained from comparative studies thus show that there is pronounced geographical zonality in the oceanic distribution of microbial forms utilizing readily assimilable organic matter.

It is already obvious that the polar regions of the ocean – the Arctic, Antarctic, sub-Arctic and sub-Antarctic – are areas in which the density of the heterotrophic microbial population is very low. Despite the rich plant life to which the ocean waters of these regions owe their productivity, the metabolic products and dead bodies of the organisms inhabiting these waters do not create such sources of nutrient material for heterotrophic microorganisms as are found in the equatorial-tropical parts of the ocean.

The concentration of heterotrophic microbial life in those parts of the equatorial and tropical zones of the Pacific, Indian and Atlantic Oceans which we investigated was astonishingly high. These zones stand out sharply from other geographical zones of the seas and oceans in this respect, and are hardly less rich in microorganisms than many small bodies of fresh water and salt lakes in the temperate zone of the northern hemisphere. Paradoxically, a high density of microbial (heterotrophic) population is observed in the very regions where the plant and animal population is lowest in comparison with the high latitudes (Zenkevitch, 1951).

The so-called inter-trade-wind zone in the equatorial part of the Pacific, where conditions are more favourable for the development of plankton and nekton (Bogorov, 1959) is something of an exception, but even this zone is much poorer in life (apart from bacterial) than the sub-Arctic part of the Pacific.

The picture in regard to microorganic life is thus one of increasing heterotroph concentration in the water column of the ocean with distance from the polar regions and proximity to the Equator,* whereas in regard to other forms of life the converse is true: the concentration rises with distance from the equatorial-tropical zone.

The explanation of the paradox lies in the fact that the principal source determining the wealth of equatorial-tropical waters in microbial population is organic matter of allochthonous origin which has not yet undergone humification and has hardly been transformed. It is further obvious that the concentration of this organic material in the equatorial-tropical zone will be much higher than the concentration of analogous forms of autochthonous organic matter reaching the ocean from land in higher latitudes. †

The enrichment of the equatorial-tropical waters of the Pacific and Indian Oceans in organic matter readily accessible to the action of hydrolytic microbial enzymes occurs mainly, we must assume, in the so-called Coral Sea. Here, as in the Australasian archipelago at the junction of the Indian and Pacific Oceans, there is an immense number of islands rich in vegetation and animal life. The waters washing the shores of these islands are supplied with organic matter in forms highly suitable as food for heterotrophic microorganisms and thus occasioning their active multiplication.

These waters, drawn in by the equatorial currents and counter currents, enrich the entire column of the equatorial-tropical zone of the Pacific and Indian Oceans, particularly in the western part of the Pacific and the eastern part of the Indian Oceans. In the section along 172°E a higher content of heterotrophic microorganisms was observed in the water than at stations in the section along 174°W, which runs through the eastern half of the Pacific (Table 40).

In the Indian Ocean, where deep currents carry equatorial-tropical water to the high latitudes as far as the shores of Antarctica, the subtropical, sub-Antarctic and Antarctic regions are richer in heterotrophic microorganisms in the eastern than in the western half (Table 42).

The conspicuously higher concentration of barely transformed organic

* It is interesting that according to Mishustin's data (1958) the mass of soil microorganisms increases with transition from northern to southern soils.

† (Editor's footnote). Alternatively it may be related to a proportionately greater liberation of extracellular products of photosynthesis at low population densities of phytoplankton, such as W. D. Watt has observed in freshwaters (see G. E. Fogg and W. D. Watt in *Symposium on Primary Productivity in Aquatic Environments, Mem. Ist. Ital. Idrobiol.*, (1965) 18 Suppl., pp. 165–174). This type of extracellular product might provide an ample carbon-source for bacterial growth whereas possible competitive and antibacterial effects of phytoplankton, being more related in intensity to the biomass of the algae, would be minimal.

Table 43. Quantitative ratio of heterotrophic microorganisms in various geographical zones of the Atlantic Ocean, Norwegian and Greenland Seas and Central Arctic

Latitude	No. of water samples investigated	%age of samples yielding various nos. of colonies on filters		
		0 – 9	10 – 99	More than 100
		Atlantic Ocean		
22—11° S	81	2.5	20.0	77.5
8° S—8° N	167	3.0	20.0	77.0
10—21° N	121	1.6	33.9	64.5
24—38° N	104	44.3	38.4	17.3
40—48° N	88	90.0	10.0	0
50—58° N	78	98.7	1.3	0
60—66° N	71	95.7	4.3	0
		Norwegian Sea		
60—70° N	575	35.0	54.0	11.0
60—65° N	203	14.9	57.6	27.5
64—70° N	372	46.5	51.6	1.8
		Greenland Sea		
78—83° N	448	78.8	16.5	4.7
		Central Arctic		
83—90° N	115	85.0	15.0	0

matter in the equatorial-tropical waters of the Atlantic is evidently due to discharge from such huge rivers as the Amazon, Orinoco, Congo and Niger, which collect water from the vast expanses of equatorial America and Africa, with their dense vegetation and animal life. Some importance as a source of allochthonous organic material must be attributed also to the numerous Caribbean islands, which are reached by branches of the equatorial currents.

Very interesting in this respect are Kolbe's discoveries (1957) of the cell walls of freshwater diatoms in muddy deposits of the equatorial zone of the Atlantic. In bottom samples obtained thousands of kilometres from the coast of Africa, Kolbe found more than 1000 valves of freshwater diatoms on one slide. In view of the considerable distance from land at which these diatoms were found, the great depth of the ocean and the high concentration of the diatom valves, it appears that the contribution to the organic and inorganic matter in the water mass of the equatorial-tropical zone of the Atlantic made by discharge from equatorial Africa caught up by trade-wind currents can hardly be overestimated. The strong north-easterly winds carry such dense clouds of dust from the African continent that they sometimes reduce visibility to 1 – 2 kilometres or even 150 metres in the sea area adjacent to Africa, between 15°N and 5°S. These winds also deposit terrigenous organic material in the water of the North and South Equatorial Currents which start at the African coast.

15

Biochemical activity of heterotrophic microorganisms in various geographical zones of the seas and oceans

More than 3000 strains of heterotrophic microorganisms obtained from various geographical zones of the sea were studied to discover their capacity to convert proteinaceous substances and carbohydrates and to utilize combined oxygen and mineral compounds of nitrogen in their vital processes. This was important in order to assess the biochemical activity of these microorganisms in decomposing readily assimilable forms of organic matter in the sea. More than 500 strains, or 17% of the entire collection, caused pronounced hydrolytic breakdown in such protein substances as gelatine and milk protein (Table 44). Thorough decomposition of the proteins in meat-peptone bouillon, with formation of hydrogen sulphide, was observed in 4% of the cultures.

According to the data of ZoBell and Upham (1944), half the total number of 60 strains obtained by them from Pacific Ocean water and mud off the Californian coast hydrolysed casein and 47 liquefied gelatine. The higher percentage of proteolytically active strains found by these authors may well have been due to the fact that they obtained their strains from coastal waters.

The same reason would obviously account for the predominance of strains liquefying gelatine in the collection of microorganism cultures obtained from the Black Sea (451 cultures out of a total of 733) (Kriss et al., 1954), since the Black Sea is an intracontinental basin with considerable continental effluent.

The activity of bacterial cultures obtained from the ocean in converting various carbohydrates, with the formation of acids, is shown in Table 44. The highest percentage of strains (26.4) fermented glucose, acidifying the medium. Acid formation in media containing sucrose and maltose occurred in roughly the same number of cultures (18 – 19%); then followed media containing mannitol (15%) and lactose (10%). These data indicate only the capacity of the cultures from the oceanic collection to ferment certain carbohydrates and mannitol with formation of acids. The great majority of the strains (more than 80%) multiplied well on media containing glucose, sucrose, maltose, lactose and mannitol.

Table 44. Biochemical activity of heterotrophic

Sea area	Liquefaction of gelatine	Formation H_2S	Peptonization of milk protein	Acidificatic	
				Mannitol	Gluco
Atlantic Ocean, Greenland and Norwegian Seas, Central Arctic	1089/1052 (31.2)	1068/961 (7.7)	1021/1021 (29.5)	1067/790 (25.6)	1084/886 (47
Indian Ocean and Antarctic seas	909/889 (14.7)	864/790 (3.5)	898/898 (15.2)	883/805 (17.1)	899/852 (21
Pacific Ocean	1202/1155 (7.6)	1184/1097 (1.3)	1203/1203 (8.2)	1179/1068 (5.2)	1191/1099 (13
All oceans	3200/3096 (17.7)	3116/2848 (4.1)	3122/3122 (17.1)	3129/2663 (14.9)	3174/2837 (26

Numerators - number of strains investigated; denominators - number of strains g of strains growing which were capable of effecting the given enzymatic proc

Similar results were obtained on a medium containing starch as the only source of carbon. The percentage of strains hydrolysing starch, however, proved relatively high (63.3). ZoBell and Upham (1944) state that 75% of the strains from their collection fermented glucose, with formation of acids. Among the Black Sea cultures the percentage of those decomposing glucose, maltose, sucrose, lactose and mannitol with acidification of the medium was considerably higher than among the strains in the oceanic collection.

It is interesting that 2873 out of 3158 strains of microorganisms obtained from various ocean areas multiplied on a medium containing a mineral source of nitrogen (Table 44), but only 40% of the strains reduced the nitrates which were the source of nitrogen in this medium. The percentage of Black Sea strains utilizing nitrates and reducing them to nitrites was approximately the same – slightly more the 30% of the whole collection.

There were notable differences in the numbers of microbial forms hydrolysing proteins and converting carbohydrates in the Atlantic, Indian and Pacific Oceans respectively. The percentage of strains hydrolysing gelatine and casein, decomposing proteins with evolution of hydrogen sulphide and fermenting glucose, sucrose, maltose, lactose and mannitol with formation of acids proved highest in the Atlantic Ocean and lowest in the Pacific; the Indian Ocean occupied an intermediate position in this respect. The magnitude of these differences can be judged from the comparative data given in Table 44. In the Pacific the percentage of strains liquefying gelatine, forming hydrogen sulphide in cultures on meat-peptone bouillon and peptonizing milk proteins after their coagulation, was four or five

nisms obtained from various parts of the ocean

one water containing			Hydrolysis of starch	Assimilation of mineral nitrogen	Dentrification
crose	Maltose	Lactose			
3/5 (30.9)	1074/827 (31.9)	1077/772 (14.6)	1091/989 (46.8)	1092/1001 (91.7)	1092/503 (46.1)
(19.0)	880/828 (18.4)	883/797 (8.8)	901/820 (72.7)	893/843 (94.4)	893/351 (39.3)
7/5 (9.5)	1184/1107 (11.7)	1192/1061 (7.3)	1203/1102 (71.0)	1173/1104 (94.1)	1173/419 (35.6)
7/7 (18.7)	3138/2762 (19.7)	3152/2630 (9.9)	3195/2911 (63.3)	3158/2873 (90.97)	3158/1273 (40.3)

on given medium; figures in brackets are percentage of total number

times higher in the Atlantic than in the Pacific. The percentage of strains forming acid on media containing carbohydrates and mannitol was two, three or five times greater in the Atlantic than in the Pacific.

Since nearly all the water samples were collected from various depths of the high seas, far from land, in the Atlantic, Indian and Pacific Oceans, it is suggested that these differences are due to the geographical factor rather than to microbiologically specific characteristics of these parts of the ocean.

Reference to the map in Fig. 1 will show that the bulk of the research in the Atlantic Ocean was performed at high latitudes and covered also regions adjoining the Arctic Ocean. In the Pacific, on the other hand, the stations were made only in subtropical, tropical and equatorial regions. In the Indian Ocean the microbiological sections intersected all geographical zones from the Tropic of Cancer to Antarctica.

Closer study revealed a clear-cut geographical distribution pattern of biochemically active and inactive species of heterotrophic microorganisms in the ocean. In the Indian Ocean the highest percentage of proteolytically active cultures occurred at high latitudes (Table 45). In the Antarctic and sub-Antarctic regions the percentage of cultures liquefying gelatine and peptonizing and decomposing protein with formation of hydrogen sulphide was several times higher than in the equatorial zone. Similar ratios were observed in regard to the percentage of strains fermenting carbohydrates in cultures taken from Antarctic seas, on the one hand, and from tropical sea areas, on the other.

The Atlantic picture is similar: a higher percentage of strains hydrolysing

Table 45. Biochemical activity of heterotrophic microor-

Sea area	Liquefaction of gelatine	Formation of H_2S	Peptonization of milk protein	Acidification of	
				Mannitol	Glucose
Antarctic region 70 – 50°S	274 (19.3)	221 (5.9)	277 (16.6)	219 (29.7)	259 (28.6)
Sub-Antarctic region 50 – 40°S	111 (20.7)	91 (7.9)	111 (24.3)	104 (19.2)	106 (34.0)
South subtropical region 40 – 23°S	163 (21.5)	143 (4.2)	164 (23.2)	154 (21.4)	158 (23.4)
South tropical region 23 – 10°S	134 (5.9)	132 (0.8)	136 (8.9)	126 (7.1)	128 (11.6)
Equatorial region 10°S – 10°N	131 (5.3)	128 (0.8)	133 (6.7)	127 (3.1)	126 (8.7)
North tropical region 10 – 23°N	76 (6.6)	75 (0.0)	77 (5.2)	75 (9.3)	75 (12.0)

Figures in brackets indicate percentage of strains capable of effecting enzymatic

*In these columns the figures without brackets indicate the number of strains investigated

Table 46. Biochemical activity of heterotrophic microorgan-

Sea area	Liquefaction of gelatine	Formation of H_2S	Peptonization of milk protein	Acidification of	
				Mannitol	Glucose
10—23° S	86 (0.0)	83 (0.0)	86 (4.7)	71 (5.6)	83 (27.7)
10° S—10° N	99 (5.1)	98 (0.0)	100 (3.0)	79 (7.6)	95 (20.0)
10—23° N	123 (8.9)	118 (0.0)	123 (0.8)	78 (2.6)	117 (6.8)
23—40° N	77 (33.8)	72 (0.0)	77 (2.6)	55 (0.0)	63 (20.6)
40—60° N	32 (65.6)	29 (6.9)	32 (56.3)	24 (54.2)	26 (73.1)
60—80° N	416 (39.4)	356 (17.7)	379 (45.9)	273 (38.1)	287 (61.0)
80° N and above	219 (46.1)	205 (4.4)	224 (44.2)	210 (34.8)	215 (76.7)

Figures in brackets indicate percentage of strains capable of effecting enzymatic

*In these columns the figures without brackets indicate the number of strains investigated

ganisms from various geographical zones of the Indian Ocean

peptone water containing			Hydrolysis of starch	Assimilation of mineral nitrogen*	Denitrification*
Sucrose	Maltose	Lactose			
233 (28.8)	239 (27.2)	227 (12.3)	234 (57.7)	282 (91.1)	282 (40.8)
98 (32.7)	100 (25.0)	105 (8.6)	100 (63.0)	106 (94.3)	106 (37.7)
156 (18.6)	159 (20.1)	134 (11.2)	154 (67.5)	162 (95.1)	162 (22.2)
132 (6.8)	130 (10.0)	129 (5.4)	134 (87.3)	134 (97.0)	134 (61.6)
130 (6.9)	127 (6.3)	127 (3.9)	122 (89.3)	132 (99.2)	132 (43.9)
73 (13.7)	73 (12.3)	75 (8.0)	76 (89.5)	77 (98.7)	77 (26.0)

process, figures without brackets indicate number of strains growing on medium

isms from various geographical zones of the Atlantic Ocean

peptone water containing			Hydrolysis of starch	Assimilation of mineral nitrogen*	Denitrification*
Sucrose	Maltose	Lactose			
81 (6.2)	75 (6.7)	56 (1.8)	79 (70.9)	86 (96.5)	86 (66.3)
89 (7.9)	88 (8.0)	53 (11.3)	90 (84.4)	100 (94.0)	100 (58.0)
97 (3.1)	115 (0.0)	95 (3.2)	118 (83.1)	123 (98.4)	123 (46.3)
62 (3.2)	65 (1.5)	63 (3.2)	76 (77.6)	78 (93.6)	78 (42.3)
25 (68.0)	23 (73.9)	26 (42.3)	32 (25.0)	36 (86.1)	36 (41.7)
277 (49.1)	246 (52.4)	266 (21.1)	383 (28.5)	440 (87.0)	440 (38.4)
219 (42.5)	215 (48.8)	213 (16.0)	211 (27.0)	229 (94.3)	229 (49.8)

process, figures without brackets indicate number of strains growing on medium

Table.47. Biochemical activity of heterotrophic microorganisms from

Sea area	Liquefaction of gelatine	Formation of H_2S	Peptonization of of milk protein	Acidification of	
				Mannitol	Glucose
40—23° S	190 (15.8)	174 (1.7)	195 (14.4)	178 (7.3)	174 (23.0)
23—10° S	139 (18.7)	136 (2.2)	149 (16.1)	128 (8.6)	137 (24.1)
10° S—10° N	222 (3.2)	224 (0.0)	227 (2.6)	201 (2.5)	206 (5.8)
10—23° N	137 (0.0)	126 (0.8)	141 (5.0)	130 (0.8)	137 (2.9)
23—40° N	71 (1.4)	67 (0.0)	75 (1.3)	72 (0.0)	69 (7.3)

Figures in brackets indicate percentage of strains capable of effecting enzymatic

*In these columns the figures without brackets indicate the number of strains investigated

Table 48. Biochemical activity of heterotrophic microorganisms from

Sea area	Liquefaction of gelatine	Formation of H_2S	Peptonization of milk protein	Acidification of	
				Mannitol	Glucose
40—23° S	94 (11.7)	90 (2.2)	97 (8.3)	88 (9.1)	87 (13.8)
23—10° S	74 (2.7)	73 (1.4)	76 (7.9)	75 (2.7)	69 (11.6)
10° S —10° N	137 (2.9)	128 (0.0)	143 (4.9)	121 (8.3)	132 (12.1)
10—23° N	53 (7.6)	50 (0.0)	57 (10.5)	46 (6.5)	51 (17.7)
23—40° N	38 (7.9)	29 (13.8)	43 (11.6)	29 (10.3)	37 (13.5)

Figures in brackets indicate percentage of strains capable of effecting enzymatic

*In these columns the figures without brackets indicate the number of strains investigated

various geographical zones of the Pacific Ocean (section along 172°E)

peptone water containing			Hydrolysis of starch	Assimilation of mineral nitrogen*	Denitrification*
Sucrose	Maltose	Lactose			
188 (14.9)	183 (24.0)	174 (12.6)	178 (59.6)	193 (93.3)	193 (43.0)
144 (20.8)	136 (24.3)	137 (18.9)	125 (63.2)	136 (89.0)	136 (30.2)
224 (3.1)	218 (3.7)	218 (2.8)	213 (79.8)	221 (96.4)	221 (28.5)
137 (2.9)	129 (1.6)	134 (0.0)	128 (79.7)	136 (97.1)	136 (44.9)
74 (0.0)	70 (2.9)	72 (1.4)	67 (82.1)	73 (97.3)	73 (52.1)

process, figures without brackets indicate number of strains growing on medium

various geographical zones of the Pacific Ocean (section along 174° W)

peptone water containing			Hydrolysis of starch	Assimilation of mineral nitrogen*	Denitrification*
Sucrose	Maltose	Lactose			
92 (10.9)	79 (10.1)	85 (8.2)	93 (66.7)	95 (89.5)	95 (32.6)
71 (8.5)	73 (5.5)	61 (1.6)	73 (75.3)	75 (98.7)	75 (29.3)
139 (8.6)	136 (8.8)	105 (0.95)	137 (76.6)	144 (94.4)	144 (24.3)
52 (17.3)	47 (19.2)	44 (15.9)	48 (62.5)	57 (93.0)	57 (40.4)
34 (11.8)	36 (19.4)	31 (9.7)	40 (45.0)	43 (90.7)	43 (51.2)

process, figures without brackets indicate number of strains growing on medium proteic substances and fermenting carbohydrates in the sub-Arctic and Arctic regions than in the tropical regions (Table 46).

The biochemical activity of the great majority of cultures from the Pacific Ocean collection was not high. Investigations in the Pacific confirmed that the proteolytic and fermenting activity of the microbial population in the low-latitude sea areas is relatively low. It is noteworthy that the north subtropical zone in the section along 172°E (Table 47) emerges as distinctly poorer in biochemically active microbial species than the north subtropical zone in the section along 174°W (Table 48) and the south subtropical zones in both sections. The microbiological stations in the north subtropical zone were situated in the area affected by the powerful Japan Current which is a branch of the North Equatorial Current.

Most of the equatorial-tropical cultures hydrolysed starch but the percentage was lower in the high latitudes of the Indian and Atlantic Oceans.

Differences in the percentage of denitrifying microorganisms in the various geographical zones of the ocean were slight. The data obtained disprove Brandt's hypothesis (1904), according to which the paucity of plant life in the tropics is due to the activity of microorganisms reducing nitrates and nitrites. The percentage of denitrifiers in the equatorial-tropical region was no higher than in the sub-Arctic and sub-Antarctic regions, where the the water is extremely rich in phytoplankton.

A strikingly large percentage of strains, roughly equal in all geographical zones of the ocean, metabolizes inorganic nitrogen compounds. 86–99% of heterotroph cultures developed well on media containing a mineral source of nitrogen, presumably because the marine microorganisms are adapted to the specific conditions of their habitat.

Since the microbiological sections crossed the equatorial-tropical areas four times (twice in the Pacific and once each in the Indian and Atlantic Oceans), the north sub-tropical zone three times (twice in the Pacific and once in the Atlantic) and the south subtropical zone three times (twice in the Pacific and once in the Indian Ocean), it was of interest to compare the biochemical activity of the heterotrophs in the various geographical zones of all the oceans.

As can be seen from Table 49, the equatorial-tropical zone is sharply distinguished by the very small proportion of microbial species decomposing proteins and fermenting carbohydrates among the heterotrophic microorganisms inhabiting it. In the Arctic, sub-Arctic, Antarctic and sub-Antarctic regions of the ocean the percentage of strains decomposing proteins is four to sixty times greater and the percentage fermenting mannitol, glucose, sucrose, maltose and lactose is two to eleven times greater than in the equatorial zone.

These data indicate that the process of organic decomposition and liberation of plant nutrients is more vigorous in the high latitudes. Although the heterotroph population in these latitudes is not so large as near the Equator and their biochemical activity is influenced by the low temperatures,

Table 49. Biochemical activity of heterotrophic microorganisms from various geographical zones of the ocean*

Sea area	Liquefaction of gelatine	Formation of H_2S	Peptonization of milk protein	Acidification of peptone water containing					Hydrolysis of starch	Assimilation of mineral nitrogen	Denitrification
				Mannitol	Glucose	Sucrose	Maltose	Lactose			
70—50°S	19.3	5.9	16.6	29.7	28.6	28.8	27.2	12.3	57.7	91.1	40.8
50—40°S	20.7	7.9	24.3	19.2	34.0	32.7	25.0	8.6	63.0	94.3	37.7
40—23°S	17.0	2.7	16.2	12.9	21.2	15.4	19.9	11.2	64.0	93.1	33.3
23—10°S	6.7	1.2	10.3	6.5	18.4	11.7	13.5	9.1	74.7	94.8	43.4
10°S —10°N	3.9	0.2	4.9	5.8	10.4	7.2	6.1	4.3	81.8	96.0	38.6
10—23°N	5.1	0.3	4.5	3.9	7.9	7.2	5.2	4.6	80.5	97.2	41.0
23—40°N	16.1	2.4	4.1	1.9	14.8	3.5	5.9	3.6	72.1	94.3	47.9
40—60°N	65.6	6.9	56.3	54.2	73.1	68.0	73.9	42.3	25.0	86.1	41.7
60—80°N	39.4	17.7	45.9	38.1	61.0	49.1	52.4	21.1	28.5	87.0	38.4
Central Arctic, 80°N and above	46.1	4.4	44.2	34.8	76.7	42.5	48.8	16.0	27.0	94.3	49.8

* Figures denote percentage of strains capable of effecting given enzymatic process

the presence of a comparatively large number of microbial forms displaying diversified enzymatic activity means that the transformation of organic matter is more thorough in the high latitudes than in the tropics. The result is that the water in Arctic, sub-Arctic, Antarctic and sub- Antarctic sea areas contains larger quantities of the nutrient substances necessary for the development of marine vegetation; and the phytoplankton biomasses observed in these zones are indeed many times greater than those found in the tropics.

The relative abundance of microbial forms producing a multiplicity of reactions decomposing organic matter in the high-latitude waters leads to increased concentrations of plant nutrient not only in the water mass at those latitudes, but also in the ocean depths at lower latitudes, to which these products of the decay and conversion of organic matter are carried by deep currents.

We do not yet know why tropical waters are poor in biochemically active microbial forms or why high-latitude waters are rich in them. It may be that the comparatively high concentration of readily assimilable allochthonous organic matter in tropical waters, which causes the high density of heterotroph population in the equatorial-tropical zone of the ocean, obviates the necessity for enzymatic reactions which would ensure total utilization of the organic material. In the high latitudes the water is poor in food reserves, with the result that adaptions are evolved in the heterotrophs, which allow them to use organic matter more economically by breaking it down and converting it more thoroughly.

16

Range of species and variants of bacteria and yeasts in the sea

The species *Act. globisporus* and *Proact. albus* are very unlikely to be indigenous to the sea; they are evidently random forms, for several thousand water and mud samples investigated yielded only seven strains of these species. As a rule, they occurred as single colonies on the membrane filters.

Mycobacteria were detected in the Indian and Pacific Oceans, the Greenland Sea and near the North Pole (Figs. 15 and 15a). *Mycobacterium filiforme* occurred only in the Greenland Sea and *Mycob. lacticolum* in the Indian Ocean. *Mycob. mucosum* and *Mycob. luteum,* the former isolated from Indian and Pacific Ocean water and the latter from the Pacific and Central Arctic, had wide areas of occurrence.

NON-SPORING RODS. The bulk of the microorganisms obtained from various geographical zones of the Atlantic, Indian and Pacific Oceans consisted of non-sporing rods assigned to the species *Bacterium agile* (see next section).

Bacterium candicans was the next commonest species in the Atlantic and Pacific (Figs. 3 and 3a). It was detected in only three water samples from the Indian Ocean.

B. candicans was isolated from samples taken at various depths in the equatorial-tropical zone of the Atlantic, at the rate of 10 to 100 or more bacteria per 40 ml of water. This species occurred in similar quantities in the 172°E section of the equatorial tropical zone of the Pacific. In the 174°W section, between 0° and 23°N, it was detected only at certain levels, and even then not at all stations; but in the 0 – 23°S zone its range was much the same as in the 172°E section, although the quantity was more often than not less than 10 bacteria per 50 ml of water.

This species was isolated at a number of stations in the subtropical part of the Atlantic. In the north subtropical zone of the Pacific, in the 174°W section, it was rare; in the south subtropical zone its incidence was usually less than 10 per 50 ml. In the 172°E section, however, the picture was different; *Bact. candicans* occurred both in the north and in the south subtropical regions at various levels, in quantities ranging from from 10 to 100 per 50 ml of water.

In the sub-Arctic part of the Atlantic *Bact. candicans* was detected in only one sample. It was more frequent, but still occurred in small quantities, in the Greenland Sea.

Bacterium parvulum was isolated from the water of several seas and oceans (Figs. 4 and 4a). It was most frequent in the Pacific, where it was found in all zones – the equatorial-tropical, the subtropical and the sub-Antarctic. In most of the samples there were fewer than 10 bacteria per 40 ml of water. Only in the equatorial-tropical zone was the population higher. This species was isolated also from Greenland Sea water.

Of the non-sporing rods assigned to the genus *Pseudomonas,* the commonest in the Atlantic, Indian and Pacific Oceans were those of the aggregate species *Ps. sinuosa* (Figs. 5 and 5a). This species was detected in quantities varying from 10 to 100 or more bacteria per 40 ml of water in the equatorial-tropical region of the Atlantic. In the same region of the Indian Ocean it was isolated from several samples in large quantities, and also from mud.

In the Pacific, occurrences of *Ps. sinuosa* were more frequent and quantities of 10 to 100 or more bacteria per 50 ml of water were found. In the 172°E section it occurred more frequently than in the 174°W section.

In the subtropical areas, *Ps. sinuosa* was found in only one sample from the Atlantic; in the Indian Ocean it was more frequent than in the equatorial-tropical zone of the same ocean, although in smaller quantities (fewer than 10 per 40 ml of water); in the Pacific it was comparatively frequent both in the north and in the south subtropical zones.

In the sub-Arctic and Arctic parts of the Atlantic *Ps. sinuosa* was isolated from only two samples, in small quantities.

In the sub-Antarctic part of the Indian Ocean it was widespread, but in small quantities (up to 10 cells per 40 ml of water).

In the Antarctic part of the Indian Ocean this species was predominant at most of the stations in the Capetown-Antarctica section, that is, in the western part of the Indian Ocean and at stations in the immediate vicinity of Antarctica. The number of bacteria of this species per 40 ml of water, however, was not great – fewer than 10. In the eastern part, along the sector from the mouth of the Ganges to Mirnyy, it was not found at all.

In the Greenland Sea *Ps. sinuosa* was detected at a number of levels at various stations, but in small quantity.

Pseudomonas liquida was isolated from various depths of the Norwegian Sea in quantities of 10 to 100 per 40 ml of water. In the Indian Ocean it was found only at the two southernmost stations near the Antarctic coast, at the surface of the water, at the rate of fewer than 10 bacteria per 40 ml of water. In the Atlantic Ocean it was found at a station in the Arctic zone (60 – 70°N) in the surface water and at great depths in the sub-Arctic and subtropical parts, at the rate of fewer than 10 bacteria per 40 ml (Figs. 5 and 6).

Rods assigned to the aggregate species *Pseudobacterium variabilis* occurred mainly in the Norwegian Sea, where they were isolated from various depths, from the surface to 1500 m. At more southerly stations more than 100 colonies or between 10 and 100 were usually incubated from 40 ml of water. At northern stations the numbers of bacteria belonging to this species were smaller. Bacteria similar to *Pseudobacterium variabilis* were found also in water from the Arctic Ocean, near the North Pole, at depths of 100, 150 and 600 m, and in the Indian Ocean at depths of 300, 800 and 3000 m in the sub-Antarctic zone and at 250 and 1500 m in the Antarctic zone (Figs. 7 and 7a).

Pseudobacterium biforme was the commonest of all pseudobacteria found anywhere in the sea (Figs. 7 and 7a). The largest number of strains of this species was isolated from Indian Ocean water in the sub-Antarctic, subtropical and tropical areas, at various depths. More often than not there were fewer than 10 bacteria of this species per 40 ml of water.

In the tropical part of the Indian Ocean the population of this species exceeded 100 cells per 40 ml of water. In the Pacific, it was isolated from 2000 m level at one station in the subtropical region.

SPORE-FORMING BACTERIA. Of the spore-forming microorganisms the commonest were *Bacillus catenula, B. idosus* and *B. filaris* (Figs. 8 and 8a, 9 and 9a).

Variants assigned to *B. catenula* occurred in the Indian Ocean, Antarctic waters, the tropical zone of the Pacific, the Arctic Ocean and the Norwegian and Greenland Seas.

The species *B. idosus* and *B. filaris* (var. A, C, D, F and G, see Figs. 8, 8a, 9 and 9a) occurred in the Arctic Ocean and the Greenland Sea. In the North Arctic these species were found in the surface layers of the water, down to 50 m, sometimes at a depth of 300 m and then at 1500 m and below, as well as at the bottom. In the Greenland Sea they occurred mainly in the surface layers.

COCCI. Among the commonest were cocci tentatively assigned to the species *Micrococcus albicans* and *Micrococcus radiatus* (Figs. 10, 10a, 11 and 11a). These were found in the Greenland and Norwegian Seas, the Atlantic Ocean, the Indian Ocean and the Antarctic seas, the Pacific and the Arctic.

In the Indian and Antarctic Oceans they occurred mainly at levels poor in microbial population. The water at these depths is all of similar origin, mostly from Antarctica, and can be traced in certain layers as far as the north tropical region (Kriss, 1963).

The Greenland Sea proved richest in coccal forms. Next, in diversity of species, were the Pacific and Indian Oceans and the Antarctic seas. A smaller variety of forms was recorded in the Arctic, the Norwegian Sea and the North Atlantic (Figs. 10, 10a, 11, 11a, 12, 12a, 13, 13a, 14, 14a).

Members of the genus *Sarcina* assigned to two species, *S. subflava* and *S. luteola,* were found in small quantities in all the ocean areas studied, mainly in the surface layers down to 200 – 300 m. At stations along the islands of the Coral Sea in the Pacific, they occurred at depths down to 400 and even 2500 m (Figs. 13 and 13a).

YEASTS. Some species of yeast organisms have wide areas of occurrence in the seas and oceans. A particular species may be found at various depths and in ocean areas far apart from one another (Fig. 16).

Of the spore-forming yeasts, the commonest species is *Debar. rosei*. This has been isolated from water near the North Pole, in the Greenland Sea and the Norwegian Sea. In the Greenland Sea it was discovered at great depths (1000 – 3040 m) and at Station 3 the number of colonies incubated on the membrane filter ran into thousands per 50 ml of water.

Debar. globosus too has a fairly wide range. It has been isolated from great depths in the Greenland Sea and from the Norwegian Sea and the Pacific.

Debar. guilliermondii was found only in the Norwegian Sea, at one station, at depths of 600 and 800 m.

Of the non-sporing forms of yeast organisms, the commonest is *Torulopsis aeria*. This species was found at various depths in the Central Arctic, in the Norwegian Sea and in the Indian Ocean.

Rhodotorula mucilaginosa and *Rh. glutinis* were also common. These were found in the Greenland Sea (mainly at great depths) and in the Indian Ocean.

Two variants of *Sporobolomyces roseus* were isolated at places far apart: var. A from Greenland Sea mud at a depth of 3500 m and var. B at a depth of 3400 m at drifting station 'North Pole 3'.

17

Bacterium agile as an indicator of water masses of tropical origin

The distribution in the high seas of forms of organic matter readily assimilable by heterotrophic microorganisms is dictated mainly by hydrographic factors.

Chemical methods are inadequate for determining the content of the water column in labile forms of organic matter. At present, heterotrophic microorganisms multiplying on proteinaceous media are the sole indicators of these forms at our disposal. The quantitative distribution of heterotrophs in the depths of the ocean precisely reflects the distribution of their food source, namely, labile organic matter.

Microbiological inspection of the whole water column, from surface to bottom, in meridional sections crossing all geographical zones of the ocean in the northern and southern hemispheres has disclosed the presence of water masses sharply differentiated in regard to concentration of heterotrophic microorganisms and, consequently of forms of organic matter readily assimilable by these microorganisms. It has been found that high-latitude water is distinguished by its extreme poverty in heterotrophs which will grow on proteinaceous media, whereas the tropical zone of the oceans is rich in this microflora.

It has further been discovered that equatorial-tropical waters with a relatively high concentration of labile organic matter are drawn by the currents into high-latitude regions. Arctic and Antarctic waters, in turn, which are poor in organic matter readily assimilable by microorganisms, appear as clearly expressed layers in the depths of the tropical zone of the Indian, Pacific and Atlantic Oceans.

It is thus established that we can supplement such criteria of the origin of oceanic water masses as temperature, salinity, oxygen and so forth by data on the distribution of labile matter, which can in turn be estimated from the density distribution of the microbial population (that is, of heterotrophs multiplying on proteinaceous media). This microbiological method of detecting water masses of diverse origin has enlarged our picture of the hydrographic structure of several vast areas of the ocean.

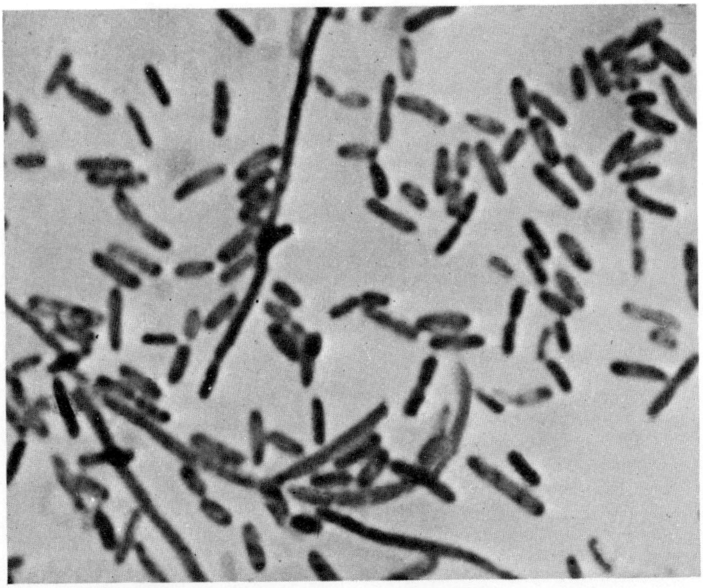

Fig. 21 Morphology of *Bact. agile* × 2400

Study of the species composition of heterotrophic microorganisms isolated from various depths and places in the Arctic Ocean (in the North Pole area), the Indian, Pacific and Atlantic Oceans, the Greenland and Norwegian Seas and the seas of Antarctica has shown that the areas of occurrence of certain species of bacteria are determined by deep currents. The most typical example of this relationship is found in the peculiar distribution of a non-sporing rod assigned in Krasil'nikov's key (1949) to the species *Bacterium agile* Jensen, 1898 (Figs. 21, 22, 22a).

Range of Bacterium agile *in equatorial-tropical water*

In the microbial heterotroph population of tropical waters *Bact. agile* is one of the mass-occurrence forms. It is found extensively throughout almost the entire water column, from surface to bottom, in this geographical zone and its population is comparatively high. The great majority of colonies incubated on membrane filters after filtration of 40 – 50 ml of water from various depths belongs to the species *Bact. agile* (filter incubation on nutrient agar). Usually, some hundreds of colonies are obtained from 40 – 50 ml, but in several water samples from the equatorial-tropical zone of the Indian Ocean the number of colonies exceeded 1000 (Fig. 23).

It can be seen from Figs. 23 – 26 that high concentration of *Bact. agile*

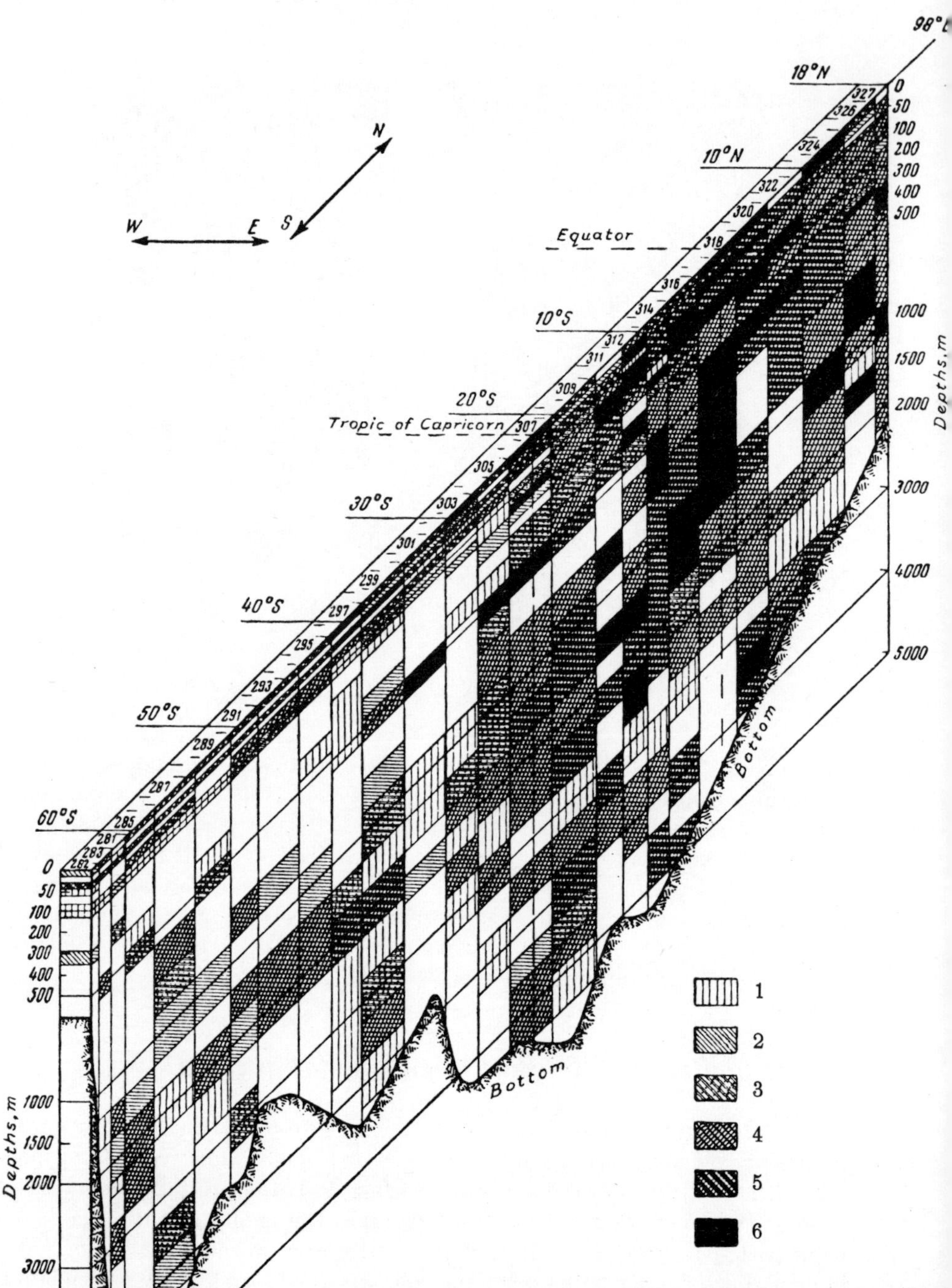

Number of bacteria per 40 ml of water: 1 - 1-10
2 - 10-50; 3 - 50-100; 4 - 100-500; 5 - 500-1000
6 - more than 1000

Fig. 22 Range of *Bact. agile* in the Indian Ocean

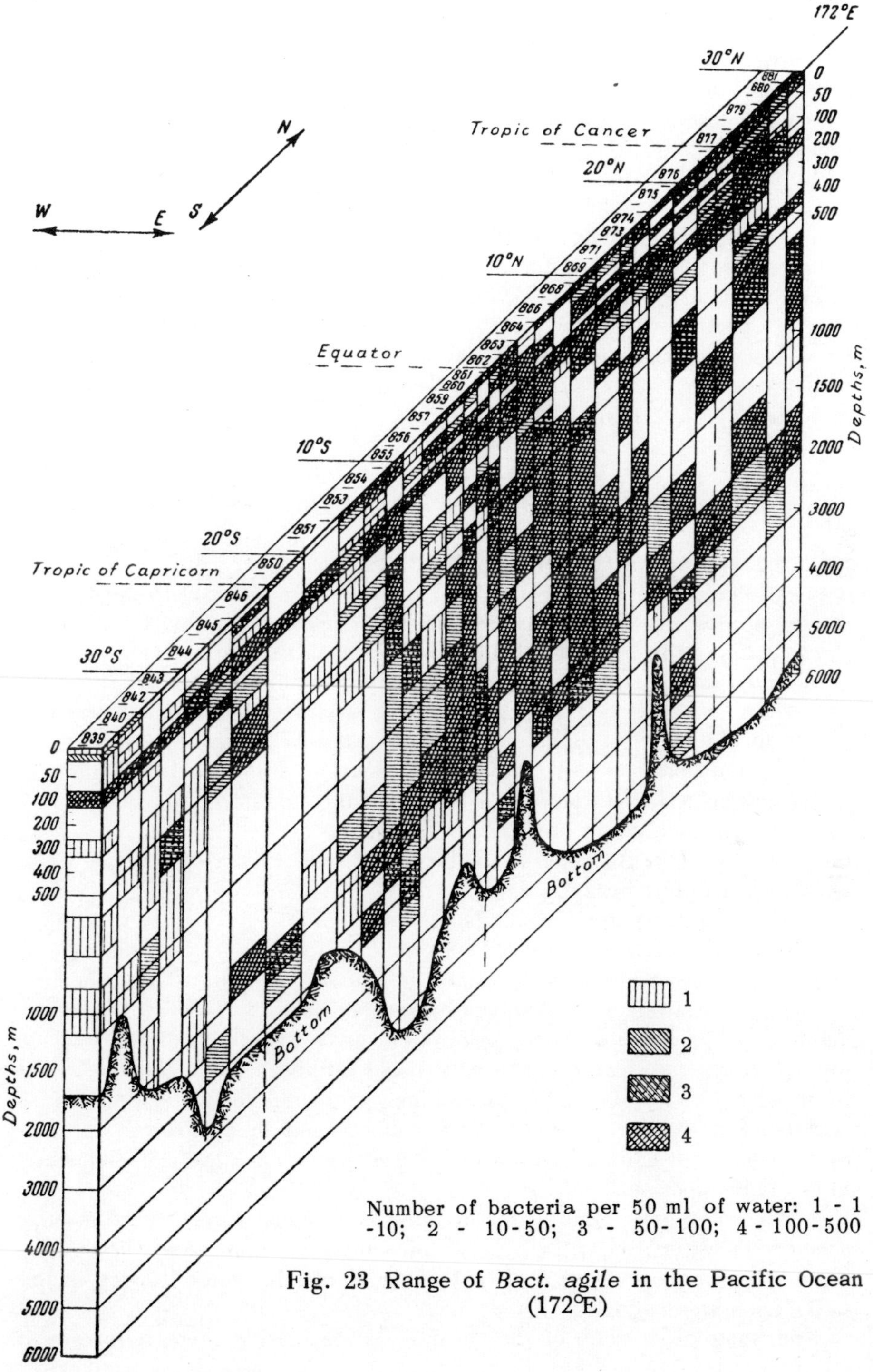

Number of bacteria per 50 ml of water: 1 - 1 -10; 2 - 10-50; 3 - 50-100; 4 - 100-500

Fig. 23 Range of *Bact. agile* in the Pacific Ocean (172°E)

is a characteristic feature of the low-latitude water mass (23°N – 23°S) of the Indian, Pacific and Atlantic Oceans. Only at certain levels does the population of this species perceptibly diminish or completely disappear; as a rule, this occurs in layers of Arctic and Antarctic origin crossing the Equator.

It is clear that *Bact. agile* multiplies only in water enriched in labile organic matter. To judge from the low *Bact. agile* population in high-latitude water reaching tropical regions through deep circulation, the degree of transformation in such water is not very high. The fact that Arctic and Antarctic water passing through the equatorial-tropical areas of the ocean does not become sufficiently enriched in organic matter readily assimilable by microorganisms, despite the fairly high concentration of such matter in the bordering water layers, supports the idea that the speed of the deep currents is greater than had been thought.

Range of Bacterium agile *in subtropical water*

In the subtropical zone, in contrast to tropical water, *Bact. agile* occurs only in certain layers – namely, in streams of equatorial-tropical water moving northwards and southwards from the Equator. Outside these layers *Bact. agile* has been found only in very small quantities or not at all.

In the Pacific, where the microbiological sections crossed the north and south subtropical zones twice, clear distinctions were observed in regard to the range of *Bact. agile* between the 172°E and the 174°W sections. In the northern part of the former section, which included the area of the powerful Japan Current – a branch of the Equatorial Current – *Bact. agile* is widespread: its area embraces almost the entire water column as far north as 30°N. Its population fluctuates from 10 to 100 or more cells per 50 ml of water (Figs. 24 and 25).

In the 172°E section of the south subtropical zone, relatively large quantities of *Bact. agile* were found only in water of equatorial-tropical origin; the Antarctic water contained few or no bacteria of this species.

The same pattern was observed at stations in the 174°W section of the subtropical zone; again, *Bact. agile* was associated with equatorial-tropical water, except that, owing to the very slight influence of the Japan Current in this section of the north subtropical zone and the more pronounced occurrence of Antarctic water in the southern part than in the 172°E section, levels with a low concentration of *Bact. agile* occurred more frequently in the 174°W section.

In the subtropical zone of the Indian Ocean *Bact. agile* occurs in large numbers in water moving from the tropics towards Antarctica. The species is less frequent, or even does not occur at all, in water flowing in the in the opposite direction.

The subtropical zone of the Atlantic is distinctive; here it is rare to

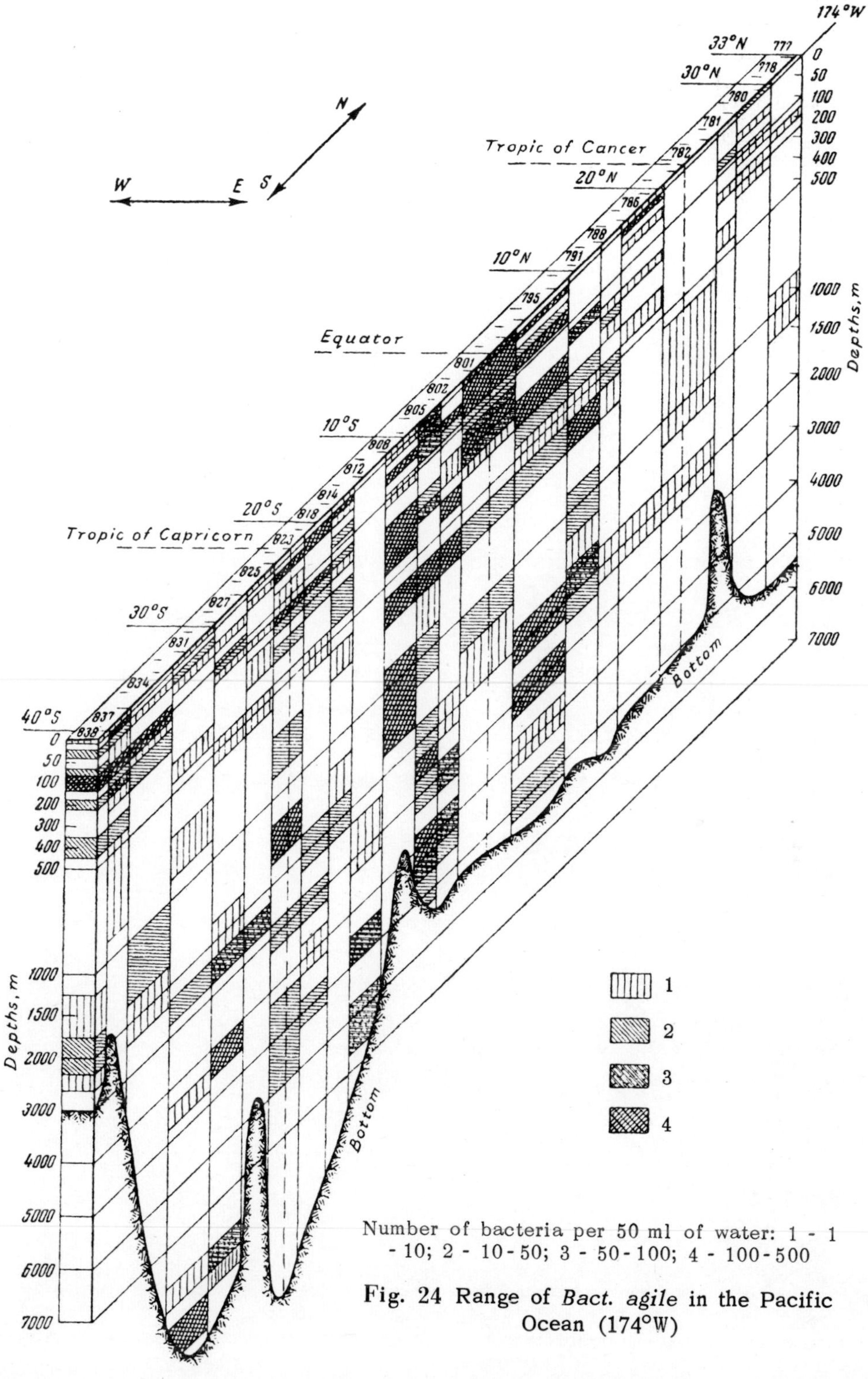

Number of bacteria per 50 ml of water: 1 - 1 - 10; 2 - 10 - 50; 3 - 50 - 100; 4 - 100 - 500

Fig. 24 Range of *Bact. agile* in the Pacific Ocean (174°W)

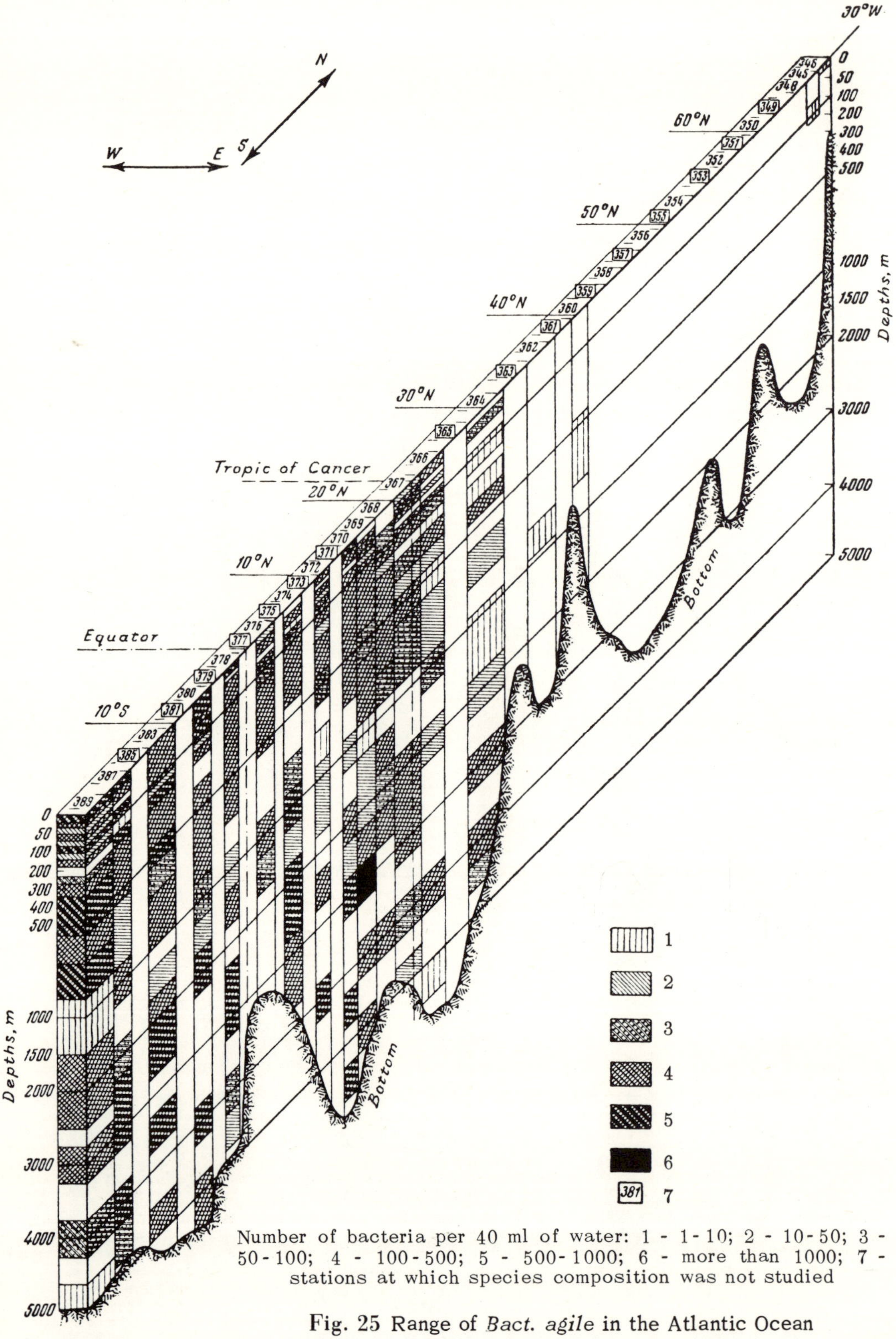

Number of bacteria per 40 ml of water: 1 - 1-10; 2 - 10-50; 3 - 50-100; 4 - 100-500; 5 - 500-1000; 6 - more than 1000; 7 - stations at which species composition was not studied

Fig. 25 Range of *Bact. agile* in the Atlantic Ocean

find *Bact. agile* at all, except in the southern part of the zone, near the tropic, where it occurs at many levels. Further north, where high-latitude water predominates, the incidence of *Bact. agile* abruptly diminishes.

Range of Bacterium agile *in high-latitude water*

In the sub-Antarctic and Antarctic zones of the Indian Ocean the range of *Bact. agile* is confined to tongues of equatorial-tropical water reaching the coasts of Antarctica.

At a number of stations the population of this species was high, indicating a rise in the concentration of labile organic matter in the corresponding layers of the water column. The main mass of Antarctic water between 40° and 70°S contains *Bact. agile* only in small quantities, or not at all.

A similar picture is observed in the sub-Arctic and Arctic zones of the Atlantic, except for occasional islets of equatorial-tropical water along 30°W where *Bact. agile* has sometimes been found in small quantities. It has not been observed outside these islets.

Eddies of equatorial-tropical water, greatly transformed, reach the highest latitudes. We can tell this from the presence of *Bact. agile* at certain depths of the Greenland Sea at 83°N. The species was found in six samples taken from the Greenland Sea at 200, 350 and 1000 – 2000 m, where water from low latitudes occurs. The very low concentration of *Bact. agile* (1 – 4 bacteria in 40 ml of water) is an indication of the considerable transformation of this water in the Greenland Sea.

Bact. agile is thus a good indicator of the presence of equatorial-tropical water. It is prolific in the water column of the tropical zone. It is carried to the coasts of Antarctica and far northwards, into Arctic regions, with the deep currents which draw equatorial-tropical water into these high-latitude areas. Outside these currents, however, it is almost non-existent; even in the contiguous layers it has been detected only in small quantities if at all. At high latitudes *Bact. agile* occurs very rarely, in small quantities and only in water which has retained characteristics of tropical origin. By the time these waters reach the extreme north and south they have become so altered that the predominant forms are other species of bacteria than *Bact. agile*.

If we compare the *Bact. agile* distribution charts for the Indian, Pacific and Atlantic Oceans (Figs. 23 – 26) with the hydrographic structure charts of these oceans (Kriss, Lebedeva et al., 1958, Figs. 6 and 10; Kriss, Mitskevich et al., 1960, Fig. 6) the almost complete coincidence of the *Bact. agile* area with the distribution of equatorial-tropical water emerges very clearly. In water of high-latitude origin *Bact. agile* occurs in small quantities or not at all, evidently as a result of the processes of water exchange.

IV

CONCLUSION

Conclusion

If the present book is regarded as a supplement to the monograph *Marine Microbiology (Deep Sea)*, the oceanic research material contained in the two as a whole can be described as an introduction to oceanic microbiology.

Before these investigations our information on marine microorganisms and their activity related mainly to shelf waters. Late 19th-century and early 20th-century observations on the high seas were episodic and until the 1950's marine microbiology was lagging seriously behind the other oceanological disciplines. By that time a good deal of information on bio-oceanology, chemical and physical oceanography and marine geology had accumulated and it had become feasible to try and build up a picture of the basic vertical and horizontal distribution pattern of the ocean's physical, chemical and biological elements.

The gap in regard to microbiology can now largely be filled, as a result of Soviet microbiologists' participation in many important oceanological and deep-sea expeditions covering vast expanses of the Pacific, Indian, Atlantic and Arctic Oceans, as well as the Black Sea, the Caspian Sea, the Sea of Okhotsk, the Norwegian Sea, the Greenland Sea and the Antarctic seas in the period 1946–1959. Material collected from the entire water column, from surface to bottom, at hundreds of stations in various geographical zones of the sea all over the world has provided a basis for the development of oceanic microbiology, which can now be studied from the same aspects as the other oceanological disciplines in their own spheres.

The research in question has entailed the use not only of culture methods, which tell us only about the negligibly small part of microbial coenoses capable of multiplying on artificial nutrient media in the laboratory, but also of direct microscopy techniques, which yield much fuller information on the concentration and morphological composition of the marine microbial population. Another aid to the research programme's successful completion was the use of the Nansen bottle for taking deep-water samples. Experience has shown that from the sterility point of view, the Nansen instrument is not only quite as good as the microbiological sampler for obtaining water samples from various depths of the ocean, but that in deep water it is also more reliable for obtaining microbiological samples from the required depth.

It is now becoming obvious that the entire water column of the sea and the surface layers of the bottom are inhabited by microorganisms. Even the Black Sea is no exception, for the water mass is contaminated with hydrogen sulphide from the 200 m level down to the maximum depth of 2200 m.

Nevertheless, the great diversity of microbial species found in the soil does not occur in the open seas. We can now take it as established that microorganisms such as *Actinomycetes,* which occur so widely in soil, are not among the indigenous inhabitants of the sea. The *Actinomycetes* occasionally isolated from samples of sea water on organic and mineral media are random occurrences, not adapted to marine life.

While we can speak of strictly land species and even of major systematic groups of microorganisms, such as the *Actinomycetes,* for which the seas and oceans do not constitute a habitat, we have as yet no conclusive proof of the existence of specifically marine species, genera or larger taxonomic units. We have no sufficient reason for assuming that microbial species and genera at present regarded as purely marine will not one day be found in soil and other land habitats; nor is it improbable that the marine heterotrophic microorganisms which multiply on proteinaceous media in the laboratory are merely variants of species inhabiting both land and sea.

In the keys of Krasil'nikov (1949), Lodder and Kreger van Rij (1952) and Kudryavtsev (1954) the microorganisms isolated from various depths of the water column and from the bottom in open parts of the ocean were assigned to the families Actinomycetaceae Buchanan, Mycobacteriaceae Chester, Coccaceae Zopf, Bacteriaceae Cohn, Pseudomonadaceae Winslow et al., Bacillaceae Fisher, Spirillaceae Migula, Cryptococcaceae Lodder a. Kreger-van Rij, Sporobolomycetaceae Lodder a. Kreger-van Rij, Saccharomycetaceae; and to the genera *Pseudobacterium* Krasil'nikov, *Pseudomonas* Migula, *Bacterium* Ehrenberg, *Vibrio* Müller, *Bacillus* Conn, *Micrococcus* Cohn, *Sarcina* Goodsir, *Mycobacterium* Lehmann et Neumann, *Proactinomyces* Jensen, *Actinomyces* Harz, *Torulopsis* Berlese, *Rhodotorula* Harrison, *Sporobolomyces* Kluyver et van Niel and *Debaryomyces* Klöcker.

The range of many species extends over vast areas; *Bact. agile* for example, has been found in various geographical zones of the Atlantic, Pacific and Indian Oceans and at various levels of the water column.

The density of the microbial population in the water and bottom mud of the high seas is considerably lower than in the soil or in many intracontinental bodies of water.

Here it must be repeated that the methods used for quantitative microbial determination are inadequate for counting the number of bacterial individuals in natural habitats. The count obtained after culturing the study material and then seeding it on to appropriate liquid or solid media will invariably be too low, even if all the required conditions are strictly observed, owing to the frequent impossibility of separating bacterial cells from one another. At best, the organisms are clumped too much for accurate titres to be obtained on liquid media or for the number of bacteria to be accurately estimated from the number of colonies incubated on solid nutrient substrates. Further, the results can be greatly distorted owing to the effect of antagonism, especially in small volumes of liquid medium or on small areas of solid substrate.

When it is essential to get a picture of the total microbial population and biomass in soil or in bodies of water, direct microscopy is far superior to culture methods, although the results obtained will be slightly exaggerated, because the preparations will contain a certain number of dead cells which have not yet undergone autolysis.

In the oceanic water column the concentration of saprophytes, or bacteria assimilating only labile organic matter, is too small for these microbial forms to be detected in every single ml of water; it is normal for a great many of the samples obtained in high-latitude or even in subtropical zones to contain only a few tens or hundreds of saprophytes per litre.

The equatorial-tropical regions and water layers through which pass currents bringing water northwards and southwards from those regions are exceptions in this respect. Here the number of heterotrophs developing on protein media rises to thousands and tens of thousands per litre.

In the bottom deposits of the high seas the number of saprophytes fluctuates between tens and thousands, more rarely, tens of thousands, per gram of surface mud, although on occasion inoculations from a 1:10 dilution of surface mud will remain sterile. Such sterile samples have in all probability been taken from bottom horizons in which saprophytes are rare. It is known that even a few centimetres below the mud surface the saprophyte concentration can fall sharply. At 1.5 m or more below the bottom surface in the Sea of Okhotsk we did not succeed in detecting any bacteria which would grow on media of organic composition, although some investigators say that in the Pacific the number of saprophytes several metres below the bottom has proved no smaller than in the surface layer of the mud.

Against this background of relative poverty in saprophytes, the numbers given for the concentration of microorganisms causing various transformations of organic matter in the bottom deposits of the hydrogen sulphide zone of the Black Sea must be high. On solid media the number of colonies incubated ran into hundreds of thousands; on liquid substrates, members of such physiological microbial groups as the ammonia-forming, denitrifying and desulphurizing bacteria, which metabolize organic matter, were counted in millions and tens of millions per gram of mud, in a number of the surface samples. Not only the population, but also the activity of these forms proved high. It is clear that, despite the high hydrogen sulphide concentration in the mud under the Black Sea, which is the only marine basin of its kind in the world, the bottom at great depths is a gigantic biochemical laboratory, in which the hydrochemical conditions of the sea are today largely determined by current microbial processes.

A world-wide geographical distribution pattern of microbial forms occurring in the sea and using readily assimilable organic matter in their vital processes clearly emerges. The polar regions – Arctic, Antarctic, sub-Arctic and sub-Antarctic – are areas of very low saprophytic bacteria population density. Although the productivity of the ocean water is conditioned by a rich plant life, the metabolic products and dead remains of the organisms inhabiting these parts of the ocean do not create such a concentration of nutrient material for saprophytic microorganisms as is observed in the equatorial-tropical regions of the ocean.

That this is so can be seen from the high concentration of microbial life (saprophytic bacteria) in the equatorial and tropical zones of the Pacific, Indian and Atlantic Oceans. These zones are in marked contrast to other geographical zones of the world's seas and oceans in respect of their microbial wealth. It is interesting that a high concentration of bacteria assimilating labile organic matter is observed in those geographical regions of the ocean which are poorest in plant and animal life by comparison with the high latitudes.

The geographical distribution pattern of microbial population density (saprophytic bacteria) in the sea corresponds to that of other life forms on land; that is, the concentration increases with distance from the polar regions and proximity to the Equator. The explanation is that in the equatorial-tropical regions the principal source of the seas' wealth in saprophytic bacteria is organic matter of allochthonous origin in a relatively untransformed and not yet humified condition. It is obvious also that in the equatorial-tropical zone the concentration of such material is far higher than the total concentration of analogous forms of autochthonous and allochthonous (that is, reaching the sea from the land) organic matter in high-latitude water.

The enrichment of water in the equatorial-tropical zone of the Pacific and Indian Oceans in organic matter readily accessible to the action of microbial hydrolytic enzymes seems to occur chiefly in the Coral Sea. Here, as well as in the Australasian archipelago, where the Indian and Pacific Oceans meet, there is an immense number of islands rich in plant and animal life. From these islands organic matter, in forms highly suitable as food for heterotrophic microorganisms and consequently causing them actively to multiply, is discharged into the surrounding water; the latter, drawn by equatorial and counter-equatorial currents, enriches the whole water column of the Pacific and Indian Ocean equatorial-tropical zone in labile organic matter, particularly in the western part of the Pacific and the eastern part of the Indian Ocean.

In the Atlantic, the conspicuously high concentration of comparatively untransformed organic matter in the water of the equatorial-tropical region is presumably due to the runoff of such powerful rivers as the Amazon,

Orinoco, Congo and Niger, which collect water from the vast expanses of equatorial America and Africa, with their prolific plant and animal life. The numerous Caribbean islands, to which branches of the equatorial currents penetrate, also make a definite contribution as a source of allochthonous organic material.

Vertically throughout the ocean water column, from surface to bottom, bacteria which grow on proteinaceous media occur at all depths.

A peculiarity of the vertical distribution of saprophytic bacteria is its focality; steep density gradients are observed from one level to another. Even in the surface layers, where one would think that vigorous mixing would create conditions for uniform distribution of the microbial cells, we find pronounced microzonality in the occurrence of saprophytes; their concentration is found to fluctuate conspicuously, not only in different samples obtained either from the same level at different stations or from different levels at the same station, but also from one ml to another of the same sample.

Along with pronounced microzonality we find also macrozonality in the vertical distribution of saprophytic bacteria in the oceanic water column. In high-latitude, subtropical and tropical regions the saprophyte concentration is found to diminish with depth. Only in certain layers are deviations observed, due to the passage of high-latitude or of equatorial-tropical water, as the case may be.

Since heterotrophs which grow on proteinaceous media are sensitive indicators of the presence of organic matter readily accessible to microbial decomposition in the water mass, the microzonality and macrozonality of their distribution gives us a picture of the distribution of labile, that is, readily assimilable organic matter in the oceanic water column.

At the present level of technique, the sole criterion of the relative concentration of labile organic matter in natural waters is the quantity of of heterotrophic bacteria in the water capable of growing on proteinaceous media. The BOD method essentially reflects the activity of saprophytes which multiply rapidly in jars containing isolated water samples; on the number and activity of these organisms depend the rate and extent of oxidation of the labile organic matter in the samples.

Data indicative of the quantitative distribution of saprophytic bacteria in the depths of the ocean can therefore give us an idea of the distribution of labile forms of organic matter, susceptible of comparatively rapid transformation. The typical pattern of horizontal distribution is one of increasingly high concentration with distance from the polar regions and proximity to the Equator; vertically, concentration decreases with depth. These global-scale patterns are disrupted in certain places and at certain depths by powerful currents drawing equatorial-tropical water northwards and southwards and drawing polar water towards the low latitudes; but such local variations do not alter the general picture.

Detailed study of heterotroph distribution in the oceanic water column enables us to estimate the stratification of waters in which the concentration of organic matter readily assimilable by heterotrophs varies according to the provenance of the water. In equatorial-tropical water, relatively high saprophyte concentration, reflecting the comparatively great wealth of this water in labile organic matter, is typical; in higher latitudes, water impoverished in these forms of organic matter and, consequently, containing a low saprophyte population, predominates.

The character of the organic matter in water, as indicated by heterotrophic microorganisms, can be taken as a reliable guide to the origin of the water masses.

Microbiological research has confirmed that equatorial-tropical water penetrates the sub-Antarctic, sub-Arctic, Arctic and Antarctic regions. There are also currents running in the opposite direction, from high to low latitudes. Water of high-latitude origin can be detected in the tropical zone and crosses the Equator.

The investigations described here, however, have shown that the deep circulation in the water column of the Indian, Pacific and Atlantic Oceans is of a more complex character than appears from the existing hydrographic structure charts. Moreover, in the light of the microbiological data, it is impossible to accept the widespread opinion that the Atlantic contains no equatorial water masses, as do the Indian and Pacific Oceans, where equatorial water masses occupy the tropical regions.

To judge from the abrupt enrichment of the water in the equatorial-tropical zone of the Atlantic in scarcely transformed, still unhumified organic matter, this water acquires new, distinctive characteristics and can therefore hardly be regarded as merely transitional between the heterogeneous central water masses of the north and south Atlantic; rather we must assume that the equatorial Atlantic water acquires, as a result of considerable transformation, specific features similar to those of the equatorial water masses of the Pacific and Indian Oceans.

We must assume that the speeds of the deep ocean currents which carry the equatorial-tropical water are by no means as low as has hitherto been supposed. Otherwise it is difficult to explain the persistence of the concentrations of readily decomposable organic matter necessary to produce such large numbers of saprophytic bacteria as we in fact find in the deep layers in temperate and higher latitudes.

Currents drawing equatorial-tropical water right up to the highest latitudes distribute terrigenous organic matter throughout the water mass of the world's seas and oceans. The contribution of allochthonous organic material as a source of the nutrient matter which makes ocean water so fecund must not be underestimated.

It is a striking fact that the equatorial-tropical zone is distinguished by the low concentration of biochemically active microbial forms among the saprophytes inhabiting it. In the Arctic, sub-Arctic, Antarctic and sub-Antarctic regions of the ocean the percentage of bacterial strains causing thorough breakdown of proteins proved to be four to sixty times greater, and the percentage of those fermenting carbohydrates two to eleven times greater, than in the equatorial zone.

These data suggest that the process of organic decay and liberation of nutrient elements is more vigorous in high latitudes. Although the saprophyte population there is not so great as near the Equator and the biochemical activity of the saprophytes is affected by the low temperatures, nevertheless, the presence of a comparatively large number of microbial forms possessing diversified enzymatic activity makes for more thorough conversion of organic matter in the high latitudes than in the tropics.

The result is that in the Arctic, sub-Arctic, Antarctic and sub-Antarctic regions the sea water contains a higher concentration of the nutrient substances essential for the development of aquatic vegetation. The phytoplankton biomass concentration in these geographical zones is indeed many times higher than in the tropics.

The comparative wealth of high-latitude water in microbial forms effecting the multifarious reactions of organic decomposition in high-latitude water leads to a higher concentration of nutrient compounds, not only in the water mass in those latitudes, but also in the depth of the ocean elsewhere in the world, in lower latitude regions to which these products of the breakdown and conversion of organic matter are carried by deep currents.

The reasons for the poverty of tropical water in biochemically active microbial forms and for the higher concentration of these forms in high-latitude water are still unknown. The relatively high concentration of allochthonous organic material readily assimilable by microbes in tropical waters, which accounts for the high density of the saprophytic population in the equatorial-tropical zone, may, perhaps, obviate the necessity for enzymatic reactions ensuring total utilization of the organic material. In high-latitude water the scanty food supply leads to the elaboration of adaptations in the saprophytic bacteria, enabling them to make more economic use of the organic matter by taking advantage of its more thorough decomposition and conversion.

It seems as though there is a special kind of exchange between the low-latitude and high-latitude regions of the ocean. Currents drawing equatorial-tropical water northwards and southwards carry along with them organic matter, mainly of allochthonous origin, which is more thoroughly broken down by the microbial inhabitants of the high latitudes. The biogenic compounds liberated are transferred by the currents to the depths of other geographical areas, thereby increasing the supply of material contributing to the primary production of those parts of the ocean.

Labile forms of organic matter, however, account for only a small part of the organic matter present in the ocean. Even in water samples with the highest content of saprophytic bacteria, the quantities of these microbes detected do not even begin to correspond to the concentration of organic matter in the same samples (2 – 5 mg/1). Two to five days in a sealed jar are sufficient to produce in a sea-water sample vigorous multiplication of microorganisms utilizing labile organic compounds; the very fact that tens and hundreds of thousands of these microorganisms will be found per ml of water shows how little of the organic matter was assimilated by the saprophytes before the sample was poured into the jar.

It is important to emphasize that the immense increase in the bacterial biomass in vessels containing water samples from natural bodies of water is due mainly to that part of the microbial biocoenosis which utilizes labile organic matter in its vital processes. The assumption is that at the water-glass interface in the jars there occurs not only a concentration of organic matter, due to adsorption effects, but also a transformation of stable forms into forms assimilable by saprophytic bacteria, and that this brings about the vigorous multiplication of the bacteria in the jars.

The proliferation of this immense biomass of bacteria in water kept in jars is an indication of the unsuitability of the BOD method proposed for determining the content of organic matter in natural waters on the basis of oxygen demand. Even when sea water samples are kept for long periods, BOD data cannot be used to estimate the extent and rate of oxygen demand under natural conditions. After six months the number of saprophytic bacteria in the jars will be hundreds and thousands of times greater than their concentration in the sea.

The ocean depths are filled with aquatic humus, if we may use this term for forms of organic matter not easily broken down by microorganisms. At great depths, however, where the organic matter, to judge from the low microbial population, consists almost entirely of aquatic humus, the organic matter may become food for heterotrophic microorganisms at the solid-liquid phase interface, as can be seen from the abrupt increase in their numbers.

The conversion of aquatic humus into forms assimilable by microorganisms occurs, to judge from experiments in keeping sea water in jars, always at boundaries where suspended particles are in contact with the water. The particles, settling on their way to the sea bottom, can create microzones where an accumulation and conversion of aquatic humus occurs, resulting in the development of heterotrophic microorganisms, which then act on the humus to produce its partial or complete mineralization.

Anyone observing the sediment obtained on membrane ultrafilters from small volumes of water will quickly realize that modern oceanography has not yet produced an evaluation, in quantitative and qualitative terms, of the influence of so powerful a physical-chemical factor as the solid-liquid phase interface in the oceanic water column. Suspended particles of microscopic dimensions, filling the depths, creat such interfaces on an immense scale, where adsorption effects promoting the concentration and catalytic conversion of various organic and inorganic compounds present in sea water have full play. In the oceanic water column microorganisms make extensive use of phase boundaries as habitats and effect highly complicated biocatalytic reactions at the interface as a result of their vital processes.

It is highly probable that the surfaces of suspended matter in deep seas and oceans have no less, possibly even greater importance, in terms of their aggregate influence, on the processes occurring in these waters, than have the interfaces created at the boundaries between mud particles and near-bottom water.

Along with labile organic matter and aquatic humus, the seas contain also forms of organic matter which, owing to a series of conversions, are accessible only to those microbial species which are not capable of multiplying on conventional microbiological media. We can get an idea of the distribution of these forms from the range of microorganisms detectable only by direct microscopy. The highest concentration of these forms of organic matter occurs in the photic zone, where the quantities of metabolic and decay products of plant and animal plankton are considerable. This accounts for the large microbial biomass in surface layers, particularly in layers of thermal discontinuity.

Determination of the microbial population and biomass by direct microscopic count has shown that the quantitative content of microorganisms in the water layer where plant life is concentrated fluctuates, in the central and south Caspian, the Black Sea and the north-western Pacific, within an order of magnitude – hundreds of thousands of bacteria per ml, or several tens of mg biomass per m^3 of water. In the central Arctic the number and biomass of the microorganisms are smaller by an order.

In the subjacent water layers (5 – 100, 100 – 200 m), the concentration of microbial cells diminishes to some tens of thousands per ml and the biomass to a few mg, not more than 10, per m^3 of water. In the 200 – 500 and 500 – 750 m layers the number of bacteria is several thousands per ml or 0.2 – 1.0 mg/m^3 of water. The same picture is observed in the Caspian and the north-west Pacific.

At depths of 750 – 3000 m in the north-west Pacific the quantity of bacteria is measured in thousands and hundreds per ml and the biomass in tenths and hundredths of a mg per m^3. At these depths the microbial population and biomass in the Central Arctic is already smaller not by an order but only by a factor of 3 or 4. In the vast depths of the Kuril'-Kamchatka depression in the Pacific Ocean, almost the deepest waters in the world, the number of microorganisms is expressed in tens per ml and the biomass in hundredths and thousandths of a mg per m^3 of water.

In the Black Sea an anomaly in the vertical distribution of microorganisms, due to the proximity of the hydrogen sulphide zone, starts in the 100 – 200 m layer; the number and, in particular, the biomass of microbial cells increase. In the hydrogen sulphide zone the microbial biomass, amounting to 32 – 43 mg/m^3, fluctuates comparatively little from the 200 – 300 m to the 1750 – 2000 m layer, in other words, until near the bottom. The considerable increase in the average biomass per m^3 in the hydrogen sulphide zone of the Black Sea, due to autotrophic bacteria, as compared with the oxygen zone, should be noted; one cubic metre of water in the 200–2000 m layer contains, on average a microbial biomass 1.5–2 times greater than the 0–200 m layer.

In the surface layer of the bottom in deep parts of the seas and oceans direct count under the microscope indicates the presence of tens and hundreds of millions of microbial cells per gram of mud; converted to biomass, this means several tenths of a gram or several grams per m^2 of bottom.

Until recently the biochemical activity of microorganisms at the surface of the bottom deposits, which produces hydrochemical changes in the bottom layer of water and geochemical changes in the sediments themselves, was estimated, in quantitative terms, mainly from the number of heterotrophic microorganisms which would grow on laboratory media, that is, it was in fact reduced simply to the conversion of unhumified organic matter.

To judge from the quantity of microorganisms which will not respond to laboratory culture and can be detected only by direct count and overgrowth methods, it is obvious that mud-dwelling microorganisms make extensive use, not only of various forms of organic matter, but also of inorganic compounds, thereby exerting a far-reaching effect on the diagenesis of sedimentary particles in deep bottom deposits.

At the same time, the millions of microbial cells occupying every square centimetre of the mud-water interface cannot fail to leave their mark on the chemistry of the processes occurring in the thin film of water contiguous with the bottom surface. Modern hydrochemistry, in particular the hydrochemistry of muds does not yet have at its disposal methods which would enable us to reach a closely approximate estimate of the intensity and resultant of the multifarious chemical reactions in the boundary layer of water due to the activity of this immense mass of bottom microorganisms.

The above data on the microbial population and biomass provide merely a statistical indication of the quantity of microbial cells in the water column. Information on the quantity of bacterial production in the seas and oceans, obtained by direct observation on the multiplication rate of microorganisms under their habitat conditions, shows that the ratio of diurnal bacterial production to bacterial biomass fluctuates between 12 and 80% from one level to another and from one sea to another. With minor exceptions, there is a perceptible diminution of the increment of bacterial biomass at great depths. It is obvious that the decisive factor is the productivity of the sea, which influences and is, in turn, influenced by bacterial productivity. The quantitative content of organic matter assimilable by microorganisms determines not only the size of the microbial population, but also the rate of microorganism multiplication.

Data on the mean microorganism biomass in the seas and oceans and on the mean diurnal ratio of production to biomass (P/B) enable us to compute the approximate amount of mineralization of organic matter per day due to the vital activity of heterotrophic microorganisms. From these calculations we find that mineralization in the photic zone of the Black Sea amounts to 6.5 mg/m^3, against 11.2 mg/m^3 in the mid and south Caspian and 2 mg/m^3 of organic matter near the North Pole in summer. In the Black and Caspian Seas these diurnal values account for about 0.1% of the quantity of organic matter in the photosynthesis zone.

The mineralization values give us an idea of the amount of phosphorus and nitrogen regenerated from dead organic matter through the activity of microorganisms. In the photic zone of the Black Sea 0.3 mg/m^3 of nitrogen and 0.03 mg/m^3 of phosphorus are liberated per day, against 0.5 mg/m^3 of nitrogen and 0.02 mg/m^3 of phosphorus in the Caspian. In the surface layer of the Black Sea bottom 6.6 mg/m^2 of mineral nitrogen and 0.66 mg/m^2 of phosphorus are regenerated daily.

It is self-evident that all the above-mentioned calculations are approximate, but they evidently express the order of magnitude of mineralizing activity by microorganisms and, consequently, the intensity of the processes by which nutrient substances are regenerated and put back into circulation.

The conversion of dead organic matter to the extent of its complete mineralization, the regeneration of nutrient compounds into forms essential for plant food, the synthesis of organic matter from inorganic compounds and direct participation in a series of food chains – all this constitutes the manifold activity of microorganisms in the creation of the biological and in particular, the fishery production of the world's seas and oceans.

With the deep-sea microbiological investigations described here, which have covered the Indian, Pacific and Atlantic Oceans, the Black Sea, the Caspian Sea, the Sea of Okhotsk, the Norwegian Sea, the Greenland Sea, the Central Polar Basin and the seas of Antarctica, a new stage has been reached in the development of marine microbiology; it has become oceanic microbiology.

References

ARLOING, F., SEMPÉ (1926 a). Pouvoir antimicrobien lytique d'eaux fluviales on marines, Françaises et étrangères. Role possible du bactériophage. *Compt. Rend. Soc. Biol.*, 94, 191.

ARLOING, F., SEMPÉ (1926 b). Recherches sur la lyse microbienne avec des eaux d'Extrême-Orient. *Compt. Rend. Soc. Biol.*, 94, 428.

ASHESHÔVA, I. (1926). Le Bactériophage du Bacille pyocyanique et les taches irisées. *Compt. Rend. Soc. Biol.*, 95, 1029.

ASHMARIN, I., VOROBYOV, A. (1962). *Statistical methods in microbiological investigations.* Moscow.

BALASAC, H., BERTOZZI, GONDIN (1952). Pouvoir antibiotique des eaux de mer vis-a-vis des germes, d'origine enterique deverses par les effluents pollues des villes. *Bull. Acad. Med.*, 136, 514.

BEARD, P., MEADOWCROFT, N. (1935). Survival and rate of death of intestinal bacteria in sea water. *Am. J. Public Health,* 25, 1023.

BEDFORD, R. (1931). The bactericidal effect of the 'Prince Rupert' sea water sampling bottle. *Contrib. Can. Biol. Fish.*, N. S., 6, 423.

BERGEY (1957). *Manual of determinative bacteriology.* Seventh ed., Baltimore.

BHAT, I., KACHWALLA, N. (1955). Marine yeasts of the Indian coast. *Proc. Indian Acad. Sci.*, 41, *Sect. B,* 1, 9.

BHAT, I., KACHWALLA, N., MODY, B. (1955). Some aspects of the nutrition of marine yeast and their growth. *J. Sci. Ind. Res.*, 14c, No. 1, 24.

BOGOROV, V. (1959). Biological structure of the ocean. *Dokl. Akad. Nauk SSSR,* 128, No. 4, 819.

BOGOYAVLENSKIY, A. (1962). On the problem of heterotrophic microorganism distribution in the Indian Ocean and Antarctic water. *Okeanologiya,* 2, 293.

BRANDT, K. (1904). Über die Bedeutung der Stickstoffverbindungen für die Produktion in Meeren. *Seih. Bot. Zbl. Orig. Arb.*, 16, 383.

BRISOU, J., (1955). *Microbiologie du milieu marin.* Paris.

BRUYEVICH, S. (1953). Chemistry and biological productivity of bodies of water. *Trudy Inst. Okeanol.*, 7, 11.

BUTKEVICH, V. (1932). Procedure for bacteriological investigation and certain data on the distribution of bacteria in the water and bottom of the Barents Sea. *Trudy Gos. Okeanog. Inst.*, 2, 5.

CAPRIOTTI, A. (1962). Yeasts of the Miami, Florida Area. III. From sea water, marine animals and decaying materials. *Arch. Mikrobiol.* 42, 4, 407.

CARPENTER, L., SETTER, L., WEINBERG, M. (1938). Chloramine treatment of sea water. *Am. J. Public Health,* 28, 929.

CHUN, C. (1880). Die Ctenophoren des Golfes von Neapel in *Fauna und flora des Golfes von Neapel.* I, Leipzig.

DREW, G. (1913). On the precipitation of calcium carbonate in the sea by marine bacteria, and on the action of denitrifying bacteria in tropical and temperate seas. *J. Marine Biol. Assoc.*, 9, 479.

DZYADZIO, A. (1938). 'True oxidizability' of effluent water and a method of determining it. *Vodosnabdzh. i Sanit. Tekhn.*, No. 8–9, 117.

EGOROVA, A. (1929). Leuchtbacterien im Schwarzen und im Azowschen Meeren. *Zbl. Bacteriol.* Pt. II, 79, 168.

FEJGIN, B. (1926). Sur la forme invisible des bactéries dans l'eau de mer. *Compt. Rend. Soc. Biol.* 95, 659.

FELL, J., AHEARN, D., MEYERS, S., ROTH, F. (1960). Isolation of yeasts from Biscayne Bay, Florida and adjacent benthic areas. *Limnol. Oceanog.*, 5, 366.

FELL, J., VAN UDEN, N., (1963). Yeasts in marine environments. 329, in *C.H. Oppenheimer* (Ed.). Symposium on marine microbiology. Springfield, Ill. *USA*.

FISCHER, B. (1894). Die Bakterien des Meeres. *Ergeb. Plankton-Expedition der Humboldtstiftung,* 4.

FRED, E., WILSON, F., DAVENPORT, A. (1924). The distribution and significance of bacteria in Lake Mendota. *Ecology*, 5, 322.

GEE, A. (1932). Estimate of bacterial activity at the Florid Keys. *Papers Tortugas Lab.*, 28, 67.

DE GIAXA (1889). Über das Verhalten einiger pathogener Mikroorganismen in Meer-wasser. *Z. Hyg.*, 6, 162.

GINZBERG-KARAGICHEVA, T., PRYANISHNIKOV, N., RODIONOVA, K. (1934). Some data on microbiological and chemical investigations of the deep-sea mud in the Black Sea. *Mikrobiologiya,* 3, 513.

GRÄF (1909) *Forschungsreise S. M. S. Planet, 1906–1907,* 4, Biol.

GURFEYN,, L. (1935). Use of bathometers for taking samples for microbiological investigation. *Dal'nevost. Med. Zh.*, No. 1, 57, Khabarovsk.

HUMM, H., SHEPARD, K. (1946). The new agar digesting actinomycetes. *Bull. Duke Univ. Marine Station,* 3, 76.

ISSACHENKO, B. (1914). Studies on Arctic Ocean bacteria. *Trudy Murmanskoi Nauchno-Promyslovoy Ekspeditsii 1906 Goda.* Petrograd: (1937). Microbiological characteristics of the bottom deposits and water of the Kara Sea. *Trudy Arkticheskogo Inst.*, 82, 7.

JOHANNESSON, J. (1957). Nature of the bactericidal agent in sea water. *Nature,* 180, No. 4580, 285.

JOHNSON, T., SPARROW, F. (1961). *Fungi in oceans and estuaries.* Weinheim.

KIRIBAYASHI, S., AIDA, T. (1934). Fate of *Cholera vibrio* in the sea water of Keelung Port, Formosa. *U.S. Public Health Eng. Abstr.*, 14, 61.

KNIPOVICH, N. (1936). The Caspian Sea, in *Hydrographical guide to the seas of the USSR.* 2, 2.

KOBAYASI, Y., TSUBAKI, K., SONEDA, M. (1953). Marine yeast isolated from little-neck clam. *Bull. Nat. Sci. Museum,* 33, 47.

KOLBE, R. (1957). Fresh-water diatoms from Atlantic deep-sea sediments. *Science,* 126, No. 3282, 1053.

KOMAI TAKU (1922). *Studies on two aberrant Ctenophores Coeloplana and Gastropodes.* Kyoto.

KRASIL'NIKOV, N. (1938). Bactericidal properties of sea water. *Mikrobiologiya,* 3, 329: (1949). *A key to bacteria and actinomycetes.* Moscow-Leningrad.

KRISS, A. (1952). The microbial population of the Chukhotsk Sea and the Bering Straits in *Krayniy Severo-Vostok Soyuza SSR,* 2, 336: (1955a). Microbiological investigations in the North Pole area. *Vestn. Akad, Nauk SSSR,* No. 1, 30: (1955b). New microbiological research in the Central Arctic, *Vestn. Akad. Nauk SSSR,* No. 9, 31: (1956). Size of the microbial population and biomass at various depths of the seas and oceans. *Dokl. Akad. Nauk SSSR,* 111, No. 6, 1356: (1957). Microbiological research in the central Arctic in 1956. *Dokl. Akad Nauk SSSR,* 114, No. 1, 199: (1959). *Marine microbiology* (deep sea). Moscow: (1963a). Quantitative distribution of the microbial population in the water column of the Pacific Ocean. *Okeanologiya,* 3, 1, 157: (1963b). *Marine microbiology* (deep sea). London.

KRISS, A., BIRYUZOVA, V., LEBEDEVA, M. (1958). Morphological description of the microbial population of the seas and oceans. *Dokl. Akad. Nauk SSSR,* 123, No. 5, 845.

KRISS, A., LEBEDEVA, M. (1953). Vertical distribution of the microbial population and biomass in deep parts of the Black Sea. *Dokl. Akad. Nauk SSSR,* 89, No. 5, 949.

KRISS, A., LEBEDEVA, M., ABYZOV, S., MITSKEVICH, I. (1958). Microorganisms as indicators of hydrological phenomena in the seas and oceans. *Zh. Obshch. Biol.* 19, 397.

KRISS, A., MARKIANOVICH, Ye. (1959). Availability of aquatic humus in the sea for utilization by microorganisms. *Mikrobiologiya,* 28, 399.

KRISS, A., MARKIANOVICH, Ye., RUKINA, Ye. (1954). New data on the species composition of Black Sea microorganisms. *Trudy Sevastopol'sk, Biol. St.,* 8, 220.

KRISS, A., MITSKEVICH, I. (1957). A new class of microorganisms inhabiting the depths of the seas and oceans (Krasil'nikoviae). *Usp. Sovr. Biol.,* 44, 2(5), 269.

KRISS, A., MITSKEVICH, I., MISHUSTINA, I., ABYZOV, S. (1960). Hydrological structure of the Atlantic Ocean and the Norwegian and Greenland Seas, on the basis of microbiological data. *Mikrobiologiya,* 29, 875.

KRISS, A., NOVOZHILOVA, M. (1954). Are yeasts inhabitants of the seas and oceans? *Mikrobiologiya,* 23, 669.

KRISS, A., RUKINA, Ye. (1947). Bacteriophage in the sea. *Dokl. Akad. Nauk SSSR,* 57, No. 8, 833: (1949a). Origin of hydrogen sulphide in the Black Sea. *Mikrobiologiya,* 18, 332: (1949b). Reduction and oxidation processes in the hydrogen sulphide zone of the Black Sea. *Mikrobiologiya,* 18, 402.

KRISS, A., RUKINA, Ye., BIRYUZOVA, V. (1950). Species composition of Black Sea microorganisms. *Trudy Sevastopol'sk. Biol St.,* 7, 50.

KRISS, A., RUKINA, Ye., TIKHONENKO, A. (1952). Range of yeast organisms in the sea. *Zh. Obshch. Biol.,* 13, 232.

KROGH, A. (1934). Conditions of life at great depths in the ocean. *Ecol. Monographs,* 4, No. 4, 430.

KUDRYAVTSEV, V. (1932). *Nadsoniomyces sphenoides* nov. gen. nov. sp.,a new yeast-like fungus found on the surface of Far Eastern seaweeds. *Dokl. Akad. Nauk SSSR,* 292: (1954). *The taxonomy of yeasts.* Moscow: (1958). Problems in the systematics and evolution of microorganisms. *Trudy Inst. Mikrobiol., Akad. Nauk SSSR,* 5, 40.

KÜKENTAL, W., KRUMBACH, Th. (1923/25). Coelenterata in *Handbuch der Zoologie.,* I, 902, Berlin and Leipzig.

KUZNETSOV, S. (1951). Comparative description of the bacterial and phytoplankton biomass in the Mid-Baykal surface water. *Trudy Baikal'sk. Limnolog. St.,* 13, 217: (1955). Use of Radioactive Isotopes for Photosynthesis and Chemosynthesis Study in Bodies of Water. *Papers presented by USSR at Internat. Conf. on Peaceful Uses of Atomic Energy*: (1961). Main trends in the study of the geological activity of microorganisms. *Trudy. Inst. Mikrobiol.,* 9, 5.

KUZNETSOV, S., IVANOV, M., LYALIKOVA, N. (1962). *Introduction to Geological Microbiology.* Izd. Akad. Nauk. SSSR.

LANKESTER, E. R. (1900). Ctenophora in *A Treatise on Zoology.* Pt. II. London.

LEBEDEVA, M. (1959). Microbiological work during the second Antarctic marine expedition. *Trudy. Sevastopol'sk. Biol. St.,* 12, 3: (1962). Microbiological indication of zones of convergence and divergence in the Indian Ocean. *Okeanologiya,* 2, No. 6, 1104.

LEBEDEVA, M., ANISHCHENKO, E. (1963). On the sterility of Nansen bathometers at the moment of taking sea-water samples for microbiological study.

Mikrobiologiya, 32, No. 6.

LEBEDEVA, M., TSIBAN, A. (1966). Comparative estimate of a Nansen and microbiological waterbottle for sterile collection of water samples from depths of seas and oceans. Deep-Sea Research, 13, 205.

LEWIS, W., McNAIL, O., SUMMERFELT, R. (1963). A device for taking water samples in sterile bottles at various depths. *Ecology,* 44, 171.

LIPMAN, Ch. (1926). The concentration of sea water as affecting its bacterial population. *J. Bacteriol.,* 12, 311.

LLOYD, B. (1937). Bacteria in stored water. *J. Roy. Tech. College, Glasgow,* 4, 173.

LODDER, I., KREGER VAN RIJ, N. (1952). *The yeasts, a taxonomic study,* Amsterdam.

MARKIANOVICH, Ye. (1954). Species affiliation of Black Sea microorganisms isolated by F. I. Kopp in 1946. *Trudy Sevastopol'sk. Biol. St.,* 8, 288.

MEFEDOVA, N. (1955). Account of bacteria from the bottom of the North-west Pacific. *Mikrobiologiya,* 24, 325.

MISHUSTIN, Ye. (1947). *Ecological-Geographical Variability of Soil Bacteria.* Izd. Akad. Nauk SSSR, Moscow-Leningrad: (1958). The geographical factor and the distribution of soil microorganisms. *Izv. Akad. Nauk SSSR, Ser. Biol.,* No. 6, 661.

MISHUSTIN, Ye, MIRZOYEVA, V. (1953). Ratio of principal groups of micro-organisms in various types of soils. *Pochvovedenie,* No. 6, 1.

MISHUSTINA, I., MITSKEVICH, I. (1963). Range of heterotrophic microorganisms in the Greenland Sea. *Izv. Akad, Nauk SSSR, Ser. Biol.,* No. 6, 914.

NADSON, G., BURGVITS, G. (1931). Yeasts of the Arctic Ocean, *Dokl. Akad. Nauk SSSR,* 4, 103.

NAKASIMA, M. (1957). Diseases in mice induced by yeasts. *Japan. J. Bot.,* 32, 261.

NISKIN, S. (1962). A water sampler for microbiological studies. *Deep-sea Research.,* 9, 501.

TAGA NOBUO, SEKI FUMITAKA (1962). Preliminary report on the microbiological survey made during the fourth cruise of the Japanese Deep-Sea expedition. *Oceanog. Mag.,* 13, No. 2, 143.

NOVOZHILOVA, M. (1955). Quantity, specific composition and range of yeast organisms in the Black Sea, the Sea of Okhotsk and the Pacific Ocean. *Trudy Inst. Mikrobiol.,* 4, 155.

OMELYANSKIY, V. (1924). *Microorganisms as Chemical Reagents.*

OSTROUMOV, E. (1953). Forms of sulphur compounds in Black Sea deposits. *Trudy. Inst. Okeanol.,* 7, 70.

PCHELIN, V. (1951). Surface Properties of Proteic Substances. Moscow.

PHAFF, H., MRAK, E., WILLIAMS, O. (1952). Yeasts isolated from shrimp. *Mycologia,* 44, 431.

PSHENIN, L. (1959). Nitrogen-fixing bacteria in the near-shore bottom deposits of the Black Sea. *Dokl. Akad. Nauk SSSR,* 129, No. 4, 930.

RODINA, A. (1956). Methods for microbiological research of water basins. *Zhizn Presnykh Vod SSSR,* 4, No. 1, 7.

ROSENFELD, W., ZOBELL, C. (1947). Antibiotic production by marine micro-organisms. *J. Bacteriol.,* 54, 393.

ROSS, S., MORRIS, E., (1962). Effect of sodium chloride on the growth of certain yeasts of marine origin. *J. Sci. Food Agr.,* 13, No. 9, 467.

RUKINA, Ye., NOVOZHILOVA, M. (1952). Species composition of yeast organisms obtained from various depths of the Black Sea. *Trudy. Inst. Mikrobiol.,* 2, 150.

SAMASSA, P. (1892). Zur Histologie der Ctenophoren. *Arch. Mikroskop. Anat.,* 40, 157.

SAWJALOV, W. (1913). Über die Schwefelwasserstoffgärung in schwarzen Heischlamme, *Zbl. Bakteriol., Parasitenkunde und Infektionskrh.*, Pt. 2, 39, 440.

SIEBERT, G., SCHWARTZ, W. (1956). Untersuchungen über das Vorkommen von Mikroorganismen in entstehenden Sedimenten. *Arch Hydrobiol.*, 52, No. 3, 321.

SIEBURTH, J., FREY., CONOVER, J. (1964). Microbiological sampling with a piggy-back device during routine Nansen bottle casts. *Deep-Sea Research*, 10, No. 6, 757.

SIEPMANN, R., HÖHNK, W. (1962). Über Hefen und einige Pilze (Fungi imp., Hyphales) aus dem Nordatlantik. *Veröffentlichungen Instit. Meeresforsch. Bremerhaven*, 8, No. 1, 79.

SKOPINTSEV, B. (1950). Organic matter in natural water (aquatic humus) *Trudy Gos. okeanograf. in-ta*, 17, (29).

SKOPINTSEV, B., MIKHAYLOVSKAYA, L. (1948). Qualitative description of organic substances in natural waters. *Gidrokhim. Mat.* 14, 108.

SMITH, L., KRUEGER, A. (1954). Characteristics of a new vibrio bacteriophage system. *J. Gen. Physiol.*, 38, 161.

SOPER, G. (1909). The discharge of sewage into tidal waters. *J. Am. Med. Assoc.*, 52, 1221.

SOROKIN, Yu. (1955). Determination of chemosynthesis value in the water of the Rybinskoye Reservoir by the use of C^{14}. *Dolk. Akad. Nauk SSSR*, 105, No. 6, 1343: (1957). Determination of chemosynthesis efficiency in methane and hydrogen oxidation in bodies of water. *Mikrobiologiya*, 26, 13: (1958). Study of chemosynthesis in mud deposits by the use of C^{14}. *Mikrobiologiya*, 27, 206: (1960). Bathometer for collecting water samples for bacteriological analysis. *Bull. Inst. Biol. Vodochranilish*, No. 6, 53: (1961). Heterotrophic assimilation of carbon dioxide by microorganisms, *Zh. Obshsh. Biol.*, 22, 265: (1962a). Vertical distribution of saprophytic bacteria in the mid-Pacific water column. *Dokl. Akad. Nauk SSSR*, 145, No. 1, 192: (1962b). Microflora in the water column in the mid-Pacific. *Okeanologiya*, 2, No. 5, 922: (1962c). Microbiological investigations in the Black Sea; methods of selecting samples for studying the bacterial population of the water column. *Mikrobiologiya*, 31, 684: (1962d). Microflora of the Black Sea bottom. *Mikrobiologiya*, 31, No. 5, 899: (1962e). Problems of technique for collecting samples for investigating marine microorganisms. *Okeanologiya*, 2, 291.

SPENCER, R. (1960). Indigenous marine bacteriophages. *J. Bacteriol.*, 79, No. 4, 614.

STEEMANN-NIELSEN, E. (1952). The use of radioactive carbon (C^{14}) for measurement organic production in the sea. *J. Conseil Explorat. Mer.*, 18, (2), 117.

STEFANOV, S. (1962). Preparation of natural suspensions of viruses for electron microscopy without altering the composition of their liquid phase. *Biofizika*, 7, 6, 725.

SUEHIRO, S., (1960). Studies on the yeasts developing in putrefied marine algae. *Sci. Bull. Fac. Agr., Kyushu Univ.*, 17, No. 4, 443: (1962). Studies on the marine yeasts. II Yeasts isolated from *Thalassiosira subtilis* (marine diatom) decayed in flasks. *Sci. Bull. Fac. Agr., Kyushu Univ.*, 20, No. 1, 101: (1963). Studies on the marine yeasts. III Yeasts isolated from the mud of tide-land. *Sci. Bull. Fac. Agr., Kyushu Univ.*, 20, No. 2, 223.

SUEHIRO, S., TOMIYASU, Y. (1962). Studies on the marine yeasts. V Yeasts isolated from seaweeds. *J. Fac. Agr., Kyushu Univ.*, 12, No. 3, 163.

SUEHIRO, S., TOMIYASU, Y., TANAKA, O. (1962). Studies on the marine yeasts. IV Yeasts isolated from marine plankton. *J. Fac. Agr., Kyushu Univ.*, 12, No. 3, 155.

TAYSI, J., VAN UDEN, N. (1964). Occurence and population densities of yeast species in an estuarine-marine area. *Limnol. Oceanog.*, 9, No. 1, 42.

VAN UDEN, N., CASTELO-BRANCO, R. (1963). Distribution and population densities of yeast species in Pacific water, air and animals off Southern California. *Limnol. Oceanog.*, 8, No. 3, 323.

VAN UDEN, N., KOLIPINSKI, M. (1962). Torulopsis haemulonii nov. spec., a yeast from the Atlantic Ocean. *Antonie van Leeuwenhoek J. Microbiol. Serol.*, 28, No. 1, 78.

VAN UDEN, N., ZOBELL, C. (1962). Candida marina nov. spec., Torulopsis torresii nov. spec., a. T. maris nov. spec., three yeasts from the Torres Strait. *Antonie van Leeuwenhoek J. Microbiol. Serol.*, 28, No. 3, 275.

VARGUES, H. (1962). Contribution a l'étude du caractère halophile chez les bactéries isolées du milieu marin. *Bull. Inst. Oceanog.*, No. 1231, Monaco.

VLAJNIC, O. (1955). Some new species of marine bacteria. *Acta adriatica*, 7, No. 2.

VOROSHILOVA, A., DIANOVA, Ye, (1937). The role of plankton in bacterial multiplication in isolated samples of sea-water'. *Mikrobiologiya*, 6, 741.

WAKSMAN, S., CAREY, C. (1935). Decomposition of organic matter in sea water by bacteria. 1. Bacterial multiplication in stored sea water. *J. Bacteriol.*, 29, 531.

WAKSMAN, S., HOTCHKISS, M. (1937). Viability of bacteria in sea water. *J. Bacteriol.*, 33, 389.

WHIPPLE, G., (1901). Changes that take place in the bacterial contents of waters during transportation. *Tech. Quart.*, 14, 21.

WILSON, E., STOUT, H., POWELSON, D., KOFFLER, H., (1953). Comparative biochemistry of the hydrogen bacteria. *J. Bacteriol.*, 65, 283.

YEGOROV, N. (1957). *Isolation of microbial antagonists and biological methods of counting their antibiotic activity*. Izd. Moskov. Gos. Univ.

ZAVARZIN, G. (1961). Gemmulating bacteria. *Mikrobiologiya*, 30, 5, 952.

ZENKEVICH, L. (1951). *The Fauna and Biological Productivity of the Sea*. 1, Izd. 'Sov. nauka', Moscow.

ZHAROVA, T. (1963). Carbon dioxide assimilation by heterotrophic bacteria and its importance in determining chemosynthesis in bodies of water. *Mikrobiologiya*, 32, 846.

ZOBELL, C. (1936). Bactericidal action of sea water. *Proc. Soc. Exptl. Biol.* Med., 34, 113: (1941). Apparatus for collecting water samples from different depths for bacteriological analysis. *J. Mar. Res.*, No. 4, 173: (1946). *Marine Microbiology*. Waltham, Mass: (1954). Some effects of high hydrostatic pressure on apparatus observed on the Danish Galathea Deep-Sea expedition. *Deep-Sea Res.*, 2, 24.

ZOBELL, C., ANDERSON, D. (1936). Observations on the multiplication of bacteria in different volumes of stored sea water and the influence of oxygen tension and solid surfaces. *Biol. Bull.*, 71, 324.

ZOBELL, C., FELTHAM, C. (1934). Preliminary studies on the distribution and characteristics of marine bacteria. *Bull. Scripps. Inst., Oceanog., Tech. Ser.*, 3, 279.

ZOBELL, C., GRANT, C. (1943). Bacterial utilization of low concentrations of organic matter. *J. Bacteriol.*, 45, 555.

ZOBELL, C., UPHAM, H. (1944). A list of marine bacteria including descriptions of sixty new species. *Bull. Scripps Inst. Oceanog.*, 5, 239.